It's another great book from CGP...

Maths exams can seem daunting — especially if you're not sure what to expect.
But they're less stressful if you've done plenty of realistic practice in advance.

Happily, this book (which includes a **free** Online Edition) is packed with exam-style questions to fully prepare you for the real thing. We've even thrown in practice exams with online video solutions.

How to get your free online extras

Want to read this book on your computer or tablet?
Just go to **cgpbooks.co.uk/extras** and enter this code...

2798 0722 5593 8833

By the way, this code only works for one person. If somebody else has used this book before you, they might have already claimed the online extras.

CGP — still the best! ☺

Our sole aim here at CGP is to produce the highest quality books — carefully written, immaculately presented and dangerously close to being funny.

Then we work our socks off to get them out to you — at the cheapest possible prices.

Contents

☑ Use the tick boxes to check off the topics you've completed.

Section Four — Geometry and Measures

Section Five — Pythagoras and Trigonometry

Section Six — Statistics and Probability

Practice Papers

How to get answers for the Practice Papers
Your free Online Edition of this book includes a link to step-by-step video solutions for Practice Papers 1 & 2, plus worked solutions you can print out.
(Just flick back to the previous page to find out how to get hold of your Online Edition.).

Published by CGP

Editors:
Katherine Craig, Ceara Hayden, Kirstie McHale, Sarah Oxley, Sam Pilgrim, David Ryan, Megan Tyler, Rachel Ward.

Contributors:
Cath Brown, Christine Graham, Rosie Hanson, Alan Mason, Mark Moody.

With thanks to Glenn Rogers for the proofreading.

ISBN: 978 1 84762 977 7

Groovy website: www.cgpbooks.co.uk

Jolly bits of clipart from CorelDRAW®
Printed by Elanders Ltd, Newcastle upon Tyne

Based on the classic CGP style created by Richard Parsons.

How to Use This Book

- Hold the book upright, approximately 50 cm from your face, ensuring that the text looks like this, not sıɥʇ. Alternatively, place the book on a horizontal surface (e.g. a table or desk) and sit adjacent to the book, at a distance which doesn't make the text too small to read.
- In case of emergency, press the two halves of the book together firmly in order to close.
- Before attempting to use this book, familiarise yourself with the following safety information:

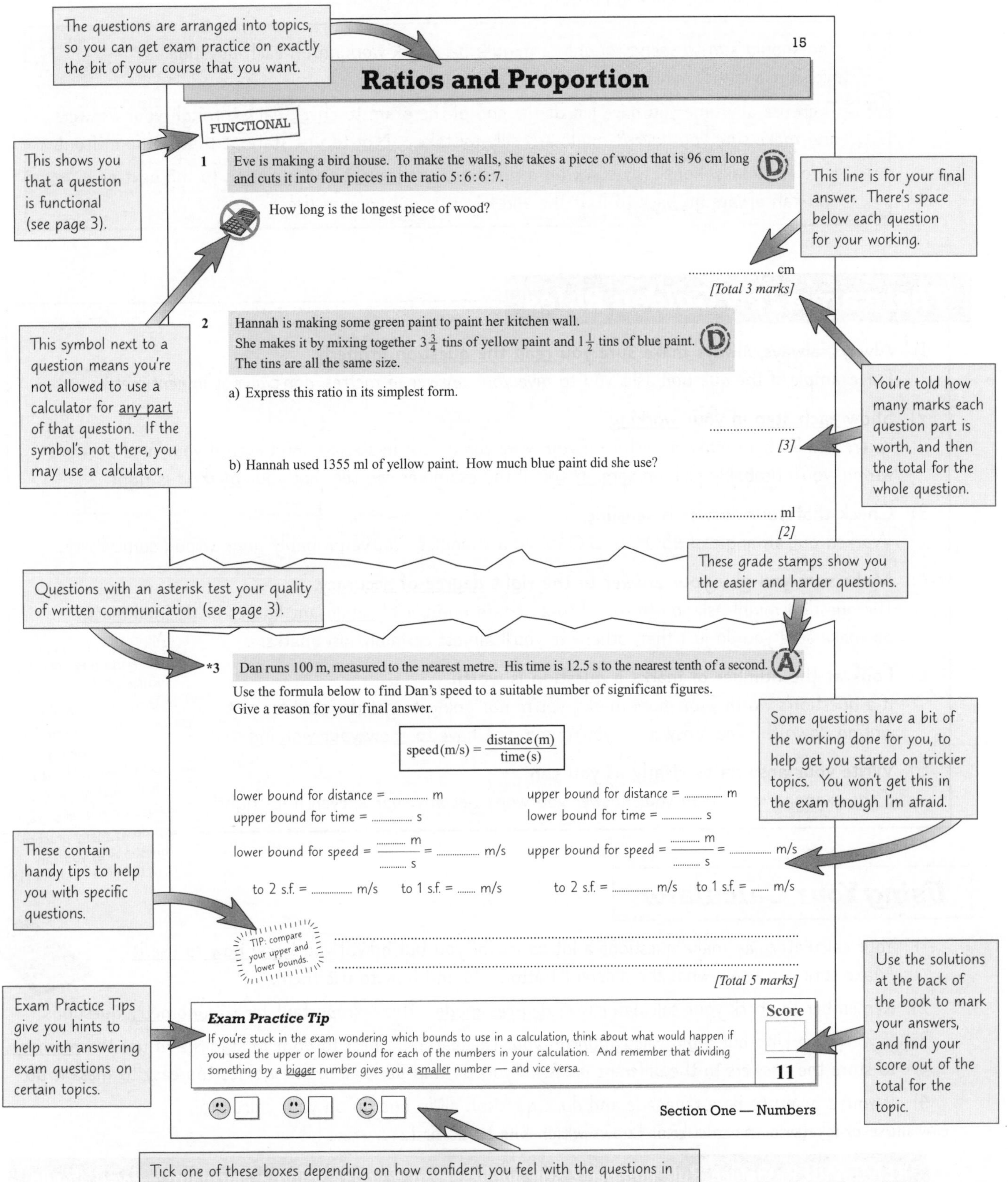

Exam Tips

Exam Stuff

1) If you're studying a linear course you will have two exams — one calculator exam and one non-calculator exam.
2) If you're studying a modular course you will have three exams — one of which is non-calculator.
3) Timings in the exam are really important, so here's a quick guide...

- You should aim to spend roughly a minute per mark working on each question (i.e. 2 marks = 2 mins).
- Then use any time you have left at the end of the exam to check back through your answers and make sure you haven't made any silly mistakes. Not to just stare at that hottie in front.
- If you're totally, hopelessly stuck on a question, just leave it and move on to the next one. You can always go back to it at the end if you've got enough time.

There are a Few Golden Rules

1) **Always, always, always make sure you read the question properly.**
For example, if the question asks you to give your answer in metres, don't give it in centimetres.
2) **Show each step in your working.**
You're less likely to make a mistake if you write things out in stages. And even if your final answer's wrong, you'll probably pick up some marks if the examiner can see that your method is right.
3) **Check that your answer is sensible.**
Worked out an angle of 450° or 0.045° in a triangle? You've probably gone wrong somewhere...
4) **Make sure you give your answer to the right degree of accuracy.**
The question might ask you to round to a certain number of significant figures or decimal places. So make sure you do just that, otherwise you'll almost certainly lose marks.
5) **Look at the number of marks a question is worth.**
If a question's worth 2 or more marks, you're not going to get them all for just writing down the final answer — you're going to have to show your working.
6) **Write your answers as clearly as you can.**
If the examiner can't read your answer you won't get any marks, even if it's right.

Obeying these Golden Rules will help you get as many marks as you can in the exam — but they're no use if you haven't learnt the stuff in the first place. So make sure you revise well and do as many practice questions as you can.

Using Your Calculator

1) Your calculator can make questions a lot easier for you but only if you know how to use it. Make sure you know what the different buttons do and how to use them.
2) Remember to check your calculator is in degrees mode. This is important for trigonometry questions.
3) If you're working out a big calculation on your calculator, it's best to do it in stages and use the memory to store the answers to the different parts. If you try and do it all in one go, it's too easy to mess it up.
4) If you're going to be a renegade and do a question all in one go on your calculator, use brackets so the calculator knows which bits to do first.

REMEMBER: Golden Rule number 2 still applies, even if you're using a calculator — you should still write down all the steps you are doing so the examiner can see the method you're using.

You Need to Understand the Command Words

Command words are the words in a question that tell you what to do.
If you don't know what they mean, you might not be able to answer the questions properly.

Calculate... This means you'll have to work something out — either using pen and paper OR your calculator.

Work out... This is a bit like 'calculate', except you might be able to do the sum in your head.

Find... You'll have to use a mixture of problem solving skills and maths to find the answer to a question. It might not be immediately obvious what calculation you have to do.

Explain... You have to use words to give reasons for something.

Show that... You have to use maths to show that something is true.

With 'explain' and 'show that' questions, the number of marks available can give you an idea of how much you need to write.

Hence... 'Hence...' means you should use your answer to the previous question to work this one out. If you don't take notice of this word, you might really struggle to do the question.

Functional Questions

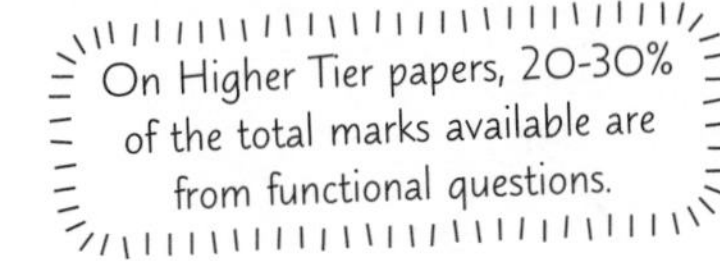

On Higher Tier papers, 20-30% of the total marks available are from functional questions.

Some of the questions in your exams will be wordy questions about a real-life situation.
These are called functional questions. Functional questions are a bit trickier than normal questions because you have to work out what you are being asked to do. Here are some useful steps to follow:

1) Read the question carefully so you can work out what maths you need to use.
2) Underline the information that you need to answer the question — you won't always have to use all of the numbers they give you.
3) Write the question out in maths and then answer it, showing your working as usual.

In this book, functional questions are marked with this stamp: **FUNCTIONAL**

Your exam paper won't mark them up though, so try to get used to how these questions look, so that you can spot them in your exam.

This may seem daft when it's a maths exam, but if the examiner doesn't think you've communicated your answer well enough, you'll lose marks.

Quality of Written Communication

In the exam, questions that have an asterisk (*) next to them are questions which test your quality of written communication. This means you'll be tested on your ability to explain things clearly, as well as your ability to do good maths. When you're answering questions like this, make sure you...

- Use your neatest handwriting so the examiner can easily read your answer.
- Check that your spelling, punctuation and grammar are ~~rigit~~ ~~rihgt~~ correct.
- Show every step of your working, and lay it out in a clear and coherent way.
- Use specialist vocabulary if you need to.

(You should already be doing all these things in every answer anyway, so they're really nothing to worry about...)

Primes and Prime Factors

1 If a and b are prime numbers, give an example to show that each of the following statements is false: 

a) $a + b$ is always even.

[1]

b) $a \times b$ is always odd.

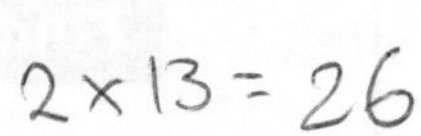

[1]

c) $a^2 + b^2$ is always even.

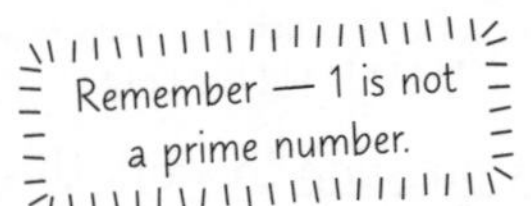

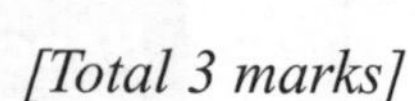

[1]

[Total 3 marks]

2 Express 90 as a product of its prime factors. 

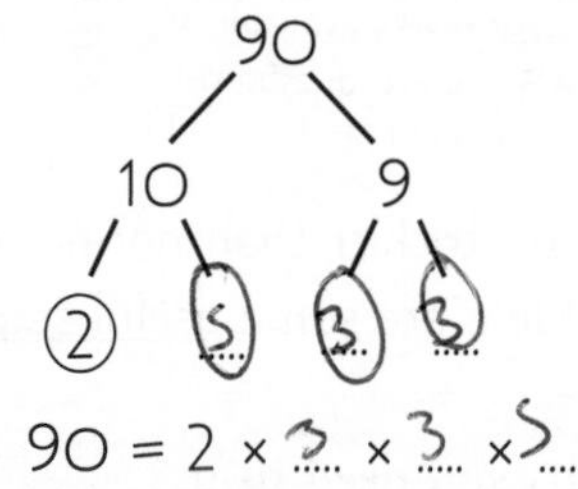

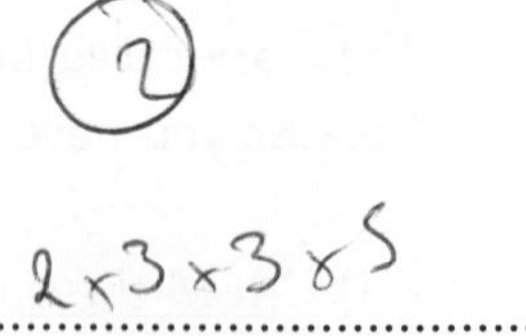

[Total 2 marks]

3 Express: 

a) 210 as a product of its prime factors.

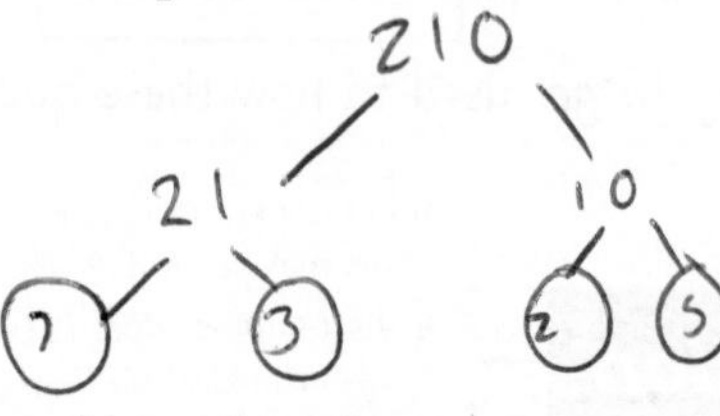

[2]

b) 105^2 as a product of its prime factors.

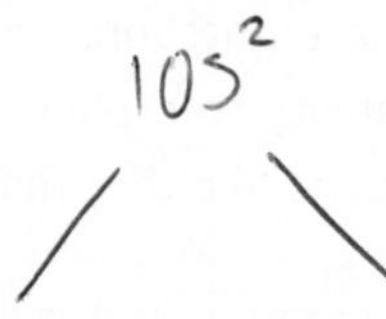

[2]

[Total 4 marks]

Score: /9

LCM and HCF

1 Find:

a) 72 as a product of its prime factors.

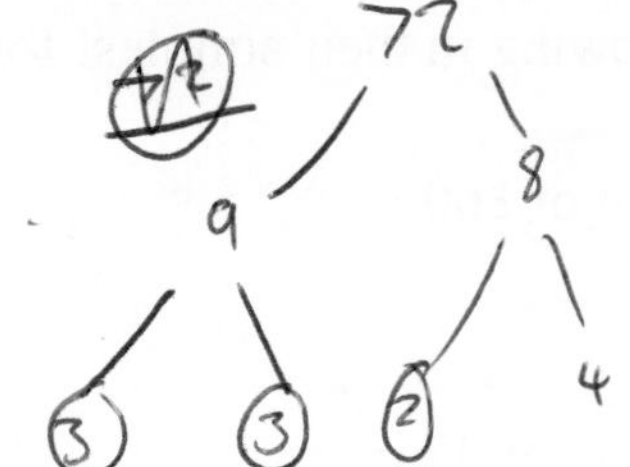

[2]

b) the HCF of 54 and 72.

[1]

c) the LCM of 54 and 72.

[1]

[Total 4 marks]

2 Find the LCM of 6, 8 and 10. 

[Total 2 marks]

FUNCTIONAL

3 Phil is making jam. 

He needs to buy mini jam jars which come in packs of 35 and lids which come in packs of 55. He doesn't want to have any jars or lids left over.

What is the minimum number of packs of jars he needs to buy?

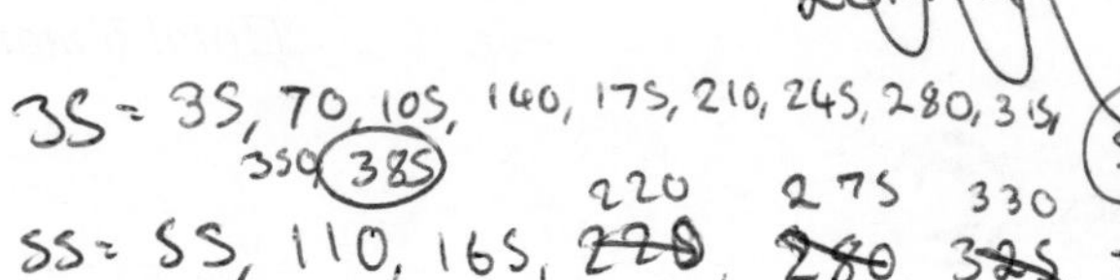

[Total 3 marks]

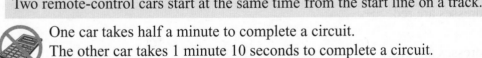

4 Two remote-control cars start at the same time from the start line on a track. 

One car takes half a minute to complete a circuit.
The other car takes 1 minute 10 seconds to complete a circuit.

If they start side by side, how long will it be before they are next side by side on the start line? State the units in your answer.

....

[Total 2 marks]

Score:  / **11**

Fractions

1 Express each of the following in their simplest form. 

a) £12 as a fraction of £60

.... [2]

b) 22 m as a fraction of 33 m

.... [2]

[Total 4 marks]

2 Which of these fractions is closest to 1? 

$\frac{5}{6}$ $\frac{3}{4}$ $\frac{7}{8}$ $\frac{4}{5}$

....

[Total 2 marks]

3 Work out:

a) $3\frac{1}{2} + 2\frac{3}{5}$

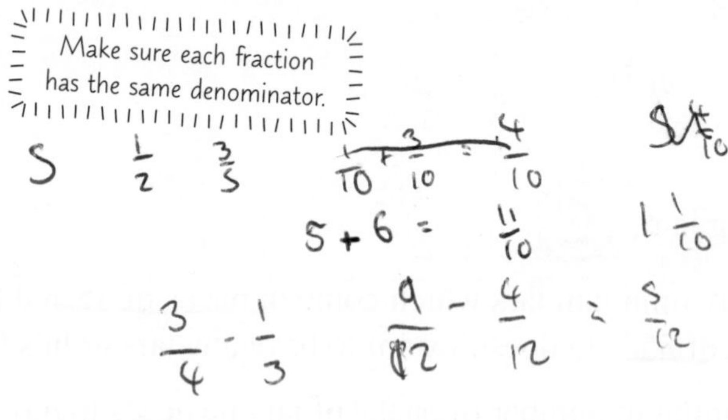

Make sure each fraction
has the same denominator.

.... [3]

b) $3\frac{3}{4} - 2\frac{1}{3}$

.... [3]

[Total 6 marks]

4 Lisa is rearranging her wardrobe. She has 24 dresses. 

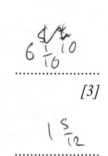

$\frac{1}{3}$ of her dresses are black.

$\frac{1}{6}$ of her dresses are red.

$\frac{1}{4}$ of her dresses are blue.

a) What fraction of her dresses are not black, red or blue?
Give your answer in its simplest form.

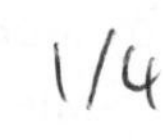

.... [3]

b) How many of her dresses are not black, red or blue?

.... [2]

[Total 5 marks]

5 If $a = \frac{3}{4}$ and $b = 2\frac{1}{2}$, find the value of $\frac{1}{a} + \frac{1}{b}$. (C)

$\frac{1}{3/4} = 1.25$

....
[Total 3 marks]

6 A rectangular field measures $1\frac{3}{4}$ km by $\frac{7}{8}$ km.

a) What is the perimeter of the field?

.... km
[1]

b) What is the area of the field? Give your answer as a fraction.

$1\frac{3}{4} \times \frac{7}{8}$

.... km^2
[1]

[Total 2 marks]

7 Work out the following, giving your answers as fractions in their simplest form.

a) $1\frac{2}{3} \times \frac{9}{10}$

$\frac{2 \times 9 = 18}{3 \times 10 = 30}$

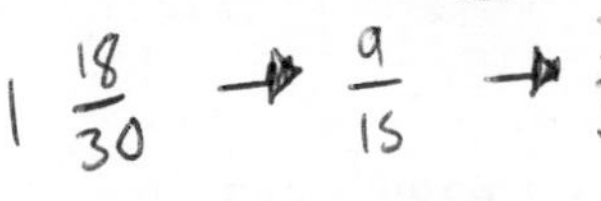

$1\frac{3}{5}$
[3]

b) $3\frac{1}{7} \times 1\frac{1}{7}$

$\frac{2}{49}$

$3\frac{2}{49}$
[2]

[Total 5 marks]

8 Give your answers to the following in their simplest form.

a) $\frac{3}{8} \div \frac{9}{10}$

$\frac{3}{8} \times \frac{10}{9} = \frac{30}{72} = \frac{15}{36} = \frac{5}{12}$

$\frac{5}{12}$
[3]

b) $3\frac{1}{2} \div 1\frac{3}{4}$

$\frac{1}{2} \div \frac{3}{4} = \frac{1}{2} \times \frac{4}{3} = \frac{4}{6} = \frac{2}{3}$

$3\frac{2}{3}$
[3]

[Total 6 marks]

Score: ☐ / **33**

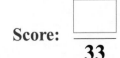

Decimals

1 Given that 56 × 427 = 23 912, find the value of: 

a) 5.6 × 4.27

23.912

[1]

b) 0.56 × 4 270 000

2,391,200

[1]

c) 2391.2 ÷ 0.427

5600

[1]

[Total 3 marks]

2 Given that 34 × 48.2 = 1638.8, find the value of: 

a) 3.4 × 4.82

16.388

[1]

b) 340 × 0.482

163.88

[1]

c) 1.6388 ÷ 482

0.34

[1]

[Total 3 marks]

3 Express 0.725 as a fraction in its simplest form. 

$\frac{725}{1000} = \frac{29}{40}$

$\frac{29}{40}$

[Total 2 marks]

4 Kath is buying new turf for her lawn. The turf costs £2.40 per square metre. She needs to buy 320 m² of turf. How much will this cost? 

2 × 320 = 640

40% of 320 · 10% = 32 × 4 = 128

640 + 128 = 768

£ 768

[Total 3 marks]

Score: $\frac{\quad}{11}$

Fractions and Recurring Decimals

1 Write $\frac{10}{11}$ as a recurring decimal. 

0. ~~aa~~ a0
....
[Total 1 mark]

2 Write $\frac{7}{33}$ as a recurring decimal. 

21
aa

$0.\dot{2}\dot{1}$ ~~$0.\dot{7}\dot{4}$~~
....
[Total 2 marks]

3 Write each of the following in the form $\frac{a}{b}$. Simplify your answers as far as possible. 

a) $0.\dot{7}$ Let r = $0.\dot{7}$

Start by naming the decimal.

so, 10r = ...

10r − r = ... − $0.\dot{7}$

9r = ...

r = ...

....
[3]

b) $0.\dot{2}\dot{6}$

....
[3]

c) $1.\dot{3}\dot{6}$

....
[4]

[Total 10 marks]

4 Show that $0.5\dot{9}\dot{0} = \frac{13}{22}$ 

Hint: start by trying to get only the non-repeating part before the decimal point.

....
[Total 3 marks]

Score: 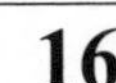 / **16**

Percentages

1 Write each of the following as a percentage. 

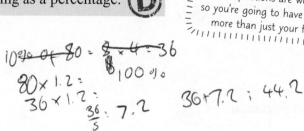

These questions are worth 2 marks, so you're going to have to write down more than just your final answer.

a) 36 out of 80

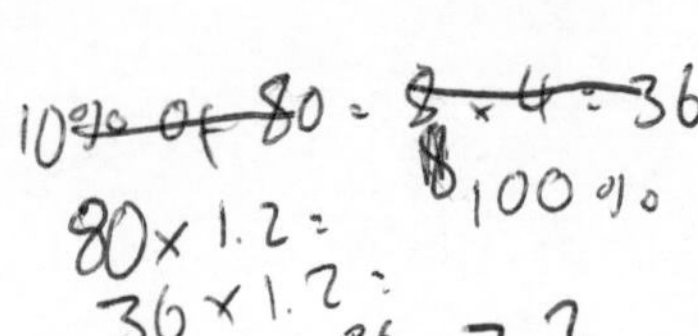

44.2 %

[2]

b) 75 out of 600

12.5 %

[2]

[Total 4 marks]

2 Ali has 40 micro pigs. 24 of them are female. 

What percentage of Ali's micro pigs are male?

40 %

[Total 3 marks]

***3** Jonny does a survey at his school asking which type of chocolate people like best. 

16% of the 25 teachers he asked said they liked white chocolate best.

$\frac{1}{4}$ of the 36 boys he asked said they liked white chocolate best.

7 out of the 35 girls he asked said they liked white chocolate best.

a) Which group had the highest percentage of people who liked white chocolate best? Show clearly how you got your answer.

....

[3]

b) What percentage of **all** the people Jonny asked liked white chocolate best? Give you answer to 1 d.p.

.... %

[4]

[Total 7 marks]

4 Kamal puts £2000 into a bank account. The account pays 3.2% per annum simple interest. 

After 2 years, what is the total amount of interest Kamal has earned?

£ ....

[Total 3 marks]

FUNCTIONAL

5 Jane has an annual salary of £45 000 before tax. 

She pays no tax on the first £9440 of her income — this is her tax-free allowance.
She pays tax at 20% on any income between £9440 and £32 010,
and at 40% on any income over £32 010.

What percentage of her £45 000 annual salary does Jane pay in tax?
Give your answer to 1 decimal place.

.... %

[Total 6 marks]

6 A computer costs £927 plus VAT, where VAT is charged at 20%.
Find the total cost of the computer. 

£ ....

[Total 3 marks]

7 After an 8% pay rise Mr Brown's salary was £15 714. 

What was his salary before the increase?

£15 714 = 108%

£ .... = 1%

£ .... = 100%

£ ....

[Total 3 marks]

8 Last year Amy weighed 30 kg. (C)

a) Amy weighs 36 kg now. Calculate her percentage increase in weight.

.... %

[3]

b) Amy is 12.5% taller than last year and she is now 135 cm tall.
How tall was she last year?

.... cm

[3]

[Total 6 marks]

9 Bill is looking at caravans. (C)

a) He sees one that cost £18 500 when it was new. It is now worth £12 600.
Calculate the percentage decrease in value to 1 d.p.

.... %

[3]

b) Another caravan has dropped 30% in value. It is now worth £11 549.
What was its original value to the nearest pound?

£ ....

[3]

[Total 6 marks]

10 José sells umbrellas. (C)

He makes £7.15 profit on each umbrella he sells, which is 65% of the price he sells the umbrellas for. José increases the price of all his umbrellas by 3%.

Work out the increase in the price of the umbrellas. Give your answer in pence.

...............................p

[Total 5 marks]

Exam Practice Tip	**Score**
One of the trickiest things about percentage change questions can be figuring out which type of question you're dealing with. Think carefully about whether the question is on percentage increase or decrease and whether you are being asked to find the amount after a % change, the actual % change or the amount before a % change.	46

Compound Growth and Decay

1 The population of fish in a lake is estimated to decrease by 8% every year. 

a) Approximately how many fish will be left after 15 years if the initial population is 2000?

population after 15 years $= 2000 \times (1 - \frac{.......}{100})^{.....}$

$= 2000 \times (..............)^{.....}$

= .... fish

TIP: think about which way you should round your answer.

[3]

b) How many years will it take for the population of fish to be less than $\frac{3}{4}$ of the initial population?

$\frac{3}{4}$ of the initial population = ...

2000 × .... = ...

.... × ....^{2} = ...

.... × ....^{3} = ...

.... × ....^{4} = ... years

[2]

[Total 5 marks]

FUNCTIONAL

***2** Alun's car has failed its MOT. He has been advised to scrap it if the repairs cost more than two thirds of its current value. Alun bought his car new for £10 500, 9 years ago, and knows that cars of the same make and model usually decrease in value by around 22% per year. 

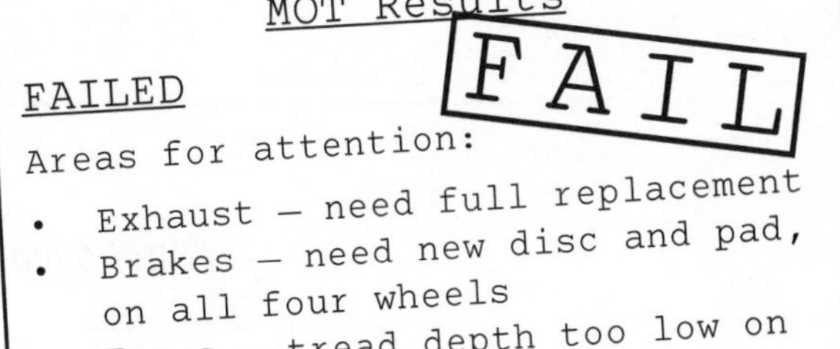

MOT Results

FAIL

FAILED

Areas for attention:

- Exhaust – need full replacement
- Brakes – need new disc and pad, on all four wheels
- Tyres – tread depth too low on all four tyres, need to replace all four
- Suspension – broken coil needs replacing
- Seat belts – needs one replacing

Price List (includes labour costs and VAT)

Tyres		Exhaust	
Each:	£28	Part Replacement:	£140
Pair:	£50	Full Replacement:	£290
Full Set:	£95		
Brakes		**Maintenance**	
		Oil Change:	£49
Pads (each):	£39	Adjust Tracking:	£62
Discs (each):	£59	Air Con Recharge:	£55
		Suspension Coil:	£98
		Seat Belts (each):	£62

Should Alun scrap his car or is it worth paying for the repairs?

....

[Total 4 marks]

3 A new house cost £120 000, but increased in value by 15% each year. (C)

Work out its value after 5 years, to the nearest £1000.

£ ....

[Total 3 marks]

FUNCTIONAL

4 Rich inherits £10 000, and wants to invest it in a high interest account.
He wants to use the money to buy a second-hand camper van, which will cost £13 000. (C)
His bank is offering him two types of account.

Compound Collectors Account	*Simple Savers Account*
5.5% compound interest per year, paid annually into your account. Rate is guaranteed for 10 years.	*5.9% simple interest paid annually by cheque. Rate guaranteed for 10 years, no further deposits permitted after opening.*

a) How much interest will Rich earn from the Compound Collectors Account if he keeps his money there for 3 years?

£ ....

[3]

b) Which of the two accounts should Rich choose to reach his target in the shortest time?

....

[3]

[Total 6 marks]

5 Mrs Khan puts £2500 into a high interest savings account.
Interest is added to the account at the end of each year.
After 2 years Mrs Khan's account contains £2704. (B)

What is the interest rate on Mrs Khan's account?

.... %

[Total 3 marks]

Score: ☐ / **21**

Ratios and Proportion

FUNCTIONAL

1 Eve is making a bird house. To make the walls, she takes a piece of wood that is 96 cm long and cuts it into four pieces in the ratio 5 : 6 : 6 : 7.

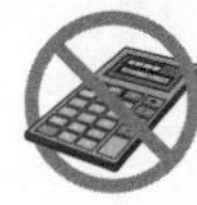

How long is the longest piece of wood?

.... cm

[Total 3 marks]

2 Hannah is making some green paint to paint her kitchen wall.
She makes it by mixing together $3\frac{3}{4}$ tins of yellow paint and $1\frac{1}{2}$ tins of blue paint.
The tins are all the same size.

a) Express this ratio in its simplest form.

....

[3]

b) Hannah used 1355 ml of yellow paint. How much blue paint did she use?

.... ml

[2]

[Total 5 marks]

3 Lucy, Peter, Edmund and Susan shared £120.
Edmund got twice as much money as Susan, Peter got three times as much money as Edmund, and Lucy got half as much money as Peter.

How much money did Lucy get?

TIP: assume Susan gets 1 'part' of the total amount.

£ ....

[Total 3 marks]

4 Last month a museum received £21 000 in donations.
They spent two thirds of the money on heating and lighting.
The rest of the money was spent on staff training and new exhibits in the ratio 2 : 5

How much did they spend on new exhibits?

£ ....

[Total 3 marks]

*5 A ship is carrying first class passengers and second class passengers in the ratio 3 : 5. There are 2928 passengers in total, and the total takings for all tickets were £666 120. 

Given that a second class ticket costs £190, how much does a first class ticket cost?

2928 ÷ (...... + ...) = 2928 ÷ ...... = ...

number of second class passengers = ... × ...... = ...

number of first class passengers = ... × .... = ...

second class ticket takings = ... × £190 = £ ....

first class ticket takings = £ .... – £ .... = £ ....

price of a first class ticket = £ .... ÷ .... = £ ....

£ ....

[Total 5 marks]

6 Mr Tailor is going to his local garage to fill his car up with petrol for a journey. Mrs Jones has just bought 25 litres of petrol from the same garage, and it cost her £31.25.  The fuel tank in Mr Tailor's car has a maximum capacity of 52 litres.

How much will it cost Mr Tailor to completely fill his petrol tank from empty?

£ ....

[Total 2 marks]

FUNCTIONAL

7 Here is a list of ingredients for making flapjacks. 

Simple Flapjack Recipe
(Makes 12)

250 g oats	150 g butter
75 g sugar	75 g syrup

a) Elenni is making 18 flapjacks. How much butter does she need?

.... g

[2]

b) Jo has 300 g of syrup. What is the maximum number of flapjacks she can make?

....

[2]

[Total 4 marks]

8 Ishmael has bought 23 identical glass slippers for £86.25. (D)

Work out the total cost of 35 of these slippers.

£ ....

[Total 2 marks]

9 12 people take 3 hours to harvest the crop from a field. (D)

Estimate how long it would it take 9 people to harvest the crop.

time for 1 person = ... × .... = ...

time for 9 people = ... ÷ ....

.... hours

[Total 2 marks]

10 A ship has enough food to cater for 250 people for 6 days. (D)

a) For how many days can it cater for 300 people?

.... days

[2]

b) How many people can it cater for on a 15-day cruise?

.... passengers

[2]

[Total 4 marks]

FUNCTIONAL

11 Simone is on holiday in Belgium. She buys a 350 g box of chocolates for €7. After returning home to England, she finds that a local supermarket sells a 500 g box of the same brand of chocolates for £12.99. (C)

The exchange rate is £1 = €1.22.
Are the chocolates better value for money in England or Belgium?

....

[Total 4 marks]

Exam Practice Tip

Exam questions on proportion usually follow a pattern — you have to work out an amount for one, then either multiply or divide by this to work out how many you've got. Don't get tripped up by trying to go straight to the answer. If you approach it step by step, you should be fine. Happy days indeed.

Score

37

Rounding Numbers and Estimating

1 Use your calculator to work out $\dfrac{197.8}{\sqrt{0.01 + 0.23}}$

TIP: part a) is worth two marks so you'll need to write more than just the final answer.

a) Write down all the figures on your calculator display.

....

[2]

b) Write down your answer to part a) correct to 3 significant figures.

....

[1]

[Total 3 marks]

2 Use your calculator to work out $\sqrt{\dfrac{12.71 + 137.936}{\cos 50° \times 13.2^2}}$

a) Write down all the figures on your calculator display.

....

[2]

b) Write down your answer to part a) correct to 2 decimal places.

....

[1]

[Total 3 marks]

3 Estimate the value of the fraction $\dfrac{215.7 \times 48.8}{460}$ 

Show all of your working.

....

[Total 2 marks]

4 Work out an estimate for $\sqrt{\dfrac{2321}{19.673 \times 3.81}}$

 Show all of your working.

....

[Total 3 marks]

Score: ____ / 11

Bounds

1 The width of a rectangular piece of paper is 23.6 centimetres, correct to 1 decimal place.
The length of the paper is 54.1 centimetres, correct to 1 decimal place.

a) Write down the lower bound for the length of the paper. 

.... cm
[1]

b) Calculate the lower bound for the perimeter of the piece of paper.

.... cm
[2]

[Total 3 marks]

2 Here is a rectangle.
$x = 55$ mm to the nearest 5 mm.
$y = 30$ mm to the nearest 5 mm.

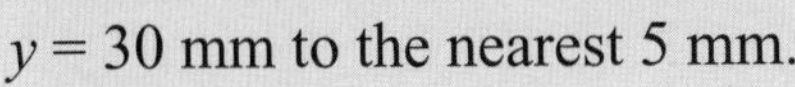

Calculate the upper bound for the area of this rectangle.
Give your answer to 3 significant figures.

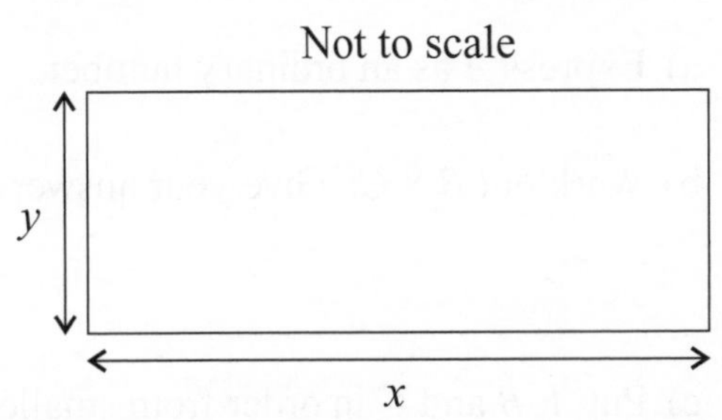

.... mm^2

[Total 3 marks]

***3** Dan runs 100 m, measured to the nearest metre. His time is 12.5 s to the nearest tenth of a second.
Use the formula below to find Dan's speed to a suitable number of significant figures.
Give a reason for your final answer.

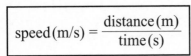

$$\text{speed (m/s)} = \frac{\text{distance (m)}}{\text{time (s)}}$$

lower bound for distance = ... m
upper bound for time = ... s
lower bound for speed = $\frac{\text{............ m}}{\text{............ s}}$ = ... m/s
to 2 s.f. = ... m/s to 1 s.f. = ... m/s

upper bound for distance = ... m
lower bound for time = ... s
upper bound for speed = $\frac{\text{............ m}}{\text{............ s}}$ = ... m/s
to 2 s.f. = ... m/s to 1 s.f. = ... m/s

TIP: compare your upper and lower bounds.

....

....

[Total 5 marks]

Exam Practice Tip

If you're stuck in the exam wondering which bounds to use in a calculation, think about what would happen if you used the upper or lower bound for each of the numbers in your calculation. And remember that dividing something by a bigger number gives you a smaller number — and vice versa.

Standard Form

1 Express the following numbers in standard form.

a) 12 500

.... *[1]*

b) 0.0064

.... *[1]*

c) 8.6

.... *[1]*

[Total 3 marks]

2 $A = 4.834 \times 10^9$, $B = 2.7 \times 10^5$, $C = 5.81 \times 10^3$

a) Express A as an ordinary number.

.... *[1]*

b) Work out $B \times C$. Give your answer in standard form.

.... *[2]*

c) Put A, B and C in order from smallest to largest.

.........., ..., ... *[1]*

[Total 4 marks]

3 Light travels at approximately 1.86×10^5 miles per second.
The distance from the Earth to the Sun is approximately 9.3×10^7 miles.

How long will it take light to travel this distance?
Give your answer in standard form.

.... seconds

[Total 3 marks]

4 A patient has been prescribed a dose of 4×10^{-4} grams of a certain drug to be given daily.

a) The tablets that the hospital stocks each contain 8×10^{-5} grams of the drug.
How many tablets should the patient be given each day?

.... tablets *[3]*

b) The doctor increases the patient's daily dose of the drug by 6×10^{-5} grams.
What is the patient's new daily dose of the drug?

.... grams per day *[3]*

[Total 6 marks]

TIP: you need matching powers to be able to add two numbers together in standard form.

Score: / **16**

Sequences

1 The nth term of a sequence is given by $3n + 2$. (D)

What are the first 3 terms of this sequence?

....

[Total 2 marks]

2 The first four terms in a sequence are 3, 8, 13, 18, … (D)

a) Write down the next two terms in the sequence.

....

[1]

b) Find the nth term of the sequence.

....

[2]

c) What is the 30th term of the sequence?

....

[1]

[Total 4 marks]

3 This question is about the sequence 3, 7, 11, 15, 19… (D)

a) Find the nth term of the sequence.

....

[2]

*b) Explain why 502 cannot be a term in this sequence.

....

....

[2]

[Total 4 marks]

Score: /10

Powers and Roots

1 Simplify the following. 

a) $a^5 \times a^{-3}$

a^2

[1]

b) $x^7 \div x$

x^6

[1]

c) $\frac{(d^9)^2}{d^4}$

$\frac{d^{18}}{d^4}$

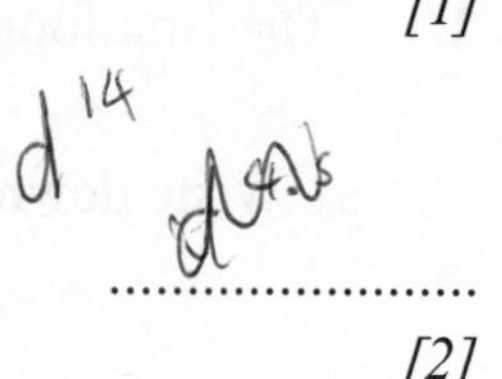

[2]

[Total 4 marks]

2 Evaluate the following. 

a) 3^0

1

[1]

b) 5^{-2}

$5^{-2} = \frac{1}{5^2}$ $\frac{1}{25}$

$\frac{1}{25}$

[1]

c) $8^{\frac{4}{3}}$

$8^{\frac{4}{3}} = (8^{\frac{1}{3}})^4 = (\,2\,)^4 = 16$

16

[2]

[Total 4 marks]

3 For values of $y \geq 2$, write the following expressions in order from smallest to largest. 

y^{-3} y^3 y^1 y^0 $y^{\frac{1}{3}}$

8 2 1

....

[Total 2 marks]

4 Simplify the following expressions fully. 

a) $3a^3 \times 2ab^2$

$6a^4b^2$

[2]

b) $\dfrac{4a^5b^3}{2ab^2}$

$\dfrac{4a^5b^3}{8ab^2}$ $\quad 2a^4b$

$2a^4b$

[2]

[Total 4 marks]

5 Find the value of k in each of the following expressions. 

a) $10^k = \dfrac{1}{100}$

$k =$ ....

[1]

b) $9^k = \sqrt{9}$

$k =$ ....

[1]

c) $3^k = (3^4)^2 \times \dfrac{3^5}{3^{11}}$

$(3^4)^2 = 3^{\dots \times \dots} = 3^{\dots}$ $\qquad \dfrac{3^5}{3^{11}} = 3^{\dots - \dots} = 3^{\dots}$

$(3^4)^2 \times \dfrac{3^5}{3^{11}} = 3^{\dots} \times 3^{\dots} = 3^{\dots}$

$k =$ ....

[2]

[Total 4 marks]

6 Completely simplify the expression below. 

$(9a^4)^{\frac{1}{2}} \times \dfrac{2ab^2}{6a^3b}$

....

[Total 3 marks]

7 Evaluate $64^{\frac{1}{3}} \times 4^{-2}$.

....

[Total 3 marks]

Score:  / **24**

Algebra Basics

1 Simplify the following. 

a) $w \times w \times w \times w \times w$

w^5 ✓ .... *[1]*

b) $4k - 2j + 5k - 8j$ 9k − 10j

9k − 10j ✓ .... *[2]*

c) $2de + 3e - 2d^2 + 4de - 3d^2$ 6de − 5d² + 3e

6de − 5d² + 3e .... *[2]*

[Total 5 marks]

2 Simplify the following. 

a) $2a \times 5b$

.... *[1]*

b) $x^2 + 15x - 7x - x^2 + x$

.... *[2]*

c) $3p^2 + pq + 2p^2q - 3pq + p^2$

.... *[2]*

[Total 5 marks]

3 The diagram below shows a rectangle with sides that are $2x + 3$ cm and $5y - 8$ cm long. 

The perimeter of the rectangle is $7y - 2x$ cm.

Show that $6x + 3y = 10$.

Diagram not accurately drawn

[Total 3 marks]

Score: ___ / 13

Multiplying Out Brackets

1 Expand the brackets in the following expressions. Simplify your answers as much as possible. 

 a) $3(x - 1)$

$3x - 3$

[1]

b) $4a(a + 2b)$

$4a^2 + 8ab$

[1]

c) $8p^2(3 - 2p) - 2p(p - 3)$

[2]

[Total 4 marks]

2 Expand the brackets in the following expressions. Simplify your answers as much as possible. 

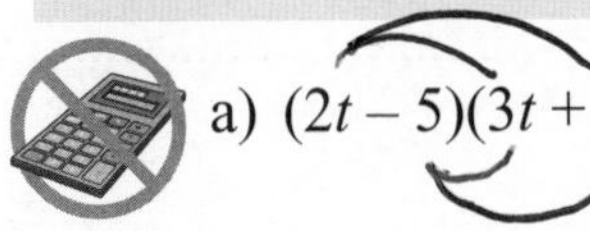 a) $(2t - 5)(3t + 4)$

$6t^2 + 8t - 15t - 20$

$6t^2 - 7t - 20$

[2]

b) $(x + 3)^2$

$x^2 + 9$

[2]

[Total 4 marks]

3 $a = 4(3b - 1) + 6(5 - 2b)$

 Show that a is always equal to 26.

[Total 2 marks]

4 Write an expression for the area of the triangle below. Simplify your expression as much as possible. 

The formula for the area of a triangle is:
Area = ½ × base × height

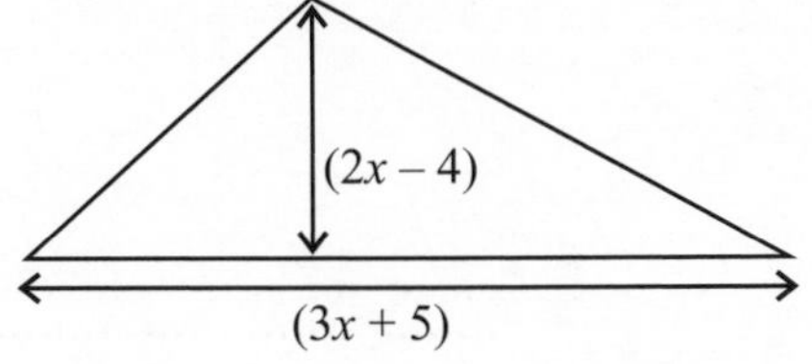

Diagram not accurately drawn

[Total 3 marks]

Exam Practice Tip

If you're struggling with double brackets in the exam, don't forget you can always use the FOIL method — multiply the First term in each bracket together, then multiply the Outside terms together, then the Inside terms, and finally multiply together the Last term in each bracket... easy.

Score

13

Factorising

1 Factorise fully $4a^2 - 24ab$. 

$4a^2 - 24ab = 4(\ldots\ldots - \ldots\ldots)$

$= 4\ldots(\ldots\ldots - \ldots\ldots)$

....

[Total 2 marks]

2 Factorise the following expressions fully. 

a) $6x + 3$

....

[1]

b) $7y - 21y^2$

....

[2]

c) $2v^3w + 8v^2w^2$

....

[2]

[Total 5 marks]

3 Factorise the following expressions fully. 

a) $x^2 - 16$

$x^2 - 16 = x^2 - (\ldots\ldots)^2$

$= \ldots\ldots\ldots\ldots\ldots\ldots$

....

[1]

b) $9n^2 - 4m^2$

....

[2]

[Total 3 marks]

Score: 

10

Manipulating Surds

1 Write $(2 + \sqrt{3})(5 - \sqrt{3})$ in the form $a + b\sqrt{3}$, where a and b are integers. 

....

[Total 2 marks]

2 Show that $\frac{(\sqrt{2} - 4)^2}{\sqrt{2}}$ simplifies to $9\sqrt{2} - 8$.

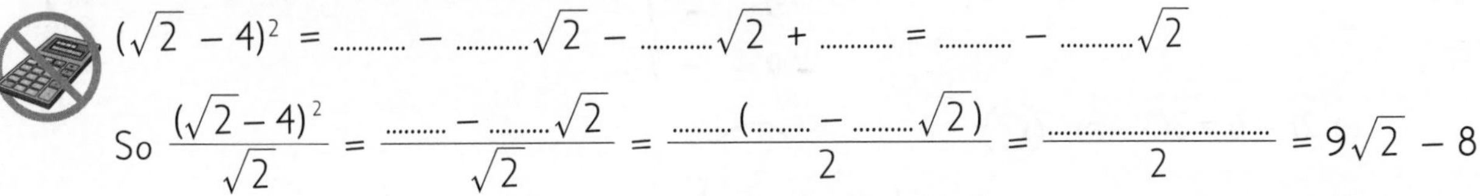

$(\sqrt{2} - 4)^2 = \ldots\ldots - \ldots\ldots\sqrt{2} - \ldots\ldots\sqrt{2} + \ldots\ldots = \ldots\ldots - \ldots\ldots\sqrt{2}$

So $\frac{(\sqrt{2} - 4)^2}{\sqrt{2}} = \frac{\ldots\ldots - \ldots\ldots\sqrt{2}}{\sqrt{2}} = \frac{\ldots\ldots(\ldots\ldots - \ldots\ldots\sqrt{2})}{2} = \frac{\ldots\ldots\ldots\ldots}{2} = 9\sqrt{2} - 8$

[Total 3 marks]

3 The expression $\frac{(\sqrt{27} + 6)}{\sqrt{3}}$ can be simplified to $a + b\sqrt{3}$, where a and b are integers. 

Find the values of a and b.

a = ...

b = ...

[Total 3 marks]

4 The diagram on the right shows a trapezium. 

The base of the trapezium is $6\sqrt{5}$ cm long, the trapezium is $2\sqrt{10}$ cm tall and the top edge of the trapezium is $4\sqrt{5}$ cm long.

Find the exact area of the trapezium.

$4\sqrt{5}$ cm

$2\sqrt{10}$ cm

$6\sqrt{5}$ cm

Diagram NOT drawn to scale

.... cm^2

[Total 4 marks]

Score: ___ / **12**

Solving Equations

1 Solve the following equations.

a) $40 - 3x = 17x$ (D)

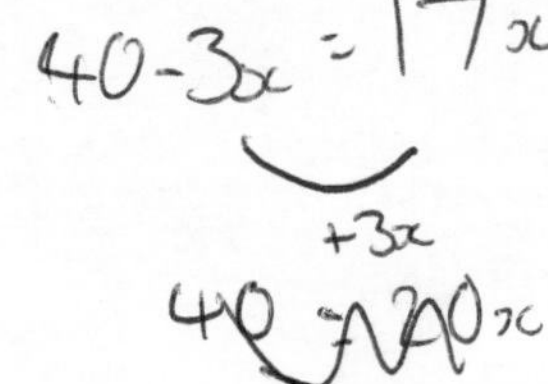

$x =$ ....

[2]

b) $2y - 5 = 3y - 12$ (D)

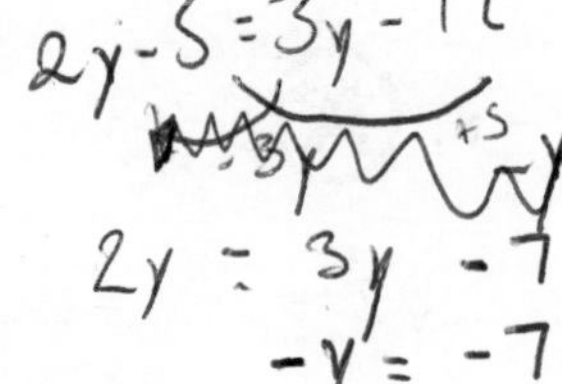

$y =$ ....

[2]

c) $2r - 6 = 3(3 - r)$ (C)

$r =$ ....

[3]

[Total 7 marks]

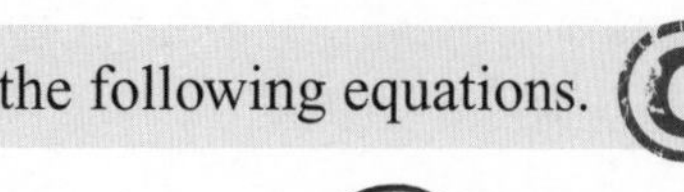

2 Solve the following equations. (C)

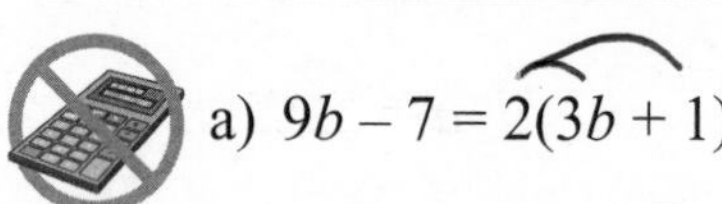

a) $9b - 7 = 2(3b + 1)$

$b =$ ....

[3]

b) $\frac{28 - z}{4} = 5$

$z =$ ....

[2]

[Total 5 marks]

3 Solve the equation $\frac{5}{4}(2c - 1) = 3c - 2$ (C)

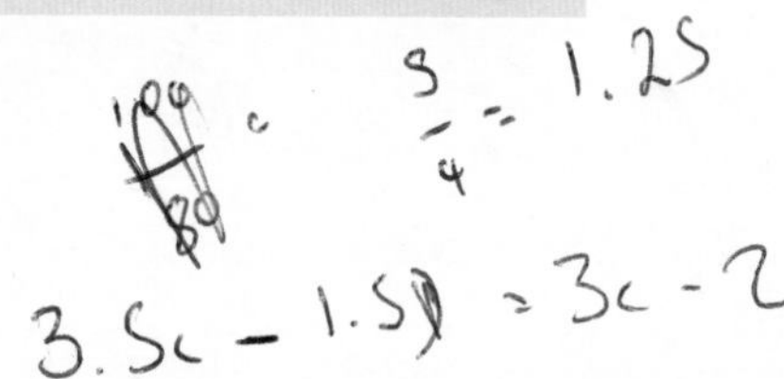

$c =$ ....

[Total 3 marks]

4 Solve this equation. 

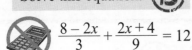

$$\frac{8-2x}{3}+\frac{2x+4}{9}=12$$

$x =$ ....

[Total 4 marks]

5 The quadrilateral below has a perimeter of 58 cm. 

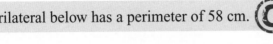

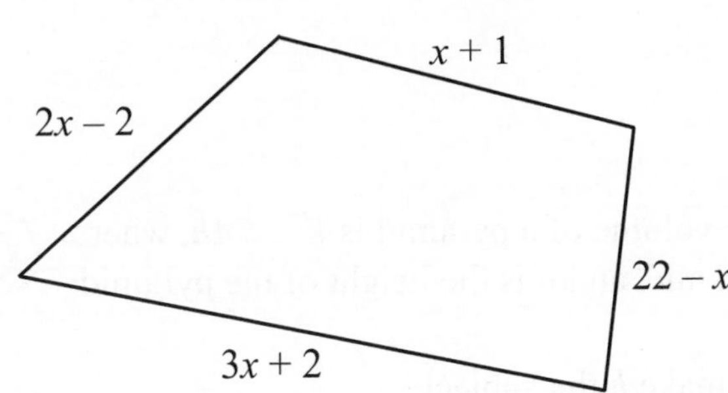

Diagram NOT drawn to scale

All of the lengths on this diagram are in cm.

Find the value of x.

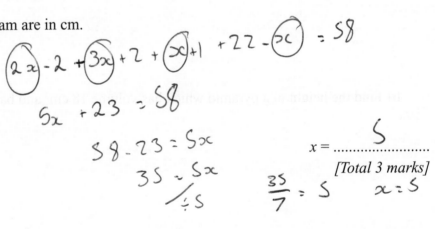

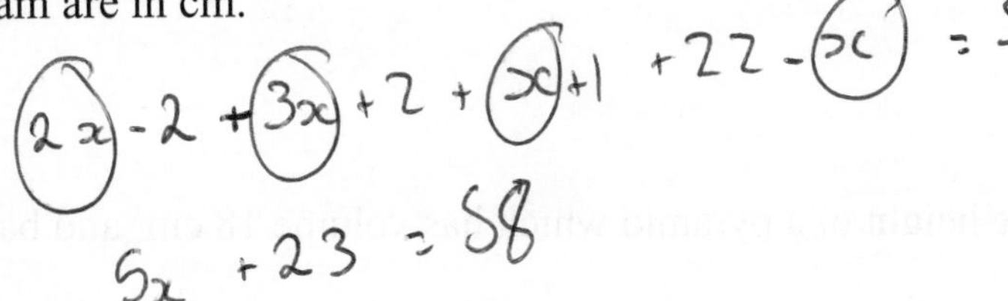

$x =$ ....

[Total 3 marks]

FUNCTIONAL

6 Liam wants to buy himself a new bike, which costs £190. He has £17.80 in his bank account. Liam gets a Saturday job as a waiter in a local café, where he gets paid £4.20 an hour. 

By writing down an equation and solving it, find out how many hours Liam will have to work before he has enough money to buy the bike.

.... hours

[Total 3 marks]

Exam Practice Tip

It's a good idea to check your solutions by substituting them back into the equation and checking that everything works out properly. It certainly beats sitting and twiddling your thumbs or counting sheep for the last few minutes of your exam.

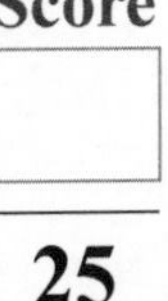

Score

25

Formulas

1 The relationship between x and y is given by the formula $y = \frac{x-2}{3}$.

a) Rearrange this formula to make x the subject.

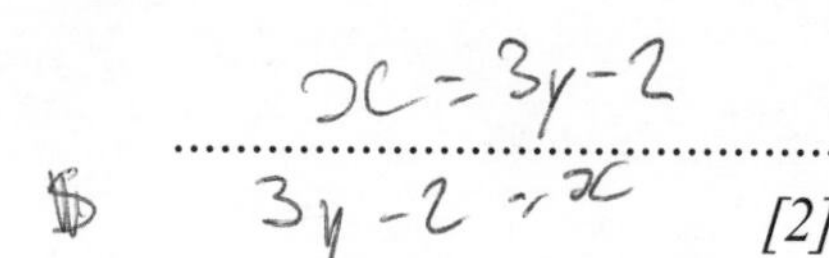

....

[2]

b) Find the value of x when $y = 5$.

$x =$ ....

[2]

[Total 4 marks]

2 The formula for finding the volume of a pyramid is $V = \frac{1}{3}Ah$, where A is the base area of the pyramid, and h is the height of the pyramid. 

a) Rearrange the formula to make h the subject.

....

[2]

b) Find the height of a pyramid which has volume 18 cm^3 and base area 12 cm^2.

.... cm

[2]

[Total 4 marks]

FUNCTIONAL

3 Neela is on holiday in New York. The local weather forecast says that the temperature tomorrow will be 41 °F. Neela wants to know what this temperature is in °C. 

The formula for converting temperatures in °C to °F is: $F = \frac{9}{5}C + 32$.

a) Rearrange the formula to make C the subject.

....

[2]

b) What will the temperature be in New York tomorrow in °C?

.... °C

[2]

[Total 4 marks]

4 Rearrange the formula $s = \frac{1}{2}gt^2$ to make t the subject. 

....

[Total 3 marks]

5 The relationship between a, b and y is given by the formula $a + y = \frac{b - y}{a}$. (B)

a) Rearrange this formula to make y the subject.

$a + y = \frac{b - y}{a}$

$a^2 + y = b - y \qquad a^2 - b + y = -y$

$-y$

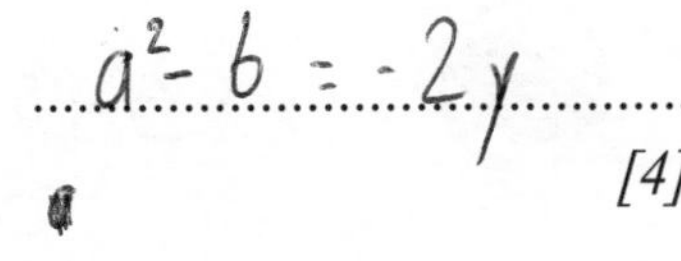

$a^2 - b = -2y$

[4]

b) Find the value of y when $a = 3$ and $b = 6$.

$y =$ ....

[2]

[Total 6 marks]

6 Rearrange the formula below to make n the subject. 

$$x = \sqrt{\frac{(1 + n)}{(1 - n)}}$$

....

[Total 5 marks]

7 Peter and Marek are both travelling to London. 

Peter took the train. The train fare for Peter's journey would normally cost £T, but Peter got a discount of a third because he had a railcard.

Marek took a taxi. The taxi fare costs £4.50 plus an extra 50p per mile. Marek's journey was d miles long and Marek paid twice as much as Peter.

a) Show that $4.5 + 0.5d = \frac{4T}{3}$

[1]

Without the railcard discount, Peter's journey would have cost £22.50.

b) Use algebra to determine how far Marek's taxi journey was.

.... miles

[3]

[Total 4 marks]

Score: $\frac{\square}{30}$

Factorising Quadratics

1 Fully factorise the expression $x^2 + 9x + 18$. (B)

$(x+6)(x+3)$

$(x+3)(x+6)$ ✓

[Total 2 marks]

2 Fully factorise the expression $y^2 - 4y - 5$. (B)

$y^2 - 4y - 5 = (y + \text{ 1 })(y - \text{ 5 })$

$(y+1)(y-5)$ ✓

[Total 2 marks]

3 Fully factorise the expressions below.

a) $x^2 + 4x - 32$ (B)

$(x+8)(x-4)$

$(x+8)(x-4)$ ✓

[2]

b) $3x^2 - 4x - 4$ (A)

$(3x+2)(x-2)$

$3x^2 - 6x + 2x - 4$

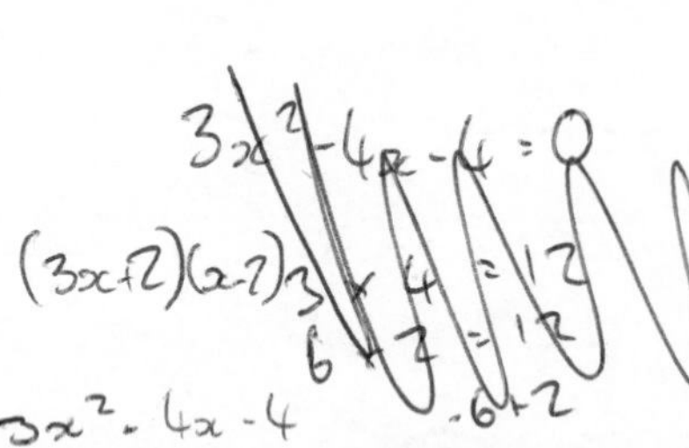

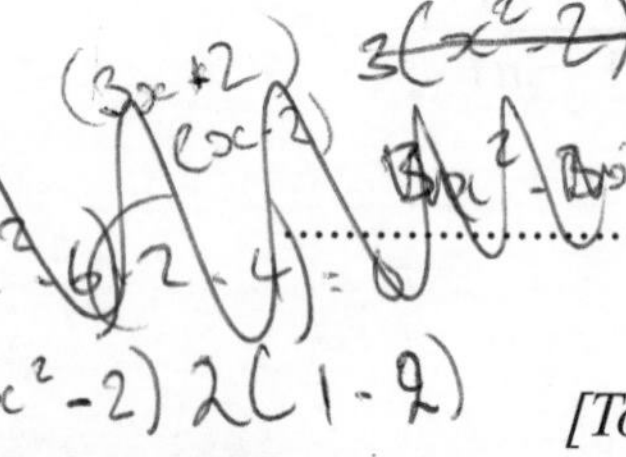

[2]

[Total 4 marks]

4 The equation $x^2 - 9x + 20 = 0$ is an example of a quadratic equation. (B)

a) Fully factorise the expression $x^2 - 9x + 20$.

$(x-5)(x-4)$ ✓

[2]

b) Use your answer to part a) to solve the equation $x^2 - 9x + 20 = 0$.

$x =$ 5 or $x =$ 4

[1]

[Total 3 marks]

5 Solve the equation $x^2 + 4x - 12 = 0$. (B)

$+6 \times -2$

$(x+6)(x-2) = 0$

$x - 6 = 0 \quad x + 2 = 0$

$x =$ -6 or $x =$ +2

[Total 3 marks]

6 The equation $2x^2 + x - 28 = 0$ is an example of a quadratic equation. **(A)**

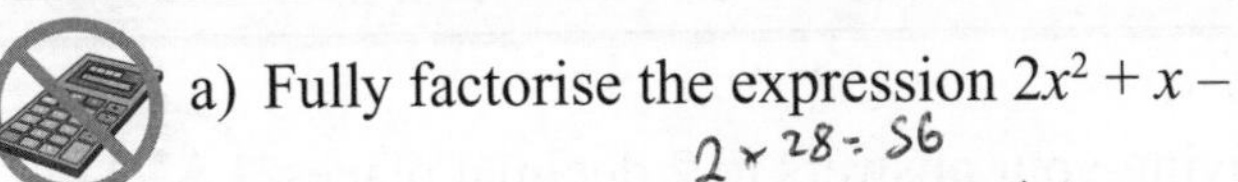

a) Fully factorise the expression $2x^2 + x - 28$.

....

[2]

b) Use your answer to part a) to solve the equation $2x^2 + x - 28 = (2x - 7)^2$.

$x =$ .... or $x =$ ....

[4]

[Total 6 marks]

7 The expression $5x^2 - 19x + 18$ is an example of a quadratic expression. **(A)**

a) Fully factorise the expression $5x^2 - 19x + 18$.

....

[2]

b) Use your answer to part a) to factorise the expression $5(x - 1)^2 - 19(x - 1) + 18$.

....

[2]

[Total 4 marks]

8 The shape on the right is made from a square and a triangle.

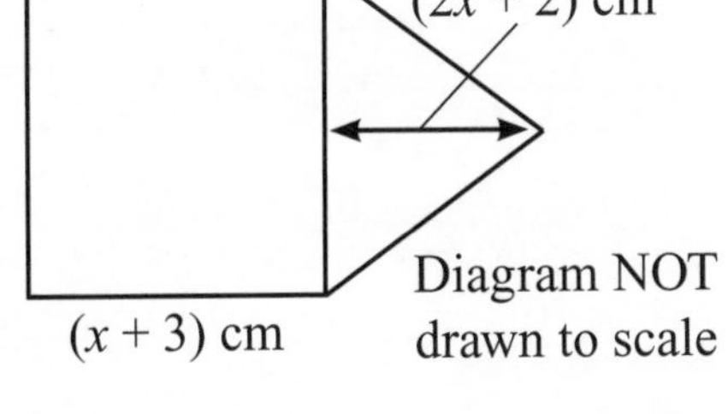

The sides of the square are $(x + 3)$ cm long and the height of the triangle is $(2x + 2)$ cm. The area of the whole shape is 60 cm².

a) Show that $2x^2 + 10x - 48 = 0$.

[4]

b) Solve the equation $2x^2 + 10x - 48 = 0$ to find a value for x.

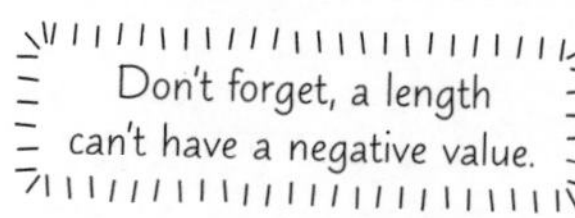

Don't forget, a length can't have a negative value.

$x =$ ....

[3]

[Total 7 marks]

Exam Practice Tip

In the exam, you can check that you've factorised an expression properly by expanding the brackets back out. You should get the same expression that you started with. If you don't then something must have gone wrong somewhere down the line and you'll need to give it another go. Sorry about that.

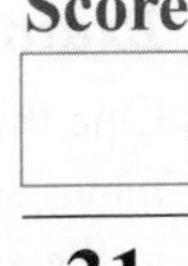

The Quadratic Formula

1 Solve the quadratic equation $x^2 + 5x + 3 = 0$, giving your answers to 2 decimal places. 

a = ..., b = ... and c = ...

$$x = \frac{-b \pm \sqrt{b^2 - 4ac}}{2a} = \frac{-.......... \pm \sqrt{..........^2 - 4 \times .... \times ....}}{2 \times ....} = \frac{-.......... \pm \sqrt{..........}}{..........}$$

$x =$ .... or $x =$ ....

[Total 3 marks]

2 Solve the equation $x^2 + 6x - 3 = 0$. Give your answers correct to 2 decimal places. 

The quadratic formula will be on your formula sheet.

$x =$ .... or $x =$ ....

[Total 3 marks]

3 Solve the equation $2x^2 - 7x + 2 = 0$. Give your answers correct to 2 decimal places. 

$x =$ .... or $x =$ ....

[Total 3 marks]

4 Solve the equation $3x^2 - 2x - 4 = 0$. Give your answers in simplified surd form. 

$x =$ .... or $x =$ ....

[Total 3 marks]

Exam Practice Tip

One thing you really need to watch out for when it comes to using the quadratic formula are those pesky minus signs. It's easy to get confused when you've got to subtract a negative number and you're under pressure in the exam. Just remember subtracting a negative number is the same as adding a positive number.

Score

12

Completing the Square

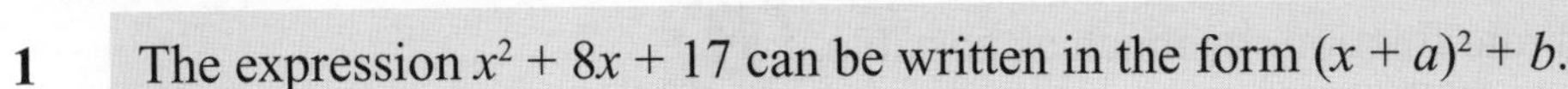

1 The expression $x^2 + 8x + 17$ can be written in the form $(x + a)^2 + b$. 

Find the values of a and b.

8 ÷ 2 = ..., so a = ... and the bit in brackets is (x + ...)^2.

Expanding the brackets: (x + ...)^2 = x^2 + ...x + ...

To complete the square: 17 − .... = ..., so b = ...

a = ... and b = ...

[Total 3 marks]

2 Write the expression $x^2 - 6x + 3$ in the form $(x + a)^2 + b$. 

$(x - 3)^2 + 3$

....

[Total 3 marks]

3 Given that $x^2 + ax + b = (x + 2)^2 - 9$, work out the values of a and b. 

a = ... and b = ...

[Total 2 marks]

4 The expression $x^2 - 10x - 5$ can be written in the form $(x + p)^2 + q$. 

a) Find the values of p and q.

p = ... and q = ...

[3]

b) Use your answer to solve the equation $x^2 - 10x - 5 = 0$.
Leave your answer in surd form.

x = ... or x = ...

[2]

[Total 5 marks]

Exam Practice Tip

Completing the square is pretty tough stuff. If you're struggling to get your head around it, just remember... when the quadratic expression is in the form $x^2 + bx + c$, the number in the brackets is always $b \div 2$ and the number outside the brackets is always $c - (b \div 2)^2$.

Score

13

Algebraic Fractions

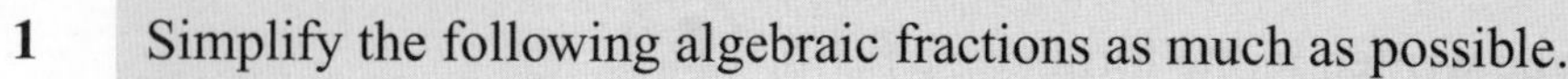

1 Simplify the following algebraic fractions as much as possible. 

a) $\dfrac{3x-12}{x^2-16}$

....

[3]

b) $\dfrac{x^2-4}{x^2+8x+12}$

....

[3]

[Total 6 marks]

2 Simplify the algebraic fraction below as much as possible.

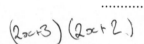

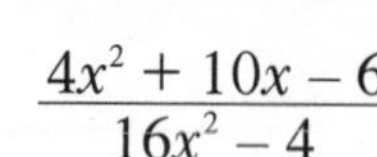

$\dfrac{4x^2+10x-6}{16x^2-4}$

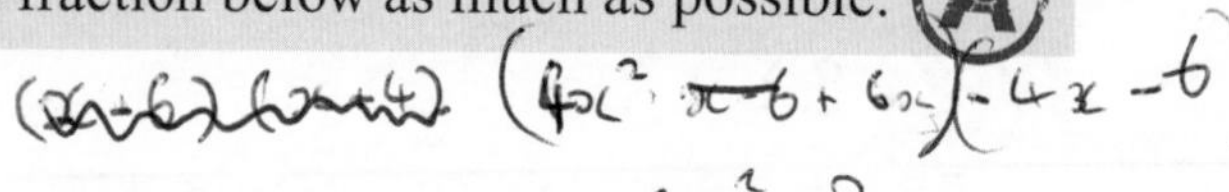

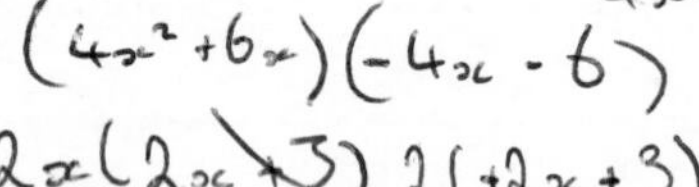

....

[Total 3 marks]

3 Simplify the following.

a) $\dfrac{x^2}{3x} \times \dfrac{6}{x+1}$

....

[2]

b) $\dfrac{10x}{3+x} \div \dfrac{4}{5(3+x)}$

....

[3]

[Total 5 marks]

4 Write $\dfrac{2}{3} + \dfrac{m-2n}{m+3n}$ as a single fraction. 

$\dfrac{2}{3} + \dfrac{m-2n}{m+3n} = \dfrac{2 \times \ldots\ldots}{3 \times \ldots\ldots} + \dfrac{\ldots\ldots \times (m-2n)}{\ldots\ldots \times (m+3n)} = \dfrac{2\ldots\ldots + \ldots\ldots(m-2n)}{\ldots\ldots(m+3n)}$

$= \dfrac{\ldots\ldots}{\ldots\ldots} = \dfrac{\ldots\ldots}{\ldots\ldots}$

....

[Total 3 marks]

5 Write $\dfrac{1}{x-5} + \dfrac{2}{x-2}$ as a single fraction. 

....

[Total 3 marks]

Score: ____ / **20**

Inequalities

1 Write down the inequality that is shown on the number line below. 

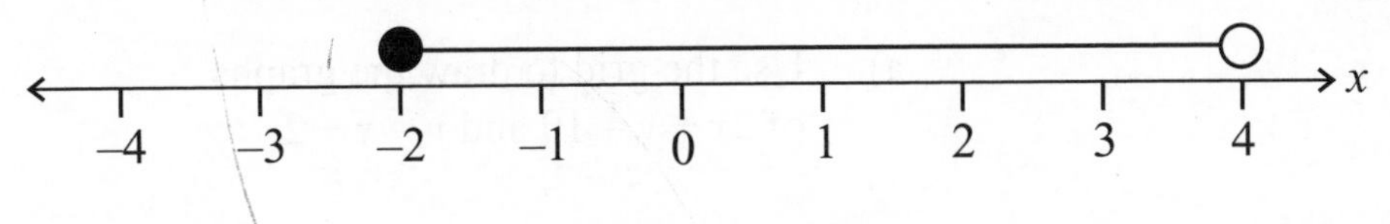

[Total 1 mark]

2 n is an integer. List all the possible values of n that satisfy the inequality $-3 \leq n < 2$. 

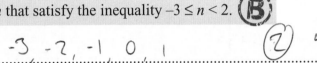

[Total 2 marks]

3 Find the integer values of p which satisfy the inequality $9 < 2p \leq 18$. 

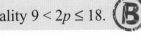

[Total 3 marks]

4 Solve the following inequalities. 

a) $4q - 5 < 23$

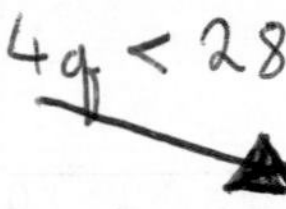

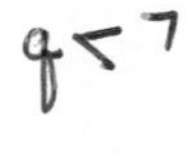

[2]

b) $\frac{2x}{5} \leq 3$

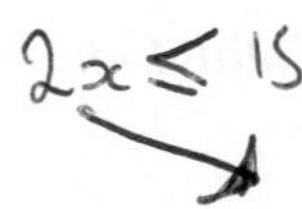

[2]

c) $4x + 1 > x - 5$

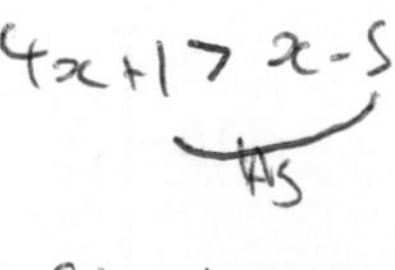

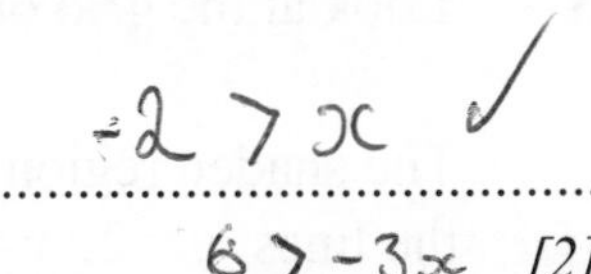

[2]

[Total 6 marks]

5 Possible values of x are given by the inequality $5 - 3x > 7 - x$.

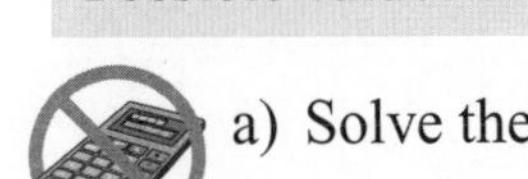

a) Solve the inequality $5 - 3x > 7 - x$. (B)

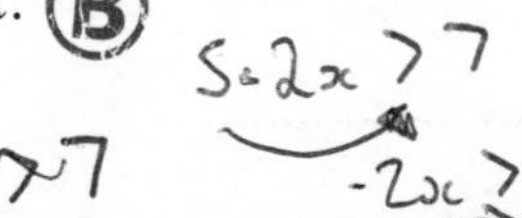

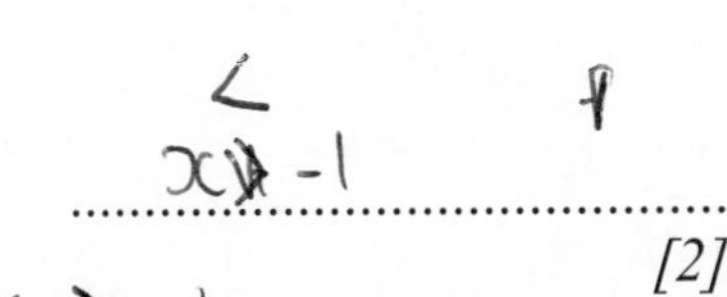

[2]

b) Represent your solution on the number line below. (C)

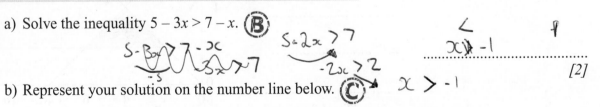

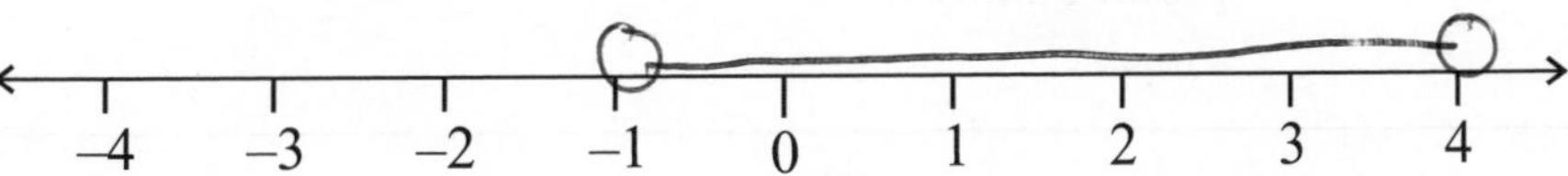

[1]

[Total 3 marks]

Score: $\frac{\quad}{15}$

Graphical Inequalities

1 Look at the grid below. 

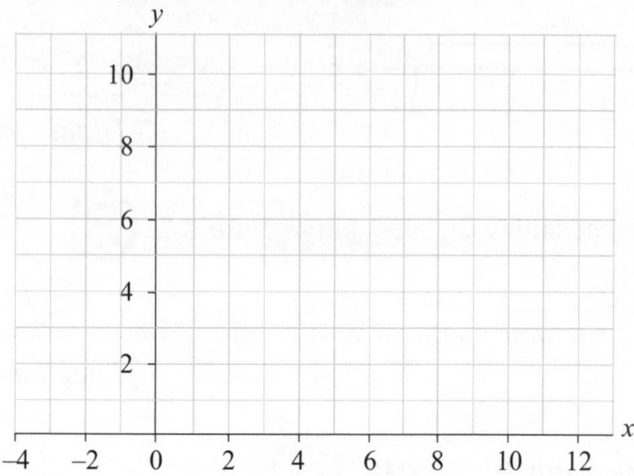

a) Use the grid to draw the graphs of $2x + y = 10$ and $y = x + 2$.

[2]

b) Shade and label, using the letter S, the area represented by the inequalities $x \geq 1$, $2x + y \leq 10$, $y \geq x + 2$.

[2]

[Total 4 marks]

2 Look at the grid on the right. 

On the grid, shade the region that represents these inequalities:

$x < 5$

$y \geq -2$

$y - x \leq 1$

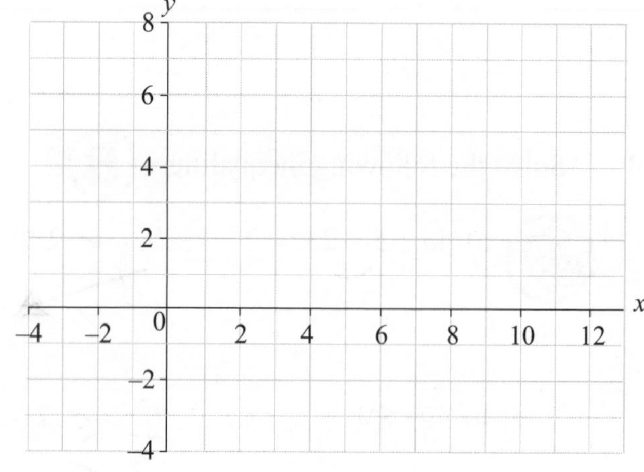

[Total 4 marks]

3 Look at the grid on the right. 

The shaded region R is bounded by the lines $y = 2$, $y = x$ and $x + y = 8$.

Write down three inequalities which define R.

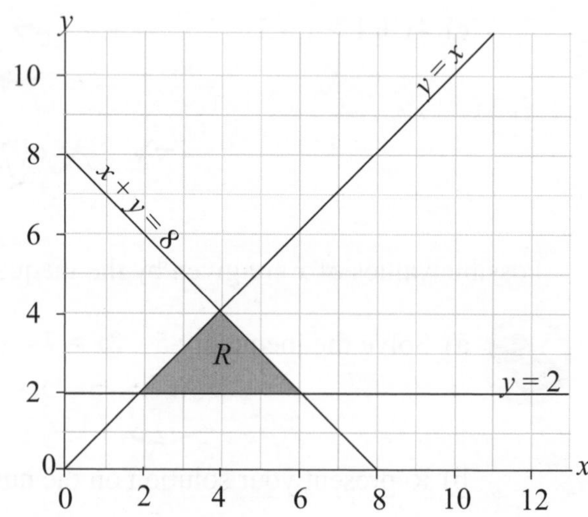

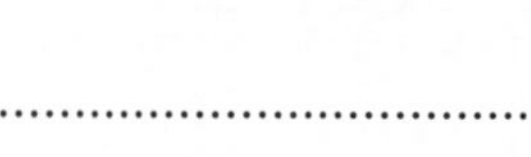

....

....

....

[Total 3 marks]

Exam Practice Tip

In the exam, you need to pay close attention to whether the symbol is just less than/greater than or whether it's less than or equal to/greater than or equal to. If it's just less than/greater than you should draw a dashed line to represent it on the graph. If it's less than or equal to/greater than or equal to you need to use a solid line.

Score
/ **11**

Trial and Improvement

1 The equation $x^3 + 4x = 24$ has a solution between 2 and 3. 

Use trial and improvement to find this solution.
Give your answer correct to 1 decimal place and show your working.

x	$x^3 + 4x$	Notes
2	16	too small
3	....	too big
2.5	....	....
....	....	....
....	....	....
....	....	....

$x =$ ....

[Total 4 marks]

2 The equation $x^2(x + 1) = 64$ has a solution between 3 and 4. 

Find this solution to 1 decimal place.
Use the trial and improvement method and show your working.

$x =$ ....

[Total 4 marks]

3 Use trial and improvement to solve $4^x = 33$. 

Give your answer correct to 2 decimal places.
Show all of your working.

$x =$ ....

[Total 4 marks]

Exam Practice Tip

With trial and improvement questions it's really REALLY important that you write down all of your working in the exam. If you don't, the examiner won't be able to tell which method you've used and you'll probably end up losing marks... which would be sad, especially if you've gone to all the effort of getting the answer right.

Simultaneous Equations and Graphs

1 The diagram below shows graphs of $2y - x = 5$ and $4y + 3x = 25$. 

Use the diagram to solve these simultaneous equations:

$2y - x = 5$
$4y + 3x = 25$

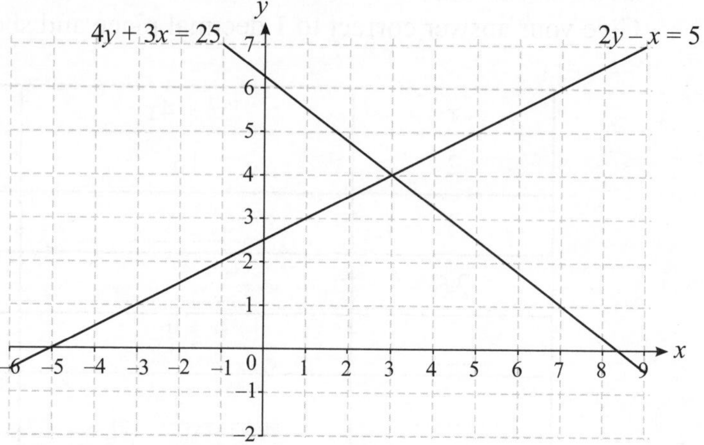

$x =$ .... $y =$ ....

[Total 1 mark]

2 The diagram below shows graphs of $y = x + 1$ and $y = 4 - 2x$. 

a) Use the diagram to solve these simultaneous equations:

$y = x + 1$
$y = 4 - 2x$

$x =$ .... $y =$ ....

[1]

b) By drawing another straight line, solve these simultaneous equations:

$y = x + 1$
$3y = x + 9$

$x =$ .... $y =$ ....

[2]

[Total 3 marks]

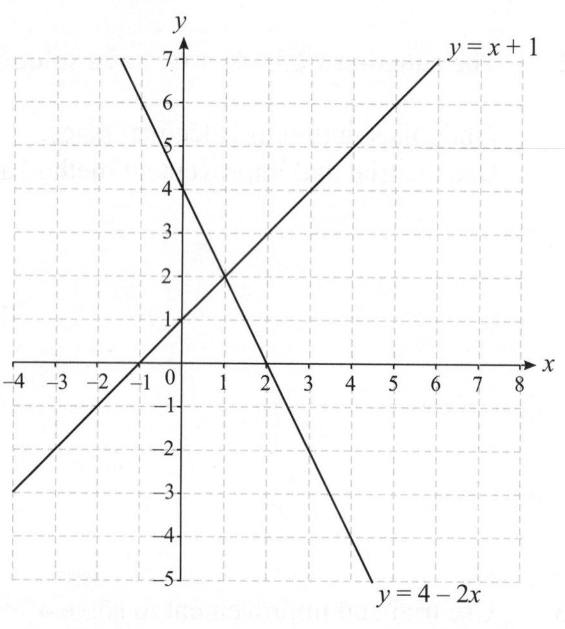

3 The diagram below shows part of the graph of $y = 4x - x^2$. 

Use the graph to solve these simultaneous equations.

$y = 5x - 2$
$y = 4x - x^2$

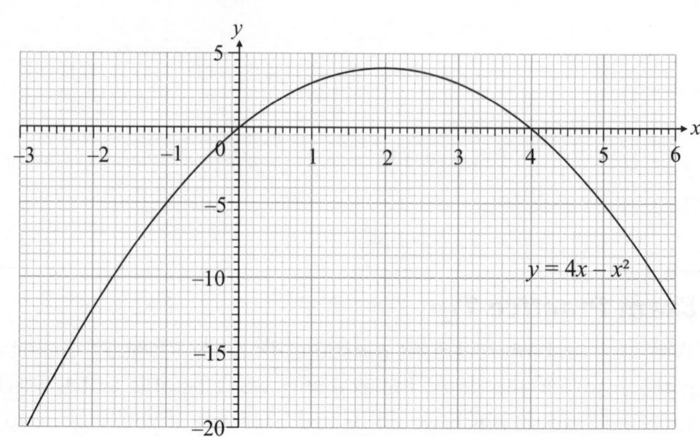

$x =$ .... , $y =$ ....

and $x =$ .... , $y =$ ....

[Total 3 marks]

4 The diagram below shows part of the graph of $y = x^2 + 2x - 2$.

Use the graph to solve these simultaneous equations.

$y = x^2 + 2x - 2$
$y = 3x + 10$

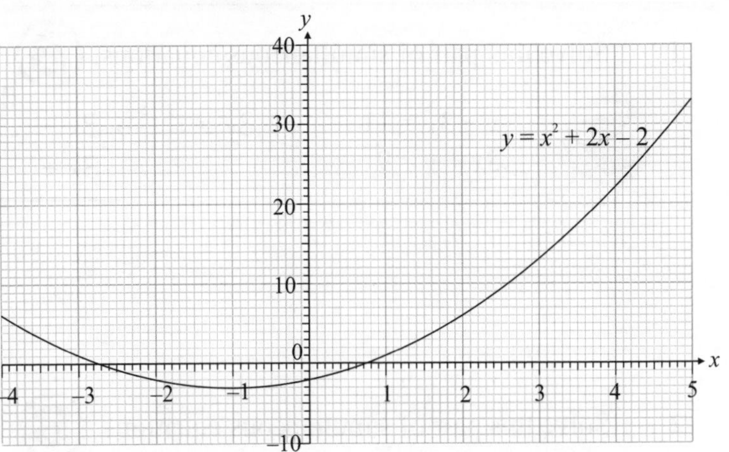

$x =$ .... , $y =$ ....

and $x =$ .... , $y =$ ....

[Total 3 marks]

5 The diagram on the right shows the graphs of $y = \dfrac{6}{x-2}$ and $y = 2x - 5$.

Using these graphs, write down the solution(s) of the equation:

$6 = (x - 2)(2x - 5)$

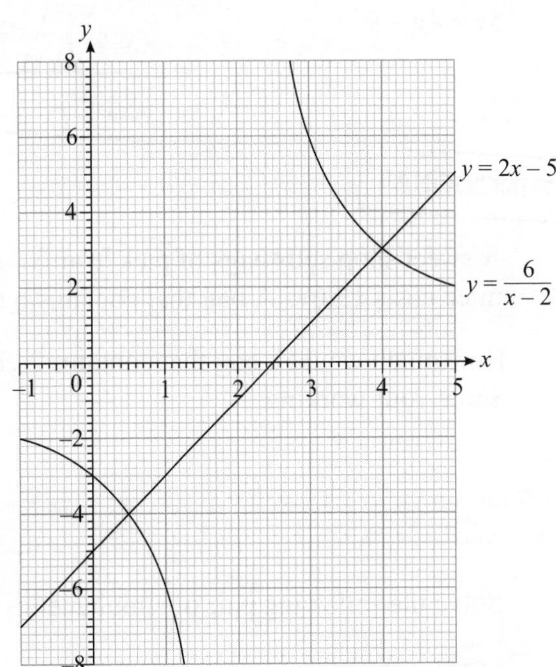

....

[Total 3 marks]

6 The diagram on the right shows the graph of $x^2 + y^2 = 16$.

Use the graph to solve these simultaneous equations.

$x^2 + y^2 = 16$
$y + x = 4$

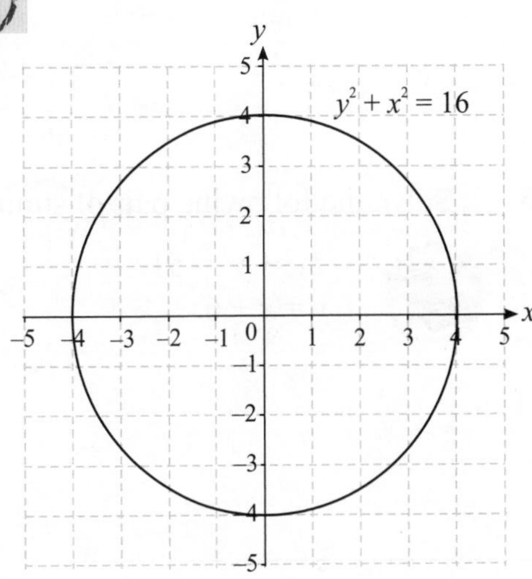

$x =$ .... , $y =$ ....

and $x =$ .... , $y =$ ....

[Total 3 marks]

Score: ______ / **16**

Simultaneous Equations

1 Solve this pair of simultaneous equations. (B)

$x + 3y = 11$
$3x + y = 9$

x + 3y = 11 $\xrightarrow{\times 3}$ 3x + ... = ...
3x + y = 9 −
............y = ...
y = ...

x + (3 × ....) = 11
x = 11 − ....
x = ...

$x =$ .... $y =$ ....

[Total 3 marks]

2 Solve this pair of simultaneous equations. (B)

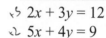

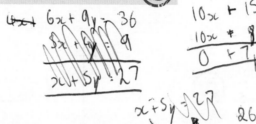

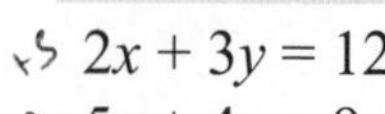

$2x + 3y = 12$
$5x + 4y = 9$

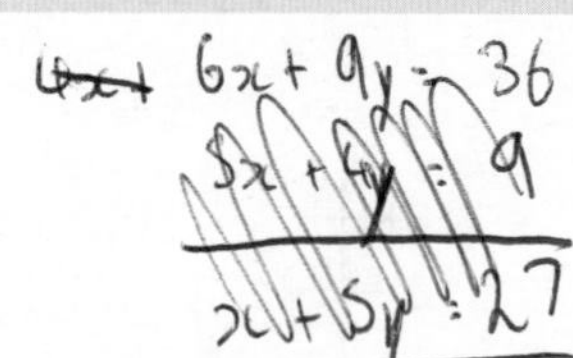

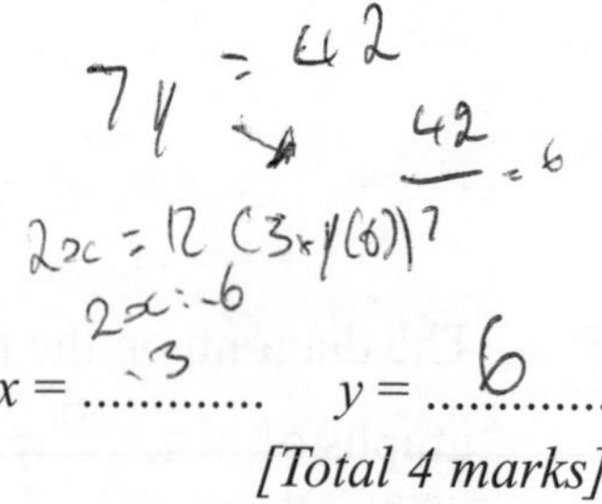

$x =$ .... $y =$ ....

[Total 4 marks]

FUNCTIONAL

3 A sweet shop sells bags of pick 'n' mix. A bag that contains 4 chocolate frogs and 3 sugar mice costs £3.69. A bag that contains 6 chocolate frogs and 2 sugar mice costs £3.96.

How much would a bag that contains 2 chocolate frogs and 5 sugar mice cost?
Show your working.

£ ....

[Total 4 marks]

4 Solve the following pair of simultaneous equations.

$x^2 + y = 4$
$y = 4x - 1$

$x =$ .... , $y =$ ....

and $x =$ .... , $y =$ ....

[Total 5 marks]

5 Solve the following pair of simultaneous equations.

$2x^2 + y^2 = 51$
$y = x + 6$

$x =$ .... , $y =$ ....

and $x =$ .... , $y =$ ....

[Total 6 marks]

Exam Practice Tip

When you're solving simultaneous equations in the exam, it's always a good idea to check your answers at the end. Just substitute your values for x and y back into the original equations and see if they add up as they should. If they don't then you must have gone wrong somewhere, so go back and check your working.

Score

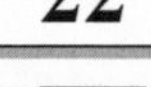

22

Direct and Inverse Proportion

1 The value of x is directly proportional to the value of y. When $y = 27$, $x = 9$. 

a) Write a formula for y in terms of x.

.... *[3]*

b) Calculate the value of y when $x = 8$.

$y =$ .... *[1]*

[Total 4 marks]

2 The value of m is inversely proportional to the value of n. When $m = 3$, $n = 12$. 

 Find the value of m when $n = 4$.

$m =$ ....

[Total 4 marks]

3 c is inversely proportional to d^2. When $c = 2$, $d = 3$.

 a) Write an expression for c in terms of d.

.... *[3]*

b) Find the values of d when $c = 0.5$.

.... *[2]*

[Total 5 marks]

4 A is directly proportional to the square root of T. When $T = 36$, $A = 4$.

 a) Write an expression for A in terms of T.

.... *[3]*

b) Explain what happens to the value of A when the value of T halves.

[1]

[Total 4 marks]

5 The value of y is inversely proportional to the cube of x. When $y = 1.5$, $x = 8$. (A)

Find the value of y when $x = 2$.

$y =$ ....

[Total 4 marks]

6 The value of p is directly proportional to the cube root of q. When $p = 15$, $q = 27$. (A)

Find the value of q when $p = 20$.

$q =$ ....

[Total 4 marks]

FUNCTIONAL

7 If you hang an object on the end of a spring, the amount that the spring stretches by, x cm, is directly proportional to the mass of the object, M g. When $M = 40$, $x = 2$. (A)

a) Write an equation connecting x and M.

....

[3]

b) How much would the spring stretch if an object with a mass of 55 g was hung on the end of it?

.... cm

[1]

[Total 4 marks]

FUNCTIONAL

8 Round a bend on a railway track the height difference (h mm) between the outer and inner rails must vary in direct proportion to the square of the maximum permitted speed (S km/h). When $S = 50$, $h = 35$. (A)

Calculate h when $S = 40$.

....

[Total 4 marks]

Score: ☐ / **33**

☐ ☐ ☐

Proof

***1** Prove that an odd number multiplied by an even number is always an even number. 

[Total 3 marks]

***2** Prove that the sum of three consecutive even numbers is always a multiple of 6. 

[Total 3 marks]

***3** Prove that the difference between the squares of two consecutive even numbers is always a multiple of 4. 

[Total 3 marks]

***4** Prove that $(3n + 2)^2 - (n + 2)^2 = 8n(n + 1)$ for all values of n. 

[Total 3 marks]

***5** Prove that $(2n - 1)^2 + 8(2n - 1)$ is always an odd number for integer values of n. 

[Total 6 marks]

Exam Practice Tip

In the exam, questions where you're asked to prove something usually test your quality of written communication. This means that you could lose marks if you don't present your answer in a clear and logical way, so make sure you show all of your working and set your answer out in a sensible way.

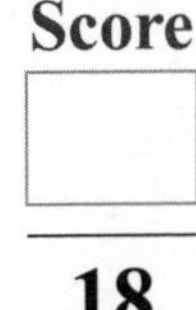

Straight-Line Graphs

1 This is a question about the function $y = 2x + 3$. 

a) Complete the table below.

x	−2	−1	0	1	2
y	−1			5	

[2]

b) Draw the graph of $y = 2x + 3$ on the grid.

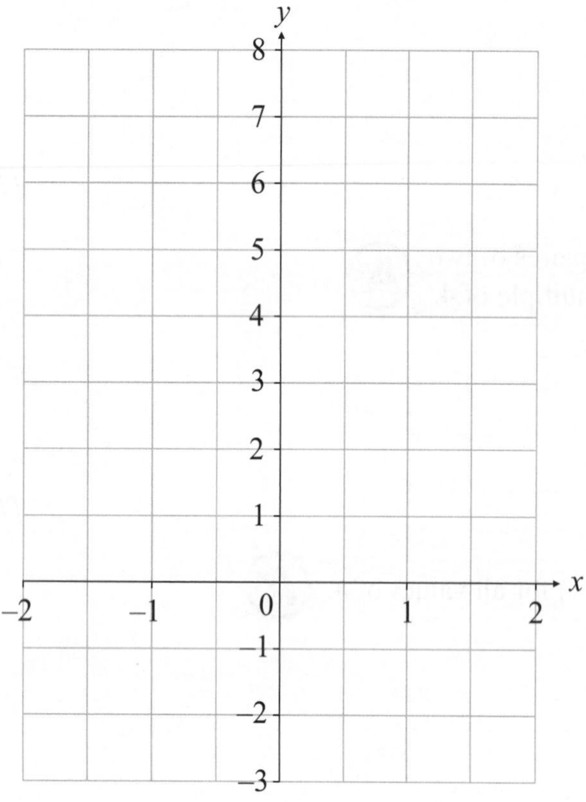

Use a ruler to draw the lines between your points.

[2]

c) Using your graph, find the value of y when $x = 1.5$.

$y =$ ....

[1]

d) Using your graph, find the value of x when $y = 2$.

$x =$ ....

[1]

[Total 6 marks]

2 Draw the graph $2y + x = 7$ on the axes below, for values of x in the range $-2 \leq x \leq 10$.

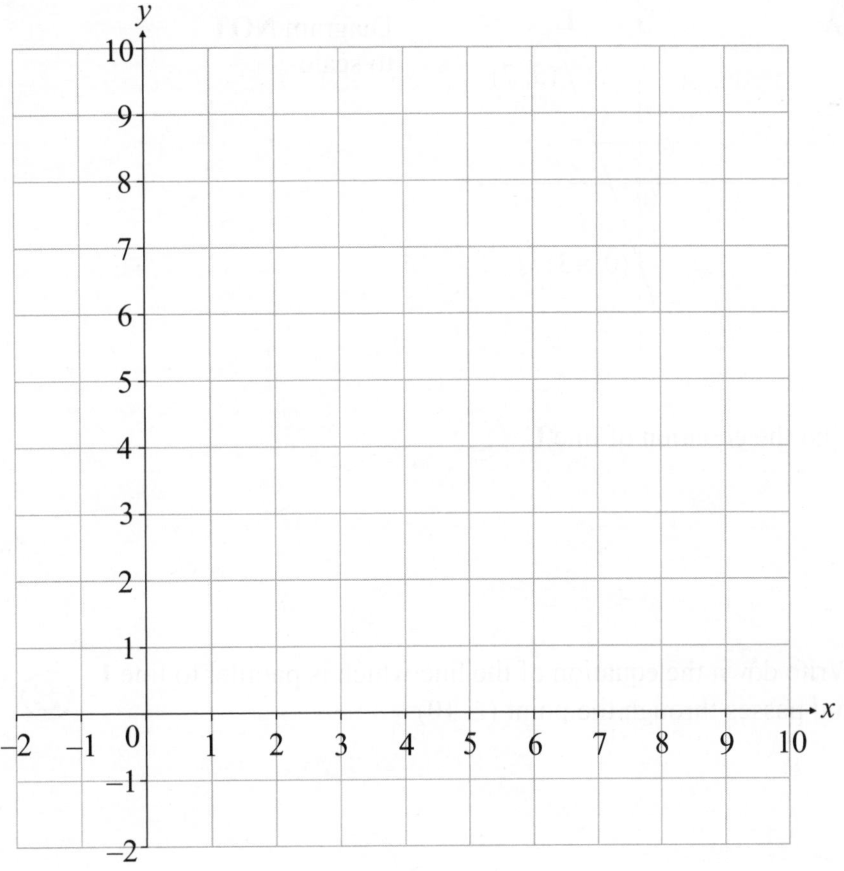

[Total 3 marks]

3 Point P has coordinates (6, 2, 1) and point Q has coordinates (–4, 1, 3).

a) Find the coordinates of the midpoint of PQ.

(................ , ..., ...)

[2]

b) Point R has coordinates $(a, b, 8)$. The midpoint of PR is (3, 5, 4.5).
Find the values of a and b.

a = ...

b = ...

[3]

[Total 5 marks]

4 Line **L** passes through the points (0, –3) and (5, 7), as shown below.

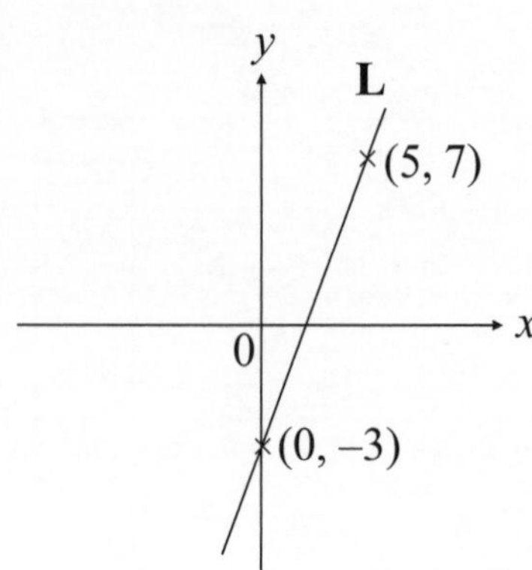

Diagram **NOT** to scale

a) Find the equation of line **L**. 

....

[3]

b) Write down the equation of the line which is parallel to line **L** and passes through the point (2, 10). 

....

[3]

[Total 6 marks]

5 The lines $y = 3x + 4$ and $y = 2x + 6$ intersect at the point M. (A)

Line N goes through point M and is perpendicular to the line $y = 2x + 6$.

Find the equation of line N.

....

[Total 5 marks]

Score: ____ / **25**

Quadratic Graphs

1 This is a question about the function $y = x^2 + 2x - 5$.

a) Complete the table below. (C)

x	-4	-3	-2	-1	0	1	2
y		-2	-5			-2	3

Check your calculation method by seeing if you can find the y-values given in the question.

[2]

b) Use your table to draw the graph of $y = x^2 + 2x - 5$ on the grid, for values of x in the range $-4 \le x \le 2$.

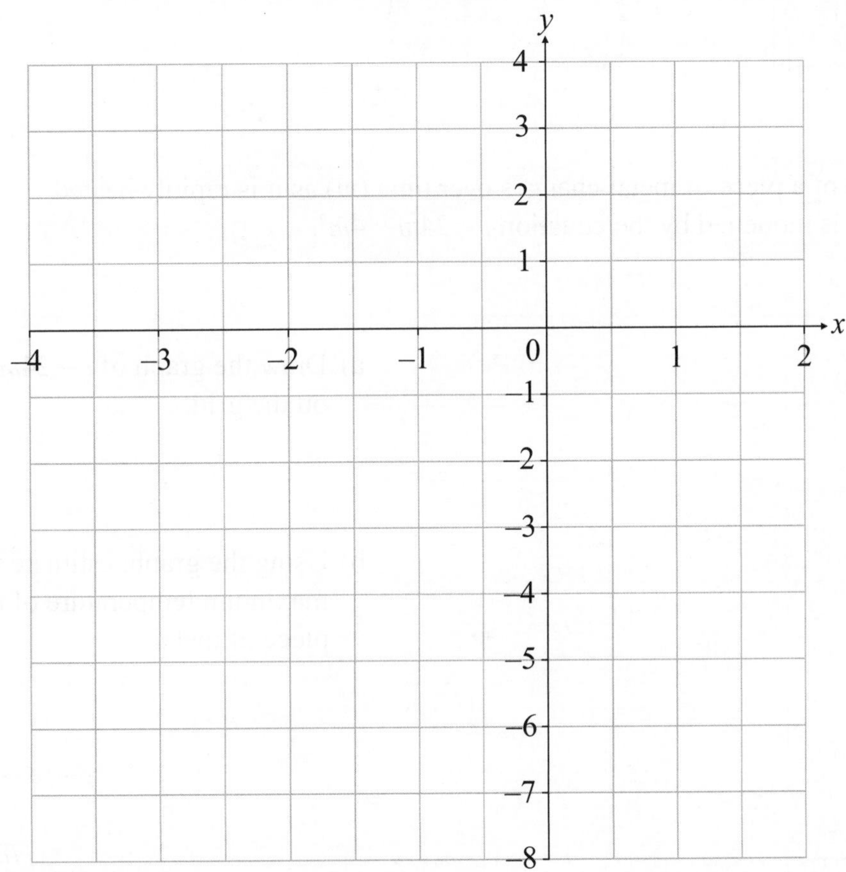

[2]

c) Using the graph above, give estimates for the solutions of $x^2 + 2x - 5 = -1$. (B)

x = ... and x = ...

[2]

[Total 6 marks]

2 This graph below shows $y = x^2 - 3x + 2$. 

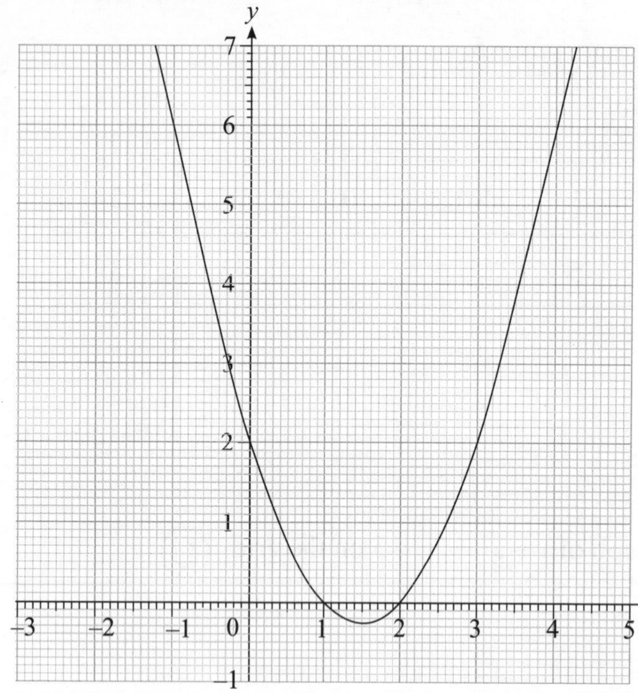

a) Find the values of x when $x^2 - 3x + 2 = 0$.

$x =$ .... and $x =$ ....

[1]

b) Using the graph, find the solutions of $x^2 - 3x + 2 = 6$.

$x =$ .... and $x =$ ....

[2]

[Total 3 marks]

3 The temperature (t) of a piece of metal changes over time (m) as it is rapidly heated and then cooled. It is modelled by the equation $t = 24m - 4m^2$.

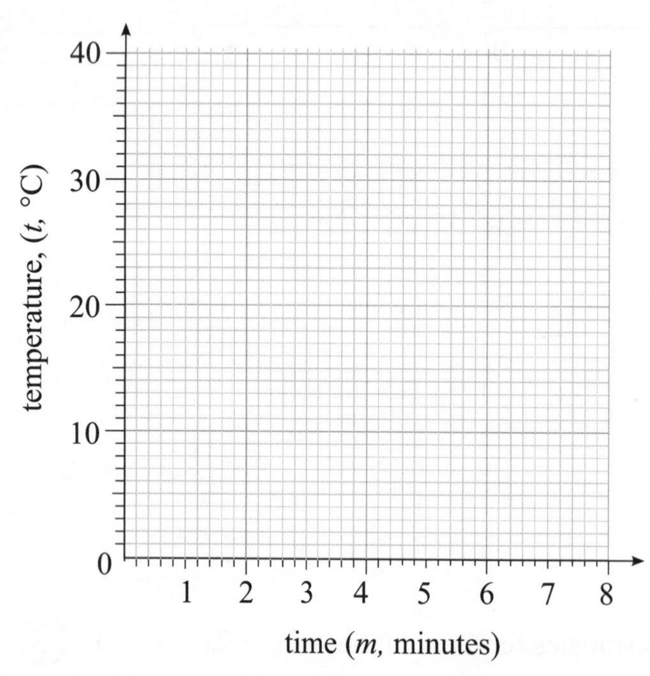

a) Draw the graph of $t = 24m - 4m^2$ on the grid. (C)

[2]

b) Using the graph, estimate the maximum temperature of the piece of metal. (B)

.... °C

[1]

[Total 3 marks]

Exam Practice Tip

If your curves aren't nice and smooth when you draw out your quadratic graphs, you can be pretty sure you've gone wrong somewhere. Just take another look at your values and plot again. You could also solve these quadratic equations using algebra, but if the question asks you to use the graph, then make sure you use it.

Score: 12

Harder Graphs

1 This question is about the function $y = x^3 - 4x^2 + 4$. 

a) Complete the table below.

x	–1	–0.5	0	0.5	1	1.5	2	2.5	3	3.5	4
y	–1	2.875	4	3.125	1	–1.625	–4				

[2]

b) Use your table to draw the graph of $y = x^3 - 4x^2 + 4$ on the grid, for values of x in the range $-1 \leq x \leq 4$.

[2]

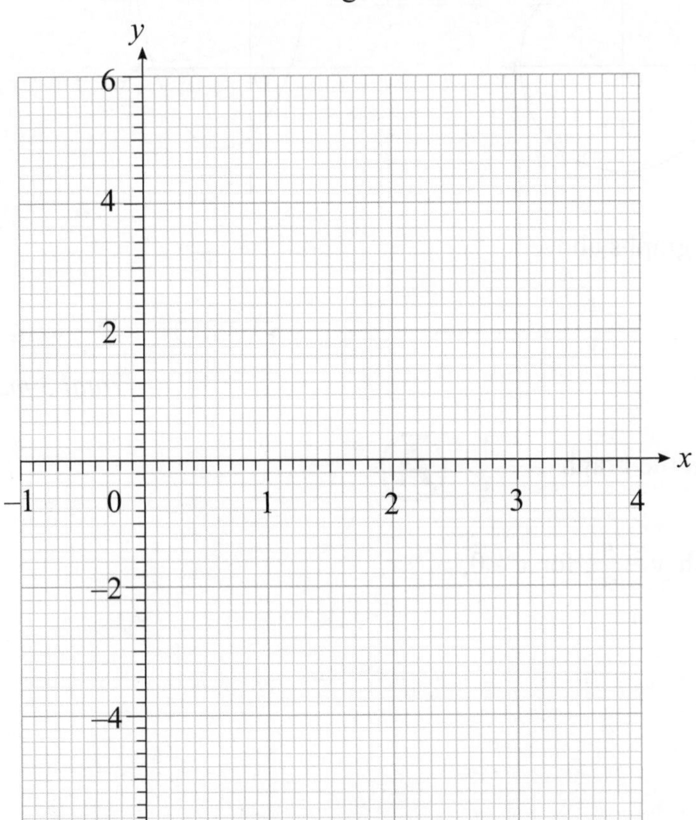

c) Estimate the solutions of the equation $x^3 - 4x^2 + 4 = 0$.

....

[1]

[Total 5 marks]

Don't use a ruler to join up the dots in curved graphs.

2 The graph of $y = \cos x$ is shown below for $0° \leq x \leq 360°$ 

As shown on the graph, $\cos 50° = 0.643$.

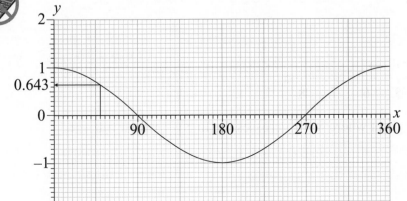

Give another value of x, found on this graph, where $\cos x = 0.643$.

$x =$ ....

[Total 1 mark]

3 Sketches of different graphs are shown below. 

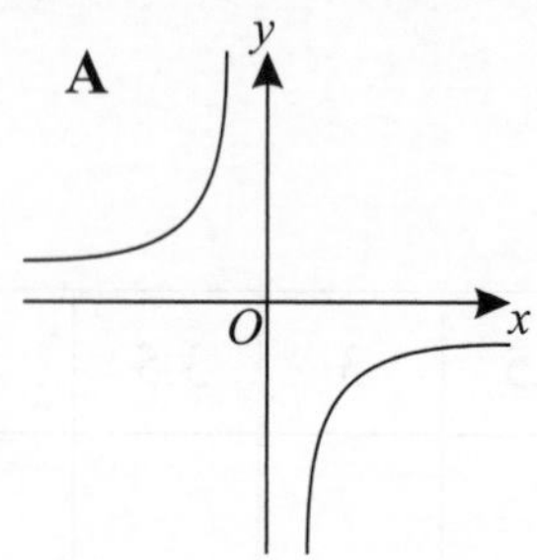

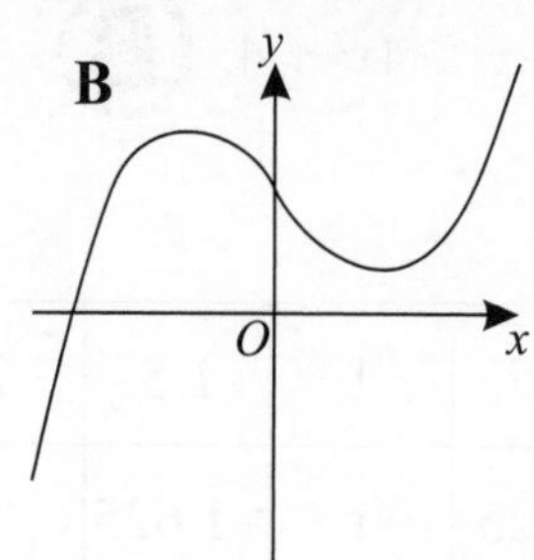

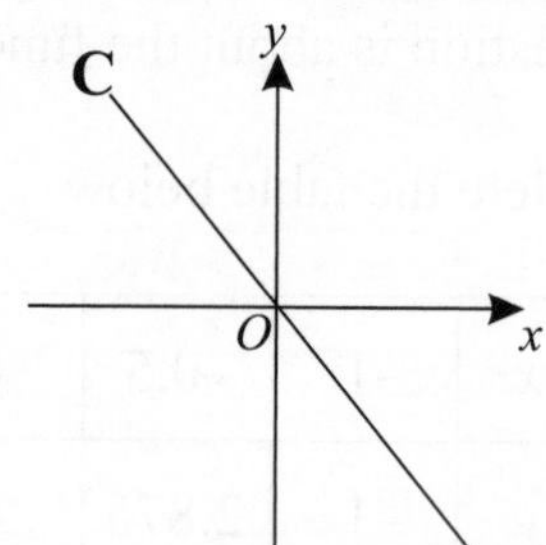

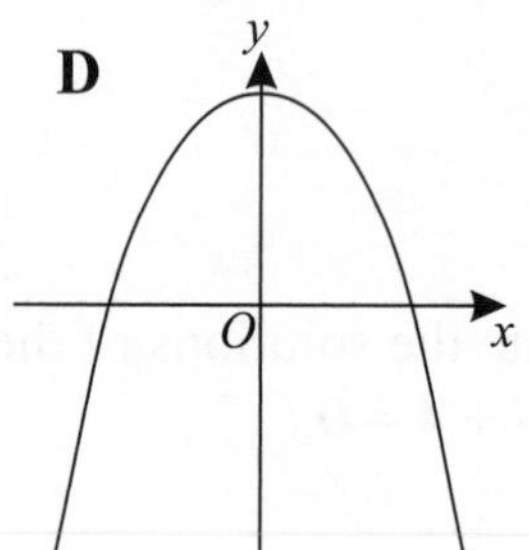

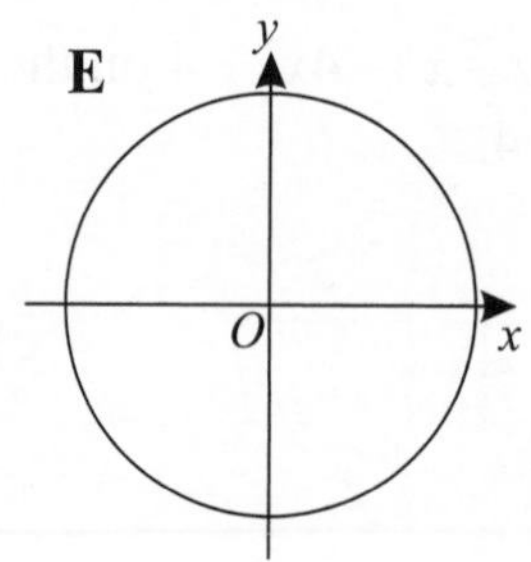

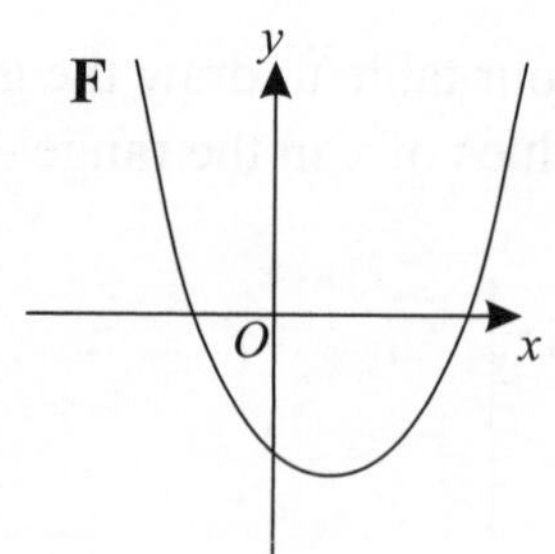

Match each equation below to one of the graphs above.

a) $3x^2 - 6x - 3$ .... b) $y = -\frac{4}{x}$ .... c) $x^2 + y^2 = 25$ ....

[Total 3 marks]

4 The sketch below shows two points from the graph $y = \frac{4}{x}$ 

a) Complete the sketch below of the graph $y = \frac{4}{x}$, for $x > 0$.

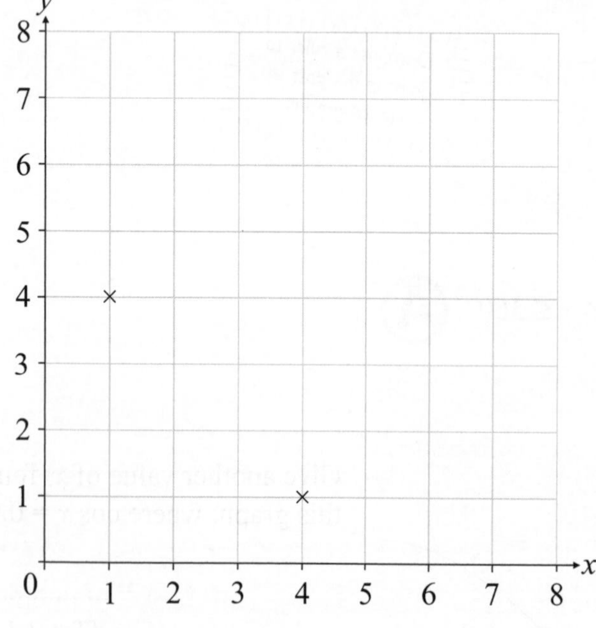

[2]

b) Find the coordinates of the point where $y = \frac{4}{x}$ crosses the line $y = x$ for $x > 0$.

(................ , ...)

[1]

[Total 3 marks]

5 Draw the graph of $x^2 + y^2 = 16$ on the grid below. 

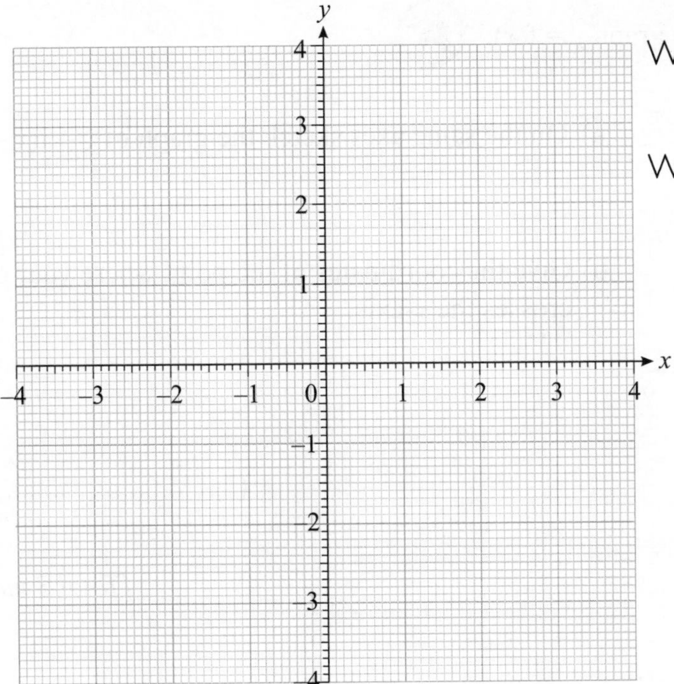

When x = 0, y^2 = 16, so y = ... and y = ...

When y = 0, x^2 = 16, so x = ... and x = ...

[Total 2 marks]

6 Cyril bought a rare book which was worth £800 on 1st January 2008.

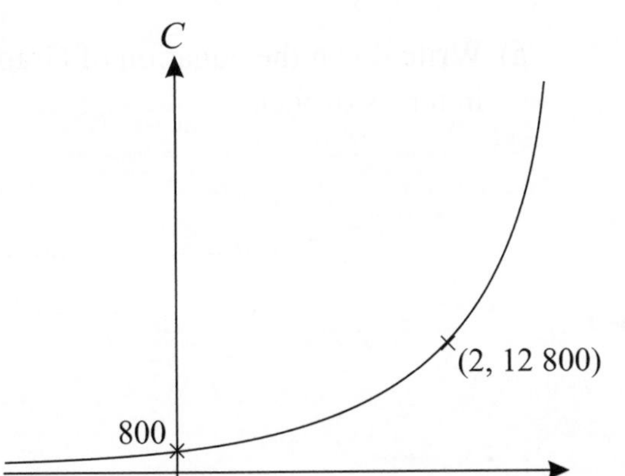

The book was worth £12 800 on 1st January 2010.

The value of the book over time is represented by the equation

$$C = xy^t$$

where x and y are positive integers and t is the number of years ($-2 \le t \le 3$). $t = 0$ on 1st January 2008.

a) Find the values of x and y, using the information given above.

x = ... and y = ...

[3]

b) What was the value of the book on 1st January 2006?

£ ....

[2]

[Total 5 marks]

Score: ☐ / **19**

Graph Transformations

1 The diagram below shows a sketch of the graph $y = f(x)$. 

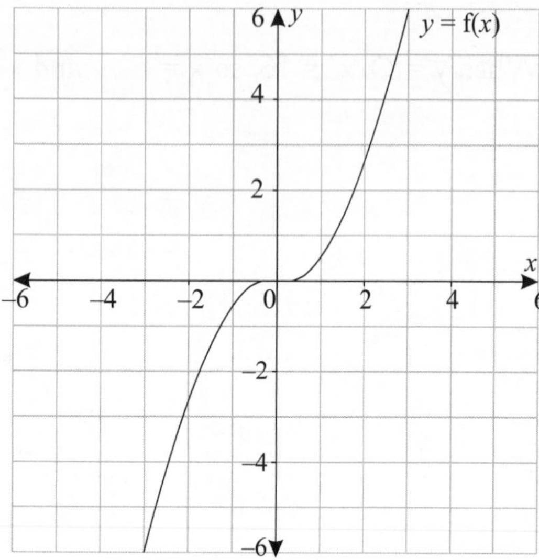

a) On the same axes sketch the graph of $y = f(x - 2)$.

[2]

b) Give the coordinates of the point where your curve crosses the x-axis.

(................ , ...)

[1]

[Total 3 marks]

2 The diagram below shows a sketch of $y = f(x)$. 

Graph **B** is a translation of $y = f(x)$.

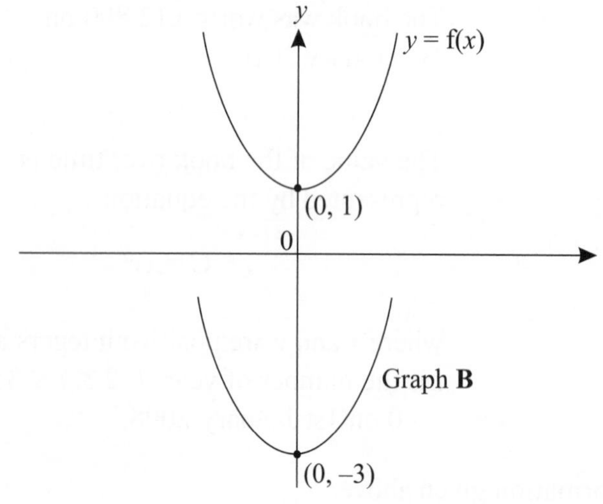

a) Write down the equation of Graph **B** in terms of $f(x)$.

$y =$ ....

[1]

b) Find the minimum point of the graph of $y = f(x + 2)$.

(................ , ...)

[2]

c) Find the minimum point of the graph of $y = f(x - 4) + 1$.

(................ , ...)

[2]

d) Sketch $y = f(x) - 2$ on the axes above. Label this Graph **C**.

[1]

e) Sketch $y = f(x + 3)$ on the axes above. Label this Graph **D**.

[1]

[Total 7 marks]

3 The graph of $y = \sin x$ for $0° \leq x \leq 360°$ is shown on the grids below. 

a) On this grid sketch the graph of $y = \sin \frac{x}{2}$

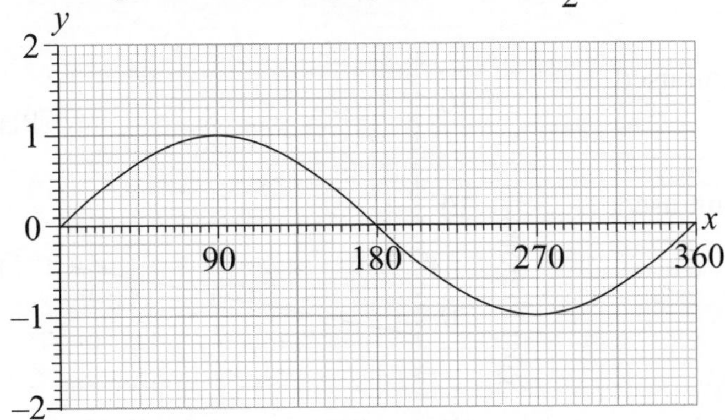

[1]

b) On this grid sketch the graph of $y = 2 \sin x$

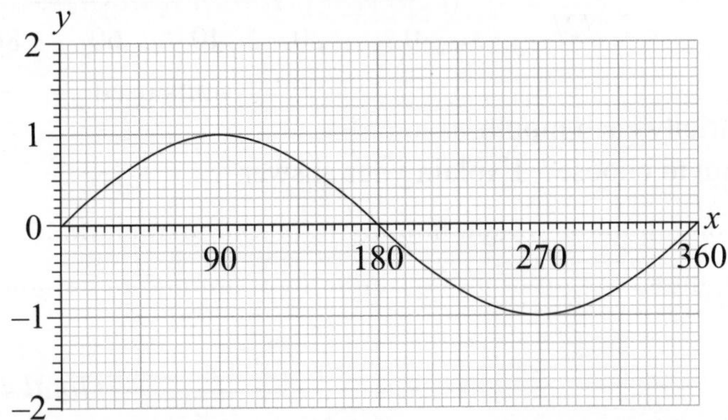

[1]

[Total 2 marks]

4 The graph of $y = \cos x$ for $0° \leq x \leq 360°$ is shown below. 

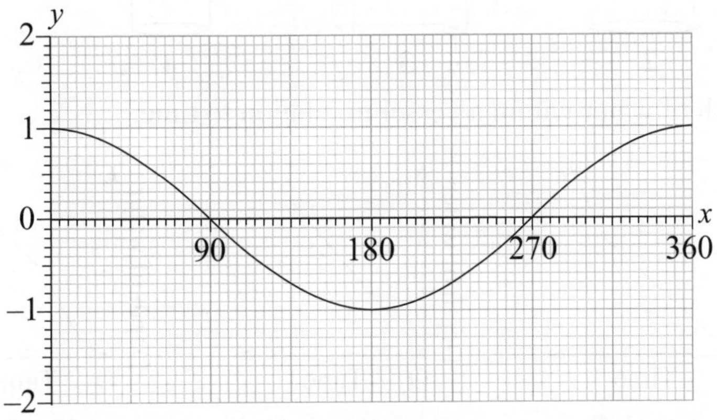

a) Sketch the graph of $y = 2 \cos (2x)$ on the grid.

[2]

b) One solution of $1 = 2 \cos (2x)$ is $x = 30$.
Work out the other solutions of $1 = 2 \cos (2x)$ for $0° \leq x \leq 360°$.

....

[2]

[Total 4 marks]

Score: /16

Real-Life Graphs

1 An electricity company offers its customers two different price plans. 

Plan **A:**
Monthly tariff of £18, plus 10p for each unit used.

Plan **B:**
No monthly tariff, just pay 40p for each unit used.

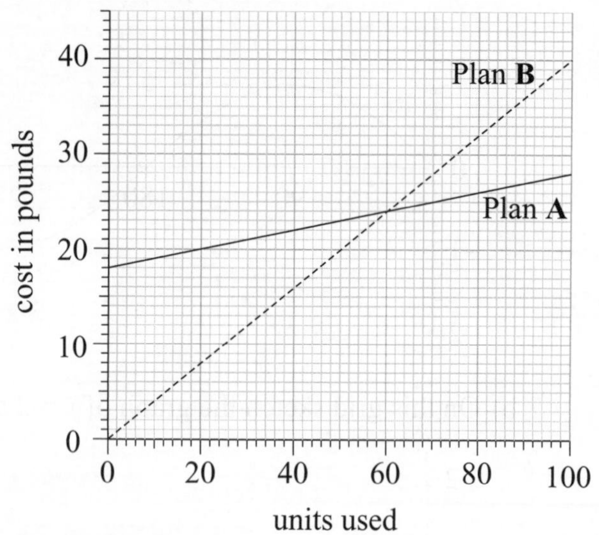

a) Use the graph to find the cost of using 70 units in a month for each plan.

Plan **A** ....

Plan **B** ....

[2]

*b) Mr Barker uses about 85 units of electricity each month.
Which price plan would you advise him to choose? Explain your answer.

....

....

[2]

[Total 4 marks]

2 Each of the vessels below is filled with water at a constant rate. (B)

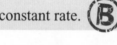

1 **2** 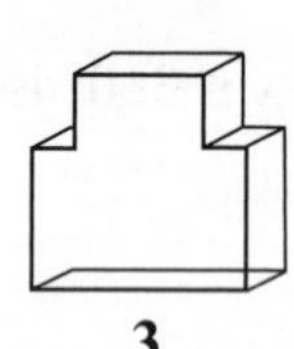 **3**  **4**

Each of these graphs show the depth of water within a vessel in relation to time.

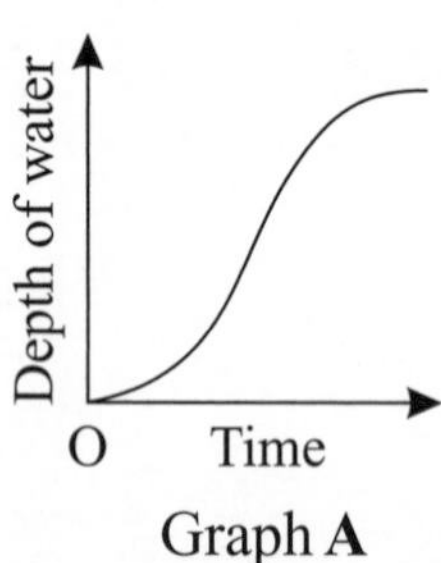

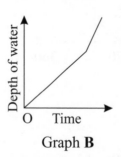

Graph **A**

Graph **B**

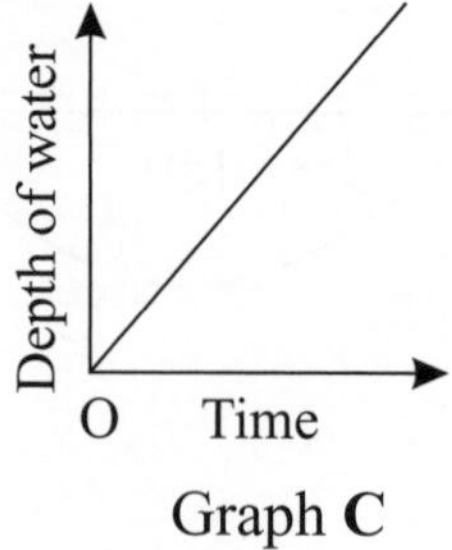

Graph **C**

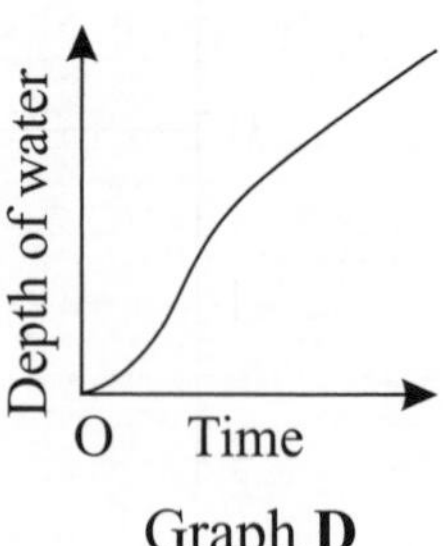

Graph **D**

Match the vessel with the correct graph.

Graph **A** and .... Graph **B** and .... Graph **C** and .... Graph **D** and ....

[2]

[Total 2 marks]

Score: ____ / **6**

Geometry

1 ABC is an isosceles triangle with $AB = BC$. ACD is a straight line. 

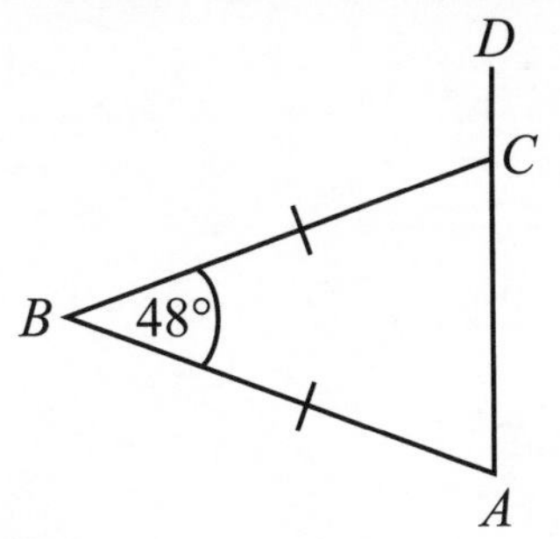

Diagram not accurately drawn

 Work out the size of angle BCD.

..................................°

[Total 3 marks]

2 $BCDE$ is a trapezium with angle $CDE = 90°$. $ABEF$ is a straight line. 

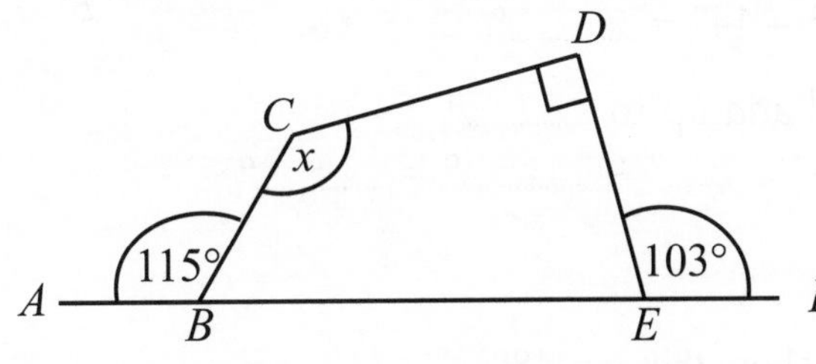

Diagram not accurately drawn

a) Work out the size of the angle marked x.

..................................°

[3]

*b) Give two reasons for your answer.

....

....

[2]

[Total 5 marks]

3 ABC is a scalene triangle. 

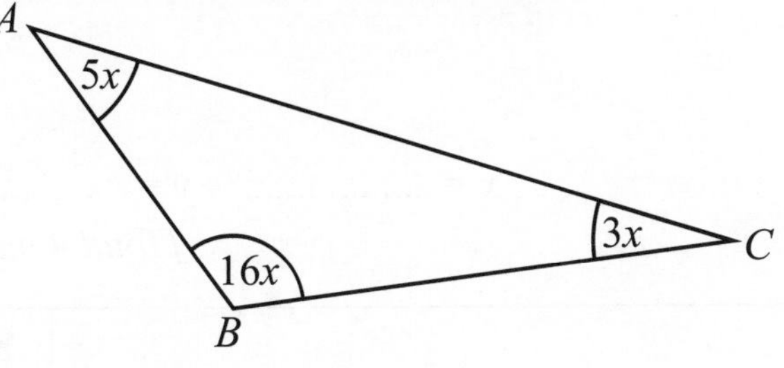

Diagram not accurately drawn

Work out the size of angle ABC.

..................................°

[Total 3 marks]

4 AB and CD are parallel lines. EF and GH are straight lines. 

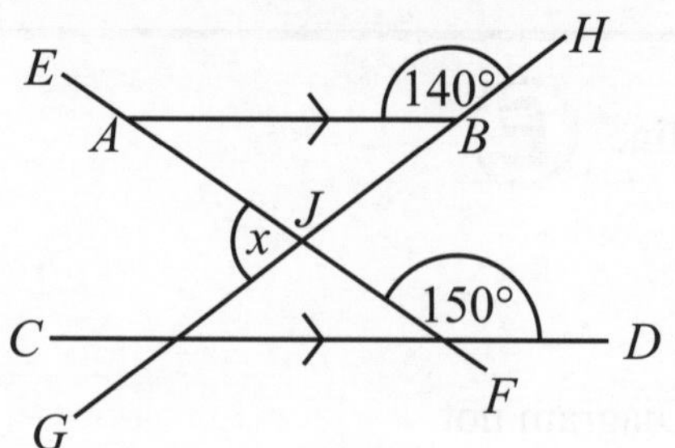

Work out the size of angle x.
Give reasons for each stage of your working.

Diagram not accurately drawn

....°

[Total 4 marks]

5 DEF and BEC are straight lines that cross at E. AFB and AC are perpendicular to each other. 

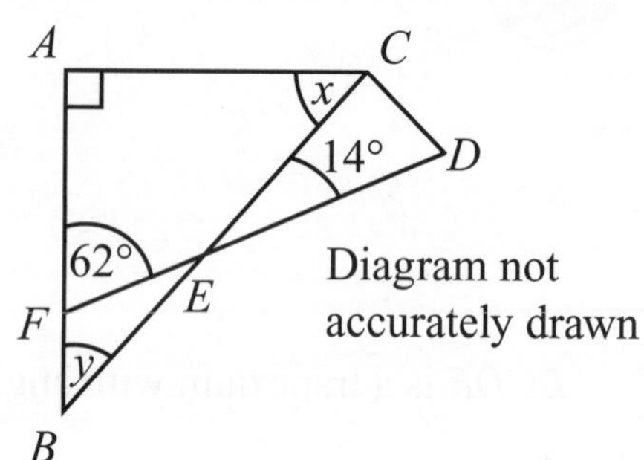

Diagram not accurately drawn

a) Find angle x.
Give a reason for each stage of your working.

Angles on a straight line add up to ....°,
so angle FEC = ...° – 14° = ...°

Angles in a quadrilateral add up to ....°,
so x = ...° – 90° – ....° – ....° = ...°

x = ...°

[2]

b) Use your answer to a) to show that $y = 48°$.

[2]

[Total 4 marks]

6 $ABCD$ is a trapezium. Lines AB and DC are parallel to each other. 

If you extend the lines in the diagram, it might be easier to see how to solve the problem.

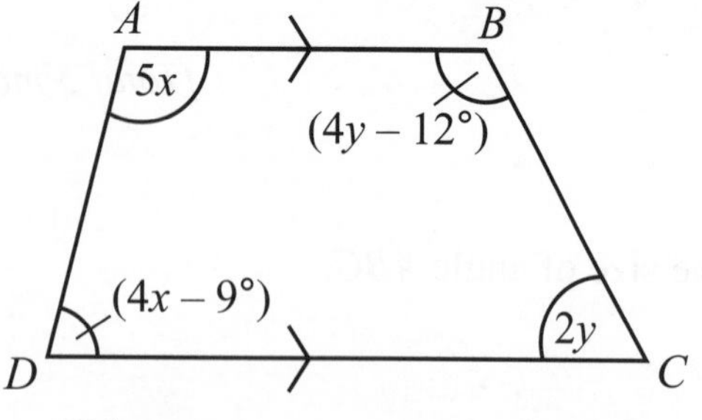

Diagram not accurately drawn

Find the values of x and y.

x = ...° y = ...°

[Total 4 marks]

Exam Practice Tip

If you find yourself staring at a geometry problem in the exam not knowing where to start, just try finding any angles you can — don't worry tooooo much at first about the particular angle you've been asked to find. Go through the rules of geometry one at a time, and apply each of them in as many ways as possible.

Score

23

Polygons

1 Part of a regular polygon is shown below. Each interior angle is 150°. 

150°

Diagram not accurately drawn

 Calculate the number of sides of the polygon.

....

[Total 3 marks]

2 The diagram shows a regular octagon. *AB* is a side of the octagon and *O* is its centre. 

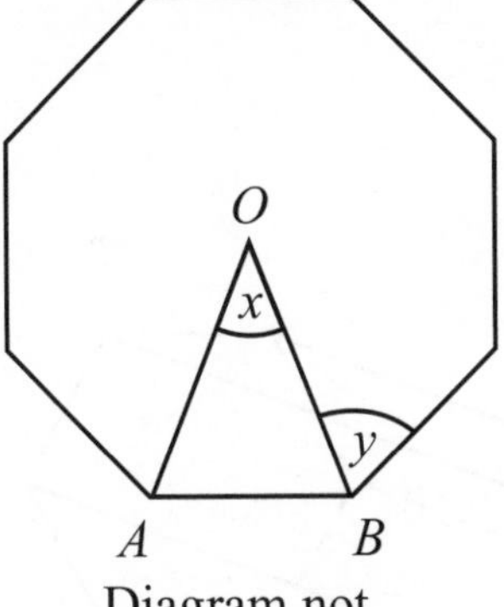

Diagram not accurately drawn

a) Work out the size of the angle marked x.

$x =$ ....°

[2]

b) Work out the size of the angle marked y.

$y =$ ....°

[2]

[Total 4 marks]

3 Part of a regular polygon is shown below. The exterior angles of the polygon are 24°. 

Diagram not accurately drawn

 Work out the number of sides of the regular polygon.

....

[Total 2 marks]

4 A regular polygon has 18 sides. 

 Prove that regular 18-sided polygons do not tessellate.

[Total 3 marks]

Exam Practice Tip

You need to know the number of sides of a regular polygon to work out its interior and exterior angles — so make sure you've swotted up on the different types of polygon. Altogether now: equilateral triangle (3), square (4), pentagon (5), hexagon (6), heptagon (7), octagon (8), nonagon (9), decagon (10).

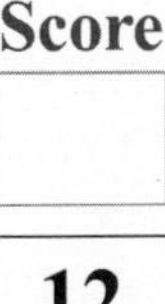

Symmetry

1 Below is an image of a cog. 

a) Draw all the lines of symmetry for the cog. *[2]*

b) What order of rotational symmetry does the cog have?

....

[1]

[Total 3 marks]

2 The diagram below shows a prism. 

 Draw in **one** plane of symmetry for the prism on the diagram.

This prism has several different planes of symmetry, but you only need to draw one.

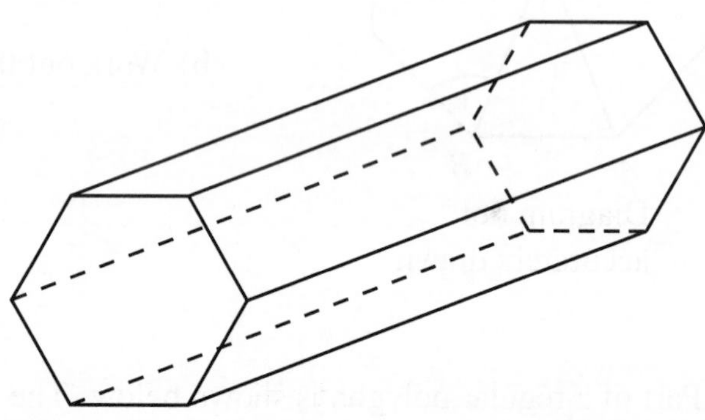

[Total 2 marks]

3 Below is a pattern made by shading part of a square grid. 

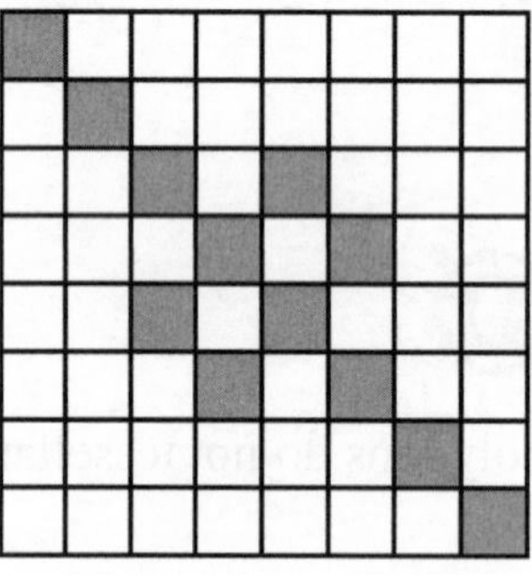

a) Draw all the lines of symmetry for the pattern. *[2]*

b) What is the order of rotational symmetry of the pattern?

....

[1]

[Total 3 marks]

Score: /8

Circle Geometry

1 The diagram shows a circle, centre O. A, B, C and D are points on the circumference. 

Not to scale

a) Work out the size of angle BCD. Give a reason for your answer.

....

....

[2]

b) Explain why angle $BAD = 105°$.

....

....

[1]

[Total 3 marks]

2 The diagram below shows a circle with centre O. A, B, C and D are points on the circumference of the circle and AOC is a straight line. 

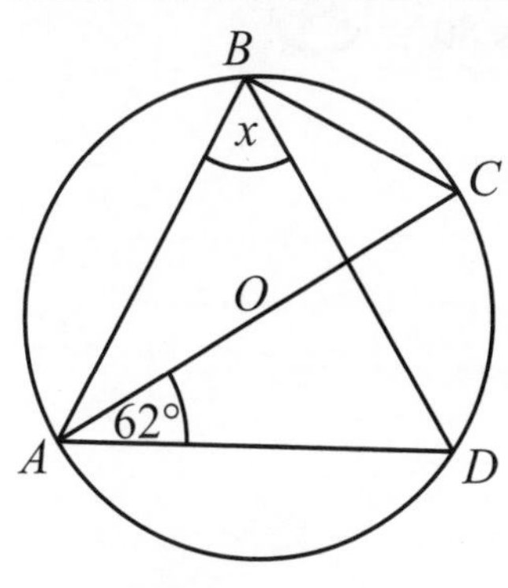

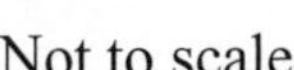
Not to scale

Work out the size of the angle marked x.

Angle DBC = ...°

Angle ABC = ...°

Angle x = ...° − ....° = ...°

x = ...°

[Total 3 marks]

3 A, B, C and D are points on the circumference of a circle. Angle BCD is 28° and angle ADC is 24°. 

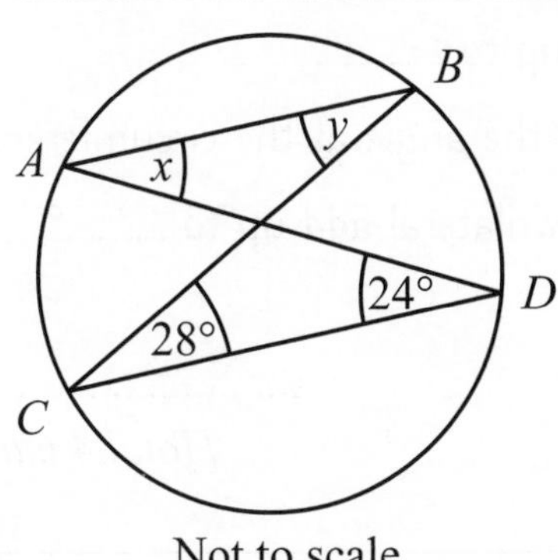

Not to scale

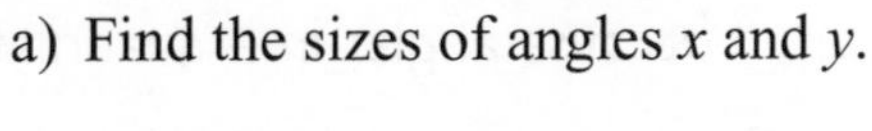

a) Find the sizes of angles x and y.

x = ...° y = ...°

[2]

b) Give a reason for your answers.

....

....

[1]

[Total 3 marks]

4 The diagram shows a circle with centre O. A, B and C are points on the circumference. AD and CD are tangents to the circle and ABE is a straight line. Angle CDO is 24°.

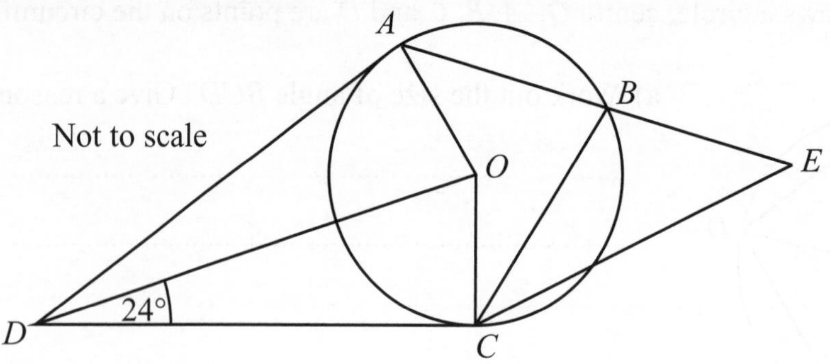

Find the size of angle CBE.

..............................°

[Total 5 marks]

5 In the diagram, O is the centre of the circle. A, B, C and D are points on the circumference of the circle and DE and BE are tangents. Angle DEB is 80°.

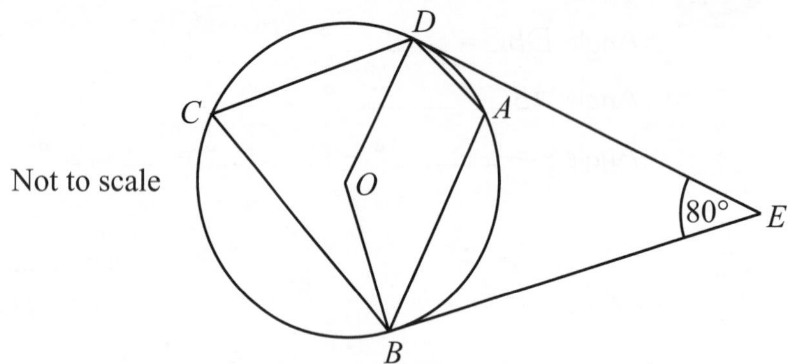

Work out the size of angle DAB, giving reasons for each step in your working.

Angles ODE and OBE are both ....° because a tangent always meets a radius at ....°.

Angle DOB = ...° because angles in a quadrilateral add up to ....°.

Angle DCB = ...° because an angle at the centre is twice the angle at the circumference.

Angle DAB = ...° because opposite angles of a cyclic quadrilateral add up to ....°.

..............................°

[Total 4 marks]

Exam Practice Tip

Make sure you know the rules about circles really, really well. Draw them out and stick them all over your bedroom walls, your fridge, even your dog. Then in the exam, go through the rules one-by-one and use them to fill in as many angles in the diagram as you can. Keep an eye out for sneaky isosceles triangles too.

Score ____ / **18**

The Four Transformations

1 Triangle **A** has been drawn on the grid below. It has vertices at (2, 1), (5, 2) and (4, 4). 

Reflect triangle **A** in the line $x = -1$. Label your image **B**.

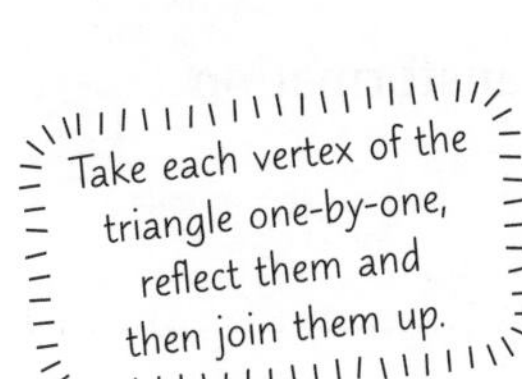

Take each vertex of the triangle one-by-one, reflect them and then join them up.

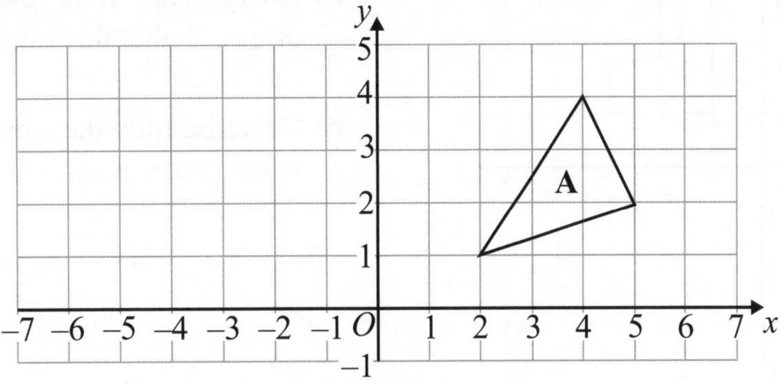

[Total 2 marks]

2 Shape **F** has been drawn on the grid below. 

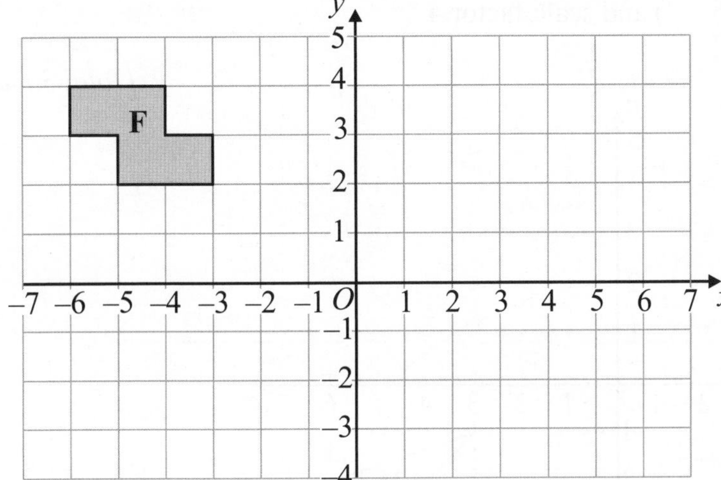

a) Translate shape **F** by the vector $\begin{pmatrix} 2 \\ -5 \end{pmatrix}$. Label your image **G**.

[1]

b) Rotate shape **F** by 90° clockwise around the point (0, –2). Label your image **H**.

[2]

[Total 3 marks]

3 In the diagram below, **B** is an image of **A**. 

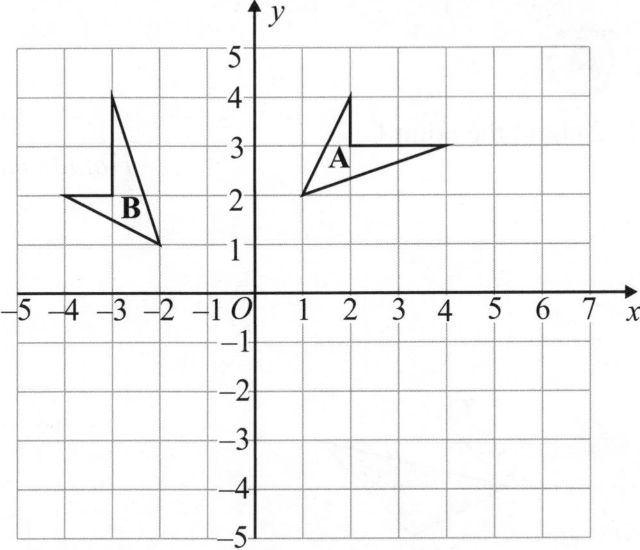

a) Describe fully the single transformation that maps **A** onto **B**.

....

....

....

[3]

b) Translate shape **B** by the vector $\begin{pmatrix} -1 \\ -4 \end{pmatrix}$. Label the image as **C**.

[1]

[Total 4 marks]

4 Shape **A** has been drawn on the grid below.

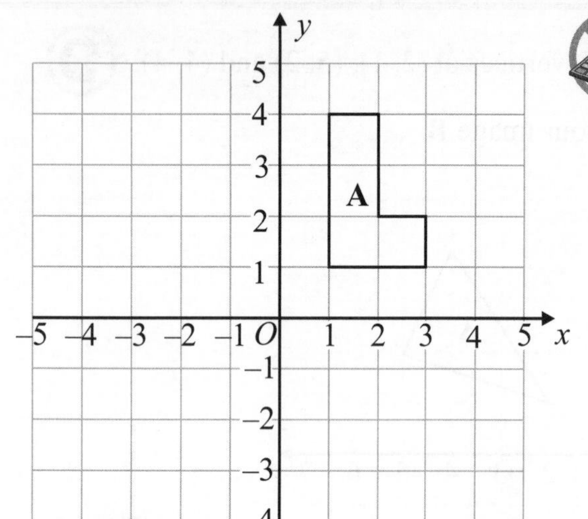

a) On the grid, reflect shape **A** in the x-axis. Label this image **B**. 

[2]

b) Rotate shape **B** 90° clockwise about the origin. Label this image **C**. 

[2]

c) Describe fully the single transformation which maps **A** onto **C**.

....

[2]

[Total 6 marks]

5 Triangle **R** has been drawn on the grid below. 

Enlarge triangle **R** with centre (6, –3) and scale factor 4.
Label your image **S**.

[Total 3 marks]

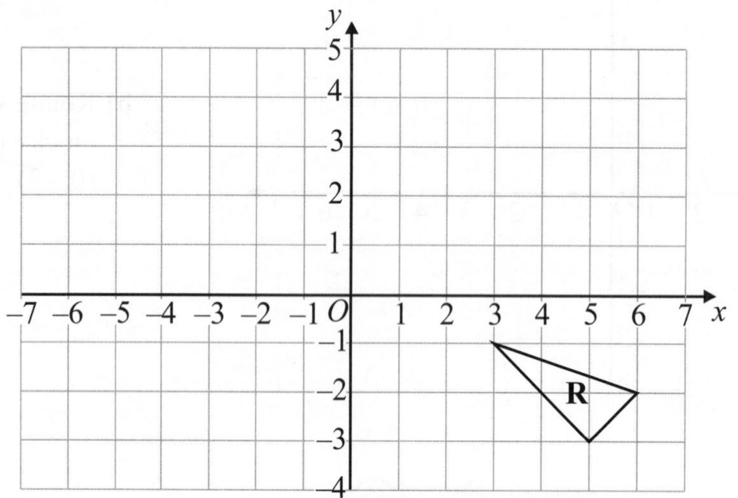

6 A triangle has been drawn on the grid below. 

Enlarge the triangle by a scale factor of –2 about the point **C**.

[Total 3 marks]

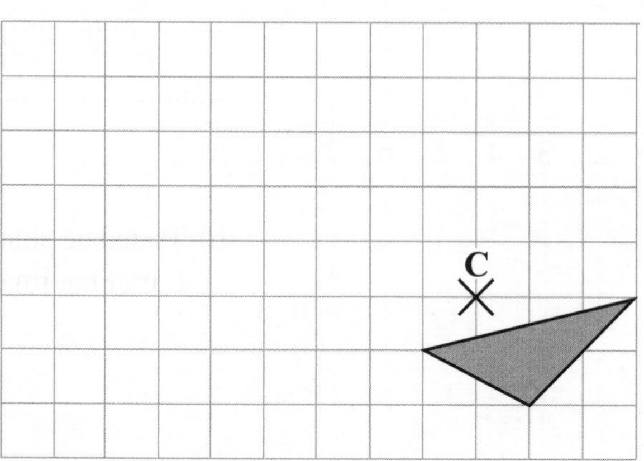

Score: ____ / **21**

More Transformation Stuff

1 A regular hexagon has sides of length 16 cm.
It is an enlargement of another regular hexagon with sides of length 4 cm. 

Write down the scale factor of the enlargement.

....

[Total 1 mark]

2 A parallelogram has an area of 7 cm^2. 

The parallelogram is enlarged with scale factor 3. Work out the area of the enlarged parallelogram.

.... cm^2

[Total 2 marks]

3 The diagram below shows two similar triangles, **A** and **B**.
The length of the base of each triangle is given. 

Remember — two objects are similar if they're the same shape, but are different sizes.

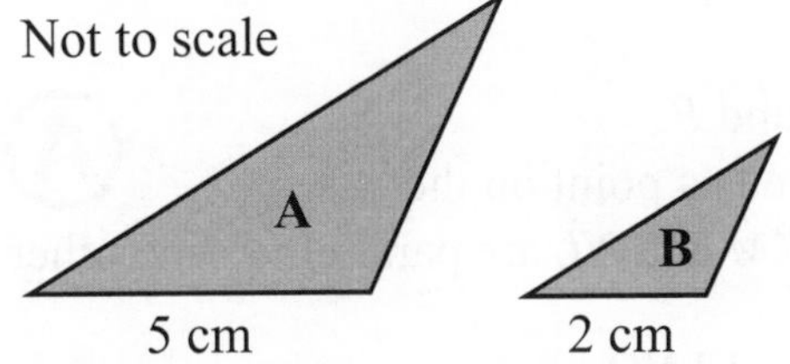

The area of triangle **B** is 6 cm^2.
Calculate the area of triangle **A**.

.... cm^2

[Total 2 marks]

4 The radius of a tennis ball and the radius of a basketball are in the ratio 1 : 7. 

Assuming both balls are spheres, work out the ratio of the volume of a tennis ball to the volume of a basketball.

....

[Total 1 mark]

5 **A**, **B** and **C** are three solid cones which are mathematically similar. The surface area of each cone is given below. The perpendicular height of **A** is 4 cm. The volume of **C** is 135π cm^3. 

Not to scale

12π cm^2 **A** 48π cm^2 **B** 108π cm^2 **C**

a) Calculate the volume of **A**.

.... cm^3

[4]

b) Calculate the perpendicular height of **B**.

.... cm

[4]

[Total 8 marks]

Score:  / **14**

Congruent Shapes

*1 ABC is a triangle. FDEC is a parallelogram such that F is the midpoint of AC, D is the midpoint of AB and E is the midpoint of BC.

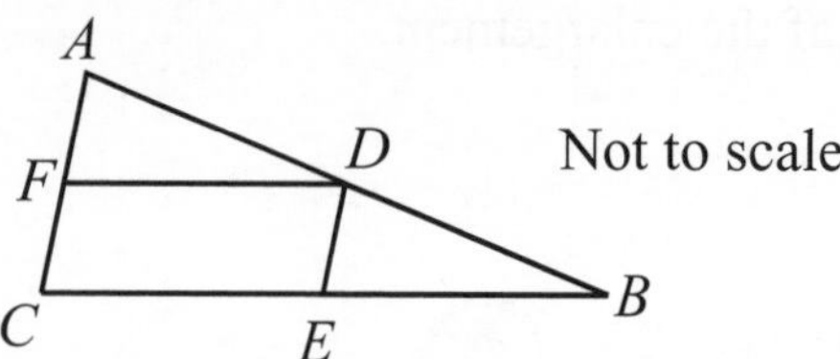

Prove that triangles AFD and DEB are congruent.

F is the midpoint of AC so AF = ..., and opposite sides of a parallelogram are equal so .... = FC. Therefore AF = ...

E is the midpoint of CB so .... = EB, and opposite sides of a parallelogram are equal so .... = FD. Therefore FD = ...

D is the midpoint of AB, so AD = ...

Satisfies condition .... so triangles are congruent.

[Total 4 marks]

*2 The diagram shows two overlapping circles, with centres O and P. The circles intersect at M and N, and the centre of each circle is a point on the circumference of the other circle. KOPL is a straight line. KM and NL are parallel to each other.

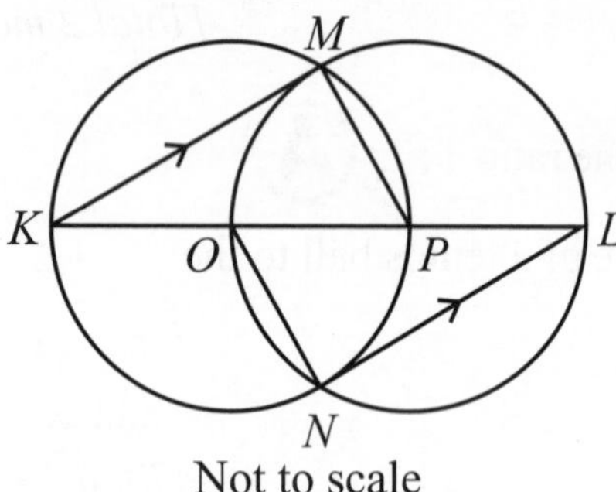

Not to scale

Prove that triangles KMP and LNO are congruent.

....

....

....

....

[Total 4 marks]

*3 A, B, C and D are points on a circle. AED and BEC are straight lines. AC and BD are the same length as each other.

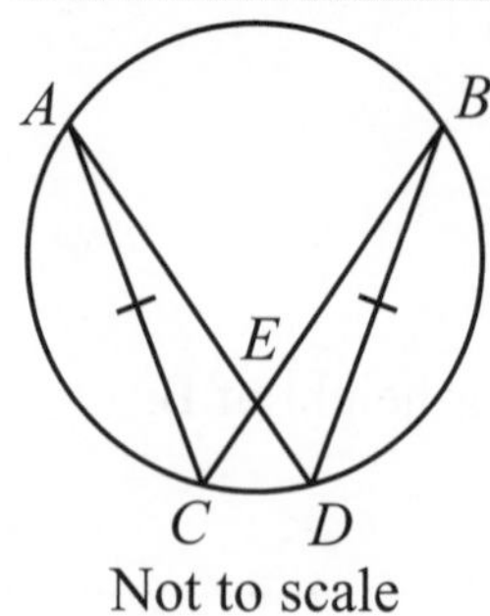

Not to scale

Prove that triangles AEC and BED are congruent.

....

....

....

....

[Total 4 marks]

Exam Practice Tip

To prove two triangles are congruent, you need to show that three pairs of angles or sides are the same, giving a reason for each step of your working. It's no good just saying that two things are equal — to get all the marks you need to explain why. Then give the condition for congruence that you've satisfied (SSS, AAS, SAS or RHS).

Score

12

Similar Shapes

1 Triangles ABC and DEF are mathematically similar. Angles BAC and EDF are equal. 

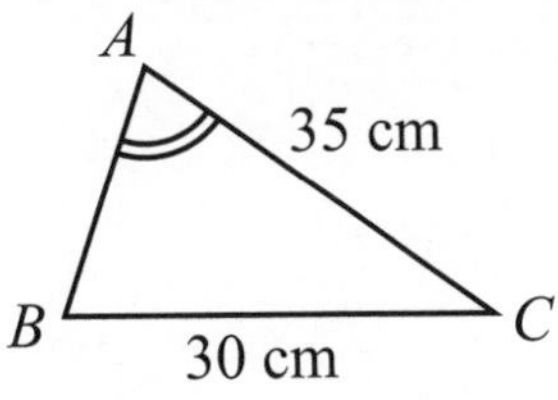
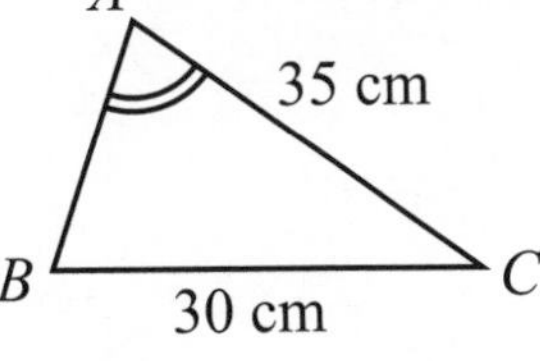

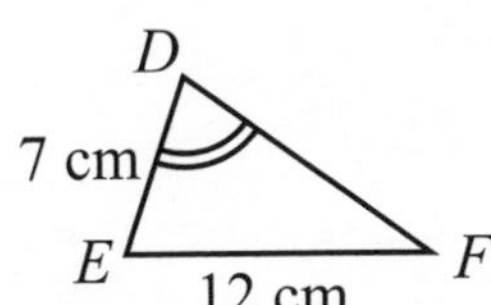

Not to scale

a) Work out the length of AB.

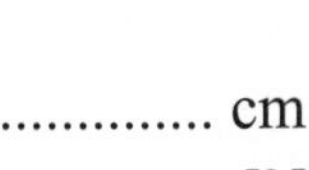

.... cm

[2]

b) Work out the length of DF.

.... cm

[1]

[Total 3 marks]

2 The shapes $ABCD$ and $EFGH$ are mathematically similar. 

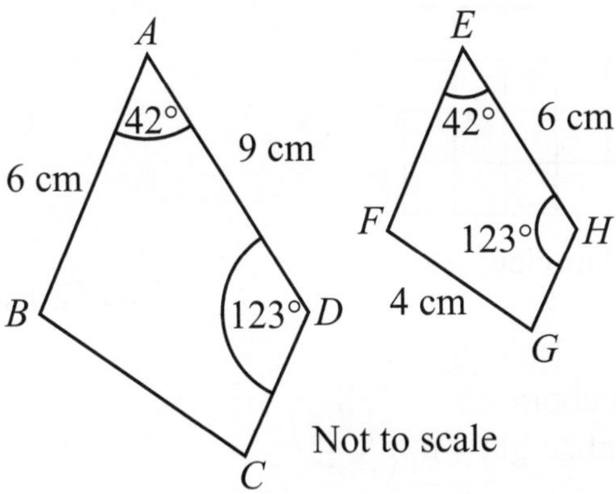

Not to scale

a) Find the length of EF.

.... cm

[2]

b) Find the length of BC.

.... cm

[1]

[Total 3 marks]

***3** $ABCD$ and $CEFG$ are rectangles that touch at C. DCE and BCG are straight lines. 

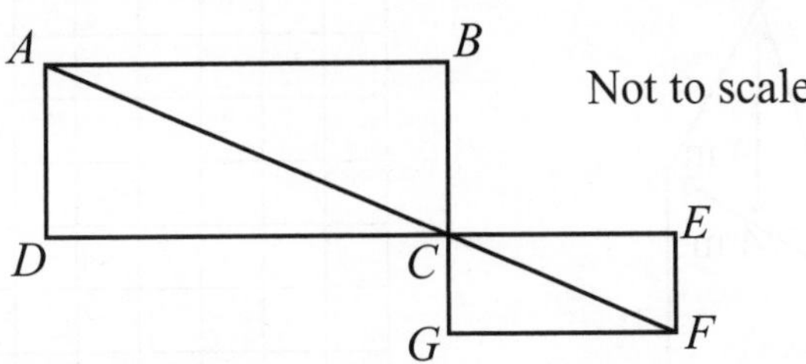

Not to scale

Prove that triangles ABC and CEF are similar triangles.

....

....

[Total 3 marks]

Score: $\frac{\quad}{9}$

Projections

1 The diagram below shows a solid made from identical cubes. The side elevation of the solid is drawn on the adjacent grid. 

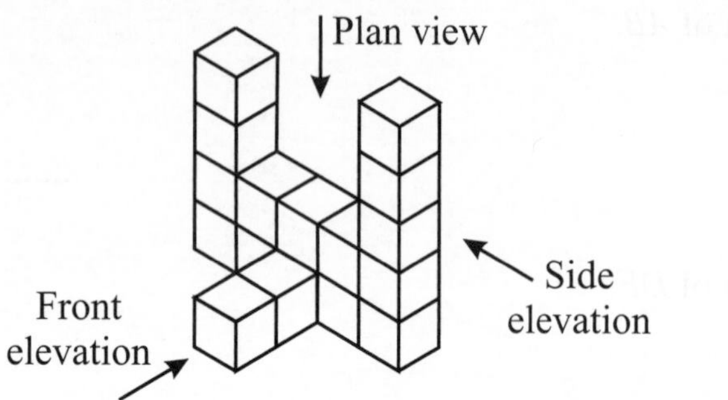

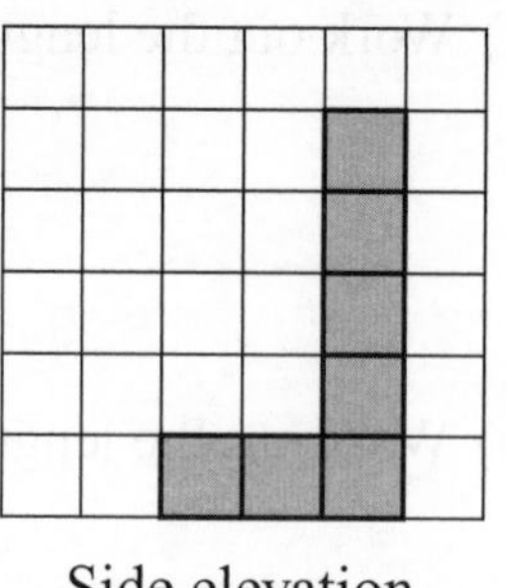

Side elevation

a) On the grid below, draw the front elevation of the solid. *[1]*

b) On the grid below, draw the plan view of the solid. *[1]*

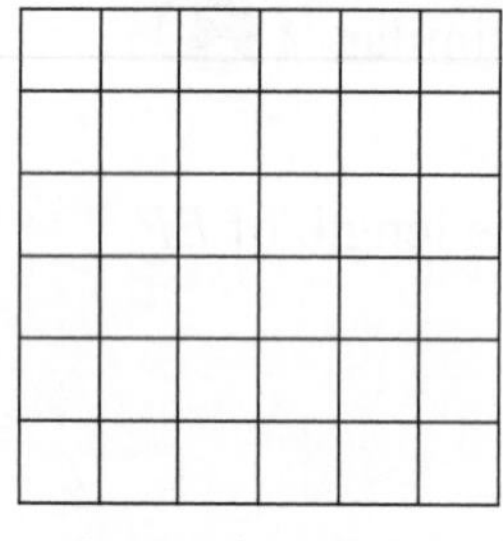

Front elevation

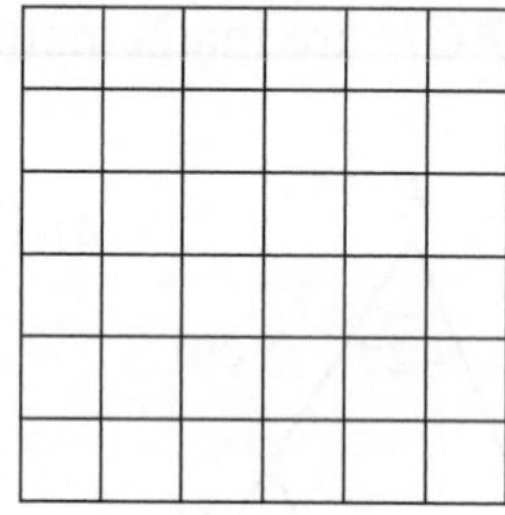

Plan view

[Total 2 marks]

2 The diagram shows a house made of a 5 m × 5 m × 6 m cuboid and a triangular roof of width 4 m, length 5 m and vertical height 4 m. 

On the grid below, draw the front elevation of the house.
Use a scale of 1 square = 1 m.

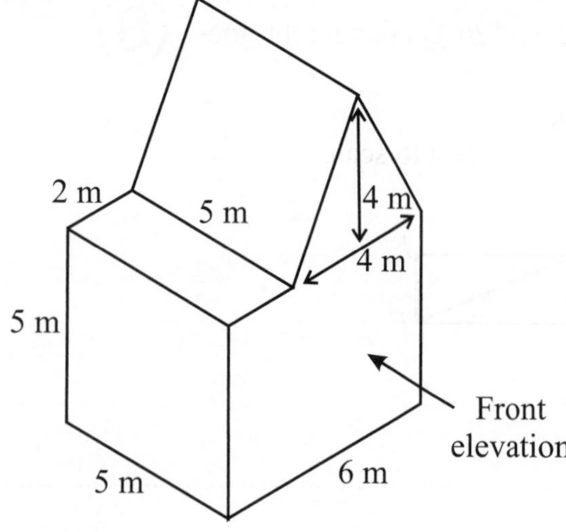

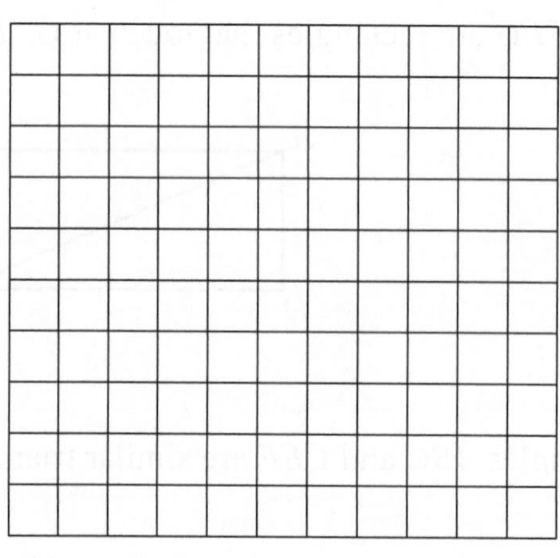

[Total 2 marks]

Score: __ / 4

Areas and Perimeters

FUNCTIONAL

1 The diagram shows a field. The farmer wants to spray weed killer on the field. Weed killer costs £0.27 per 10 m^2.

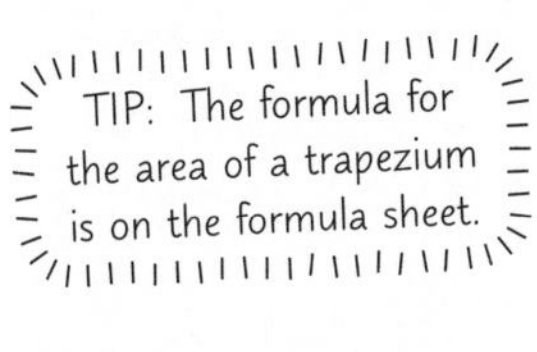

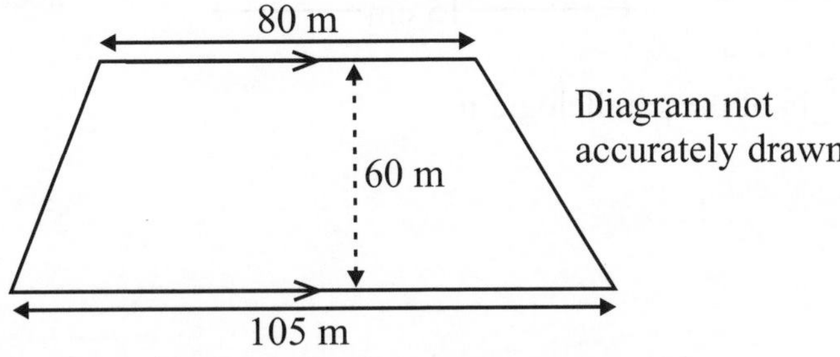

Diagram not accurately drawn

How much will it cost the farmer to spray weed killer on the whole field?

£ ....

[Total 4 marks]

FUNCTIONAL

2 Lynn is designing a garden. The diagram shows her design. (C)

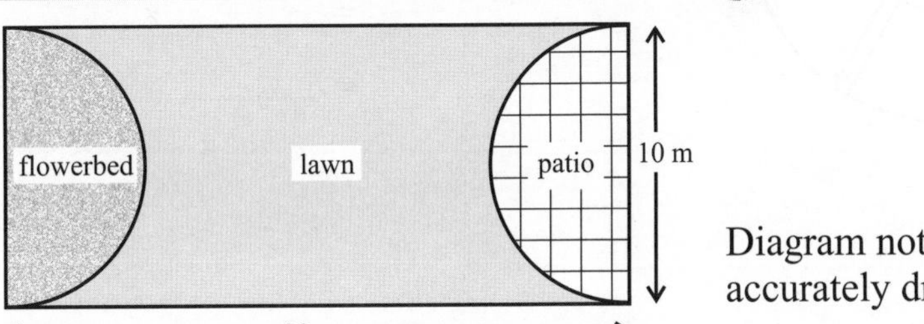

Diagram not accurately drawn

Lynn's garden will be rectangular, with a semicircular flowerbed at one end, and a matching semicircular patio at the other end. The rest of the space will be taken up by a lawn.

a) The grass seed that Lynn is planning to use comes in boxes that cost £7 each. Each box will cover 10 m^2. How much will it cost Lynn to plant the lawn?

£ ....

[6]

b) Lynn wants to put a decorative border all around the edges of the lawn. Lawn edging strip is sold by the metre. How many metres should Lynn buy?

.... m

[3]

[Total 9 marks]

3 The area of the parallelogram shown below is 105 cm^2. 

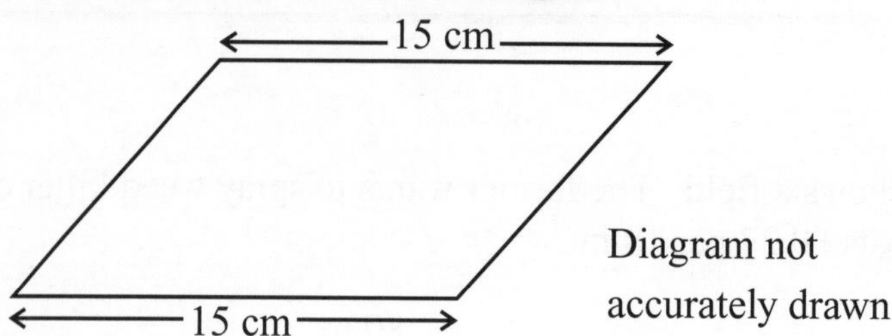

Calculate the height of the parallelogram.

.... cm

[Total 2 marks]

4 The circle below has a radius of 12 cm.
The sector S has a central angle of 50°. 

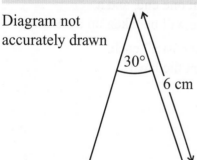

50° 12 cm

S

Diagram not accurately drawn

Find the area of the sector S of the circle.
Give your answer to 3 significant figures.

Area of full circle = ... × .... = ...π cm^2

Area of sector S = ... × area of circle

= .... × .... cm^2

= .... cm^2

.... cm^2

[Total 4 marks]

5 Look at the sector shown in the diagram below. 

Diagram not accurately drawn

30°

6 cm

Find the perimeter of the sector.
Give your answer to 3 significant figures.

Circumference of full circle = ... × .... × .... cm

= .... π cm

Length of arc = ... × circumference of circle

= .... × .... cm = ... cm

Perimeter of sector = ... cm + ... cm + ... cm

= .... cm

.... cm

[Total 4 marks]

Exam Practice Tip

Don't mix up radius and diameter. I know that sounds a bit obvious, but it's something that lots of people do in exams. The radius of a circle is half of its diameter. Think carefully about which one you're being given, and which one you need for a formula.

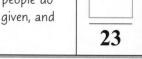

Surface Area and Volume

1 The diagram shows a regular octahedron and one of its faces.
Each of the faces is an equilateral triangle. 

Calculate the surface area of the octahedron.

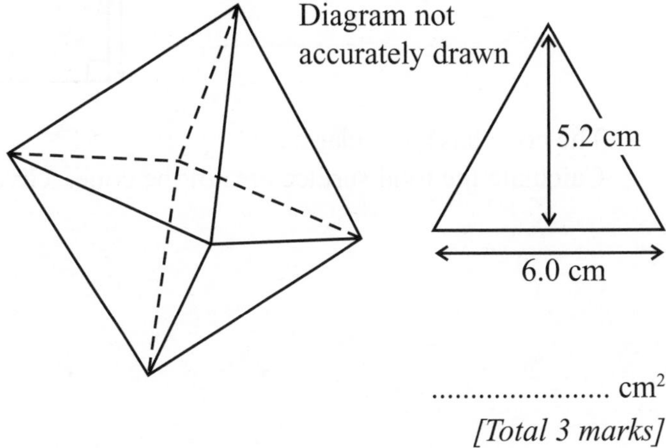

.... cm^2

[Total 3 marks]

FUNCTIONAL

2 Dan has bought a new door for his garden shed. He needs to varnish the door all over to make sure that it is weatherproof. The door is 2 m high, 1 m wide, and 3 cm thick. 

One tin of varnish will cover 2.45 m^2 of wood. Dan will need to give the door two coats of varnish. How many tins should he buy?

....

[Total 4 marks]

3 The diagram below shows a wooden spinning top made from a hemisphere and a cone. 

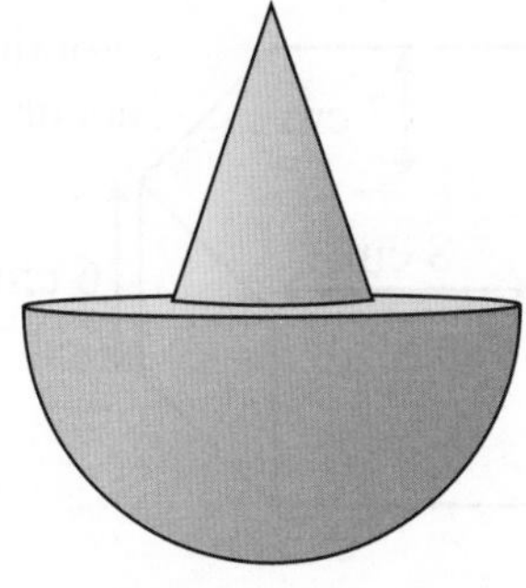

The hemisphere has a diameter of 14 cm.
The slanting length of the cone is 12 cm and the radius of its base is 2 cm.

Work out the total surface area of the spinning top.
Give your answer to 3 significant figures.

.... cm^2

[Total 6 marks]

4 The curved surface of a cone is made from the net below. 

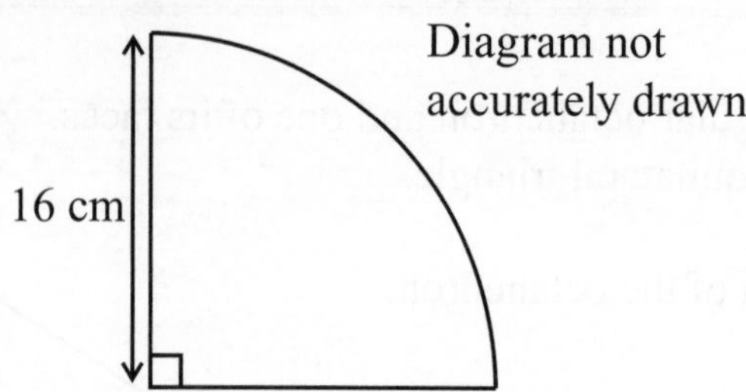

The cone has a circular base.
Calculate the total surface area of the cone. Give your answer to 3 significant figures.

.... cm^2

[Total 6 marks]

FUNCTIONAL

5 A company makes boxes of fudge. Each box is a cube with a side length of 8 cm. 

The boxes are sent in packing cases that have length 50 cm, width 40 cm and height 16 cm.
What is the maximum number of fudge boxes that can be packed into each case?

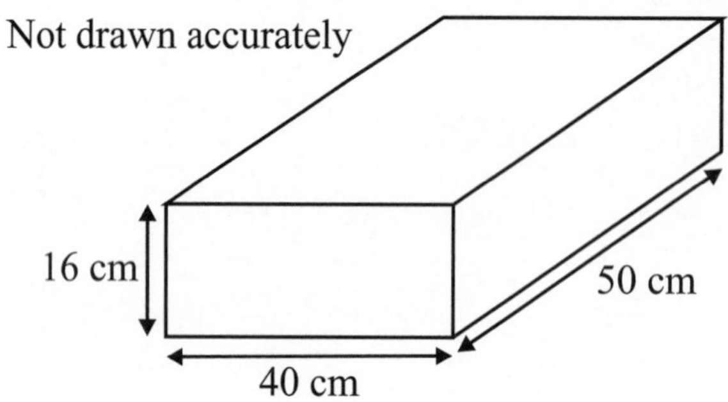

....

[Total 3 marks]

6 The cross-section of a prism is a regular hexagon. 

Each side of the hexagon has a length of 8 cm.
The distance from the centre of the hexagon to the midpoint of each side is 7 cm.
Calculate the volume of the prism.

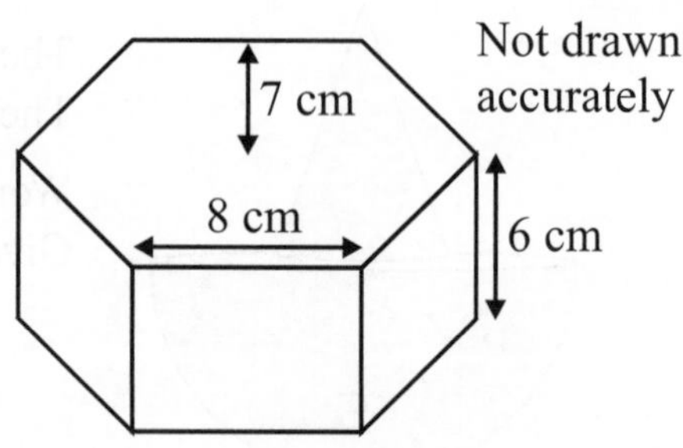

.... cm^3

[Total 3 marks]

FUNCTIONAL

7 The diagram below shows Amy's new paddling pool.
It has a diameter of 2 metres, and is 40 cm high. 

Not drawn accurately

40 cm

2 m

The instructions that came with the pool say that it should only be filled three-quarters full.
What is the maximum volume of water that Amy can put in the pool?
(Give your answer to 2 decimal places.)

.... m^3

[Total 4 marks]

8 The diagram below shows a clay bowl in the shape of a hollow hemisphere.
The radius of the inside surface is 8 cm. The radius of the outside surface is 9 cm. 

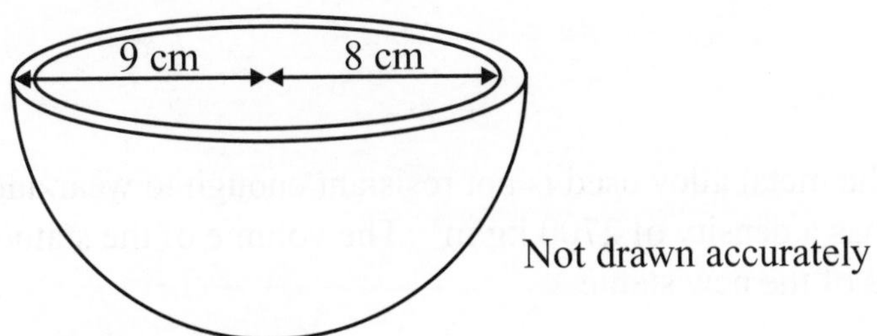

What volume of clay is needed to make the bowl?
Give your answer to 3 significant figures.

.... cm^3

[Total 3 marks]

9 The volume of the cone shown on the right is 113 cm^3 correct to 3 significant figures. 

Calculate the radius of the base of the cone.

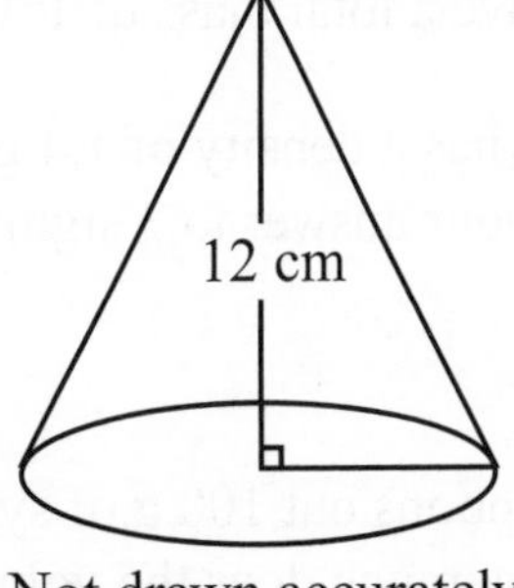

.... cm

[Total 2 marks]

Exam Practice Tip

You'll be given some of the area and volume formulas that you need in your exam paper. BUT you won't be given all of them — some of them you're going to have to learn. Check out the formula sheet inside the back cover of this book to see which formulas you'll be given. Make sure that you learn the rest off by heart.

Density

1 The diagram shows a solid prism made from iron. (C)

Not drawn accurately

a) Calculate the volume of the prism.

.... cm^3
[2]

b) Iron has a density of 7.9 grams per cm^3.
Work out the mass of the prism.

.... g
[2]

[Total 4 marks]

2 The mass of a metal statue is 360 kg.
The density of the metal alloy from which it is made is 1800 kg/m^3. (C)

a) Calculate the volume of the statue.

.... m^3
[2]

b) It is decided that the metal alloy used is not resistant enough to wear and tear so it is replaced with another that has a density of 2700 kg/m^3. The volume of the statue must remain the same. Calculate the mass of the new statue.

.... kg
[2]

[Total 4 marks]

3 A cylindrical tin with a volume of 300π cm^3 is filled with golden syrup.
The syrup and tin have a total mass of 1500 g. (C)

a) Syrup has a density of 1.4 g/cm^3. What is the mass of just the tin?
Give your answer to 3 significant figures.

.... g
[3]

b) Tom spoons out 100 g of syrup to make flapjacks with.
By how much does the volume of the syrup in the tin reduce?
Give your answer to 3 significant figures.

.... cm^3
[2]

[Total 5 marks]

Score: ____ / **13**

Speed

FUNCTIONAL

***1** Kieran is driving along a motorway on his way to watch a football match. **(D)**
The match starts at 7.45 pm.

The time on his watch shows 19:05.
The football ground is 22 miles away.

a) What time would Kieran arrive at the ground if he averaged 60 mph for the rest of the journey?

....
[3]

b) There is a 30 mph speed limit on the last 4 miles of the journey.
Assuming Kieran drives at the speed limit for the last 4 miles, what is the minimum average speed Kieran needs to drive at **before** then to get to the ground 15 minutes before kick off?
Give your answer to the nearest mph.

.... mph
[4]

[Total 7 marks]

2 Adam has been caught speeding by a pair of average speed cameras. **(C)**
The speed limit was 50 mph.

The cameras are 2500 m apart. The time taken for his car to pass between them was 102 seconds.

a) What was Adam's average speed between the cameras?
Give your answer to the nearest mph. Take 1 mile as 1.6 km.

.... mph
[3]

b) If Adam had been travelling within the speed limit, what is the minimum time it should have taken him to pass between the cameras? Give your answer to the nearest second.

.... s
[2]

[Total 5 marks]

Score: ____ / **12**

Distance-Time Graphs

1 The distance/time graph below shows Selby's bike ride from his house (**A**) to the zoo (**C**), which is 25 km away. 

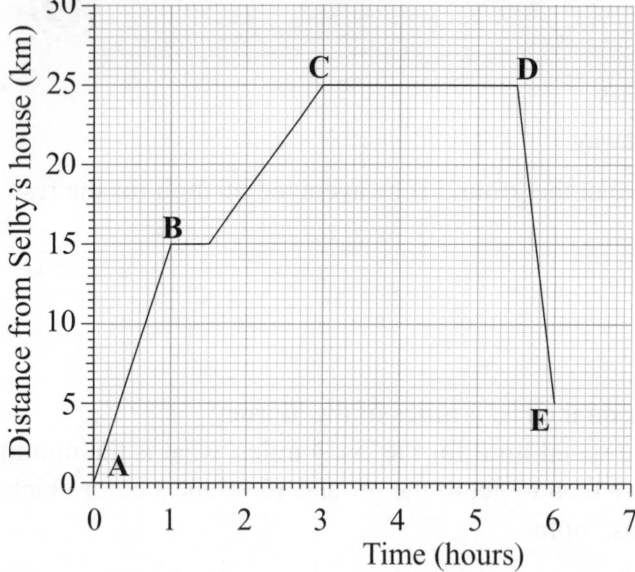

a) After one hour Selby stops at a bench (**B**) to get his breath back.
Find the gradient of the line between point **A** and point **B**.

....

[2]

b) What does the gradient of the line between point **A** and point **B** represent?

....

[1]

c) How long was Selby's journey to the zoo (**C**) from home (**A**)?

.... hours

[1]

d) How long did Selby spend at the zoo?

.... hours

[1]

e) After the zoo, Selby stopped at the shops (**E**) for 30 minutes before cycling straight home.
Given that he arrived home 7 hours after he first left, complete the graph above.

[2]

f) How many hours did Selby spend cycling in total during the day?

.... hours

[1]

[Total 8 marks]

Score: ___ / **8**

Units

1 Kevin has just competed in a long jump competition. 

His best jump measured 9½ feet. What is this distance in cm?

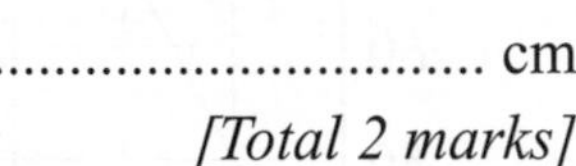

.... cm

[Total 2 marks]

2 A runner completes a 5 km race in 37.5 minutes. 

What was the runner's average speed in mph?

.... mph

[Total 3 marks]

FUNCTIONAL

3 Gemma wants to post some books to a friend in another country.
Each book weighs 1.5 lb and each package can hold a maximum weight of 2500 g. 

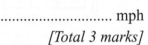

How many books can she send in one package?

....

[Total 4 marks]

4 The playing surface of a snooker table has an area of 39 200 cm^2. 

Convert the area of the snooker table into m^2.

100×100 = 10,000 $\frac{39,200}{10,000}$ = 3.92

~~392~~ 3.92 m^2

[Total 2 marks]

5 A barrel of oil has a capacity of 150 litres. 

How many cubic metres of oil does the barrel hold?

150

0.150

0.150 m^3

[Total 3 marks]

6 Below is a conversion graph to change between temperatures in °C and °F.

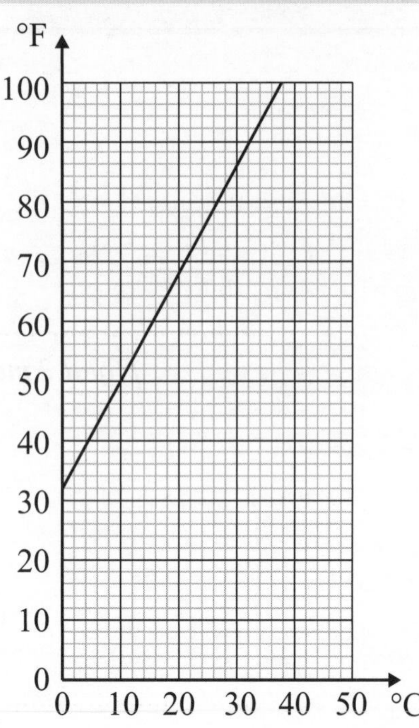

Peter wants to know how the temperature in his greenhouse changes during the day. He places a thermometer in the greenhouse and checks it at regular intervals.

a) At 7 o'clock in the morning, the thermometer recorded a temperature of 50 °F. What was the temperature in °C? 

.... °C

[1]

b) By noon, the temperature has risen by 15 °C. What is the average hourly increase in temperature between 7 o'clock and 12 o'clock? Give your answer in °F. 

.... °F

[3]

[Total 4 marks]

FUNCTIONAL

To compare the cars, you need to convert one of their fuel efficiencies so they're both in the same units.

7 Alex has a choice of two cars to hire for a holiday. He wants to hire the most efficient car. 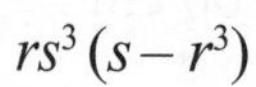

Car A will do 51.4 miles per gallon of petrol. Car B uses 6.2 litres of petrol per 100 km. Which car should Alex hire?

....

[Total 3 marks]

8 Here are some expressions. The letters r, s and t represent lengths.

$s^2 + 4t^2$ $\qquad rs^3(s - r^3)$ $\qquad 2rt^2$ $\qquad 3(r + t)$ $\qquad ts^2(s^2 + t^3)$

Write down one expression from the list above that could represent:

a) a length

....

[1]

b) an area

....

[1]

c) a volume

....

[1]

[Total 3 marks]

Exam Practice Tip

Make sure you learn the rough conversions between metric units (kg, litres, km and cm) and imperial units (pounds, pints, gallons, miles and feet). I know it's dull just memorising numbers, but you might not be given them in the exam. You also need to know metric-to-metric conversions, but thankfully those are MUCH easier.

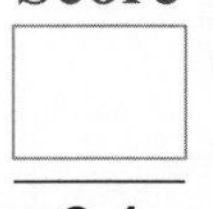

Loci and Constructions

1 *EFG* is an isosceles triangle. Sides *EG* and *FG* are both 4.5 cm long. 

Side *EF* has been drawn here.

E ——————— *F*

a) Complete the construction of triangle *EFG* by drawing sides *EG* and *FG*.

[2]

b) Construct the bisector of angle *EGF*.

[2]

[Total 4 marks]

2 *ABC* is a straight line. 

Use a ruler and compasses to construct the perpendicular to the line *ABC* that passes through the point *B*. Show all of your construction lines.

It's really important that you don't rub out your construction lines in these questions — you won't get all the marks otherwise.

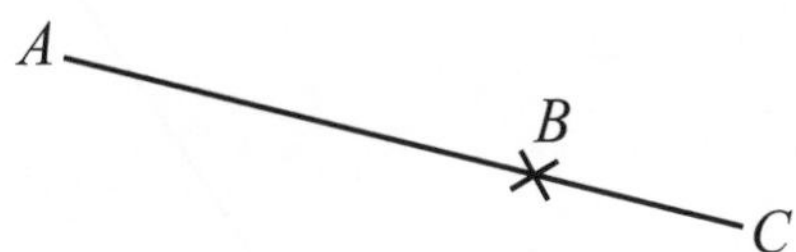

[Total 2 marks]

3 *RST* is a straight line. 

Use a ruler and compasses to construct an angle of 45° to the line *RST* at the point *S*. Show all of your construction lines.

[Total 4 marks]

4 A dog is tied to a beam *AB* by a lead which allows it to run a maximum of 2 m from the beam. 

Shade the region on the diagram where the dog may run, using the scale shown.

A  *B*

Scale: 1 cm represents 1 m

[Total 2 marks]

5 *ABC* is a triangle. 

Find and shade the region inside the triangle which is **both** closer to the line *AB* than the line *BC*, **and** also more than 6.5 cm from the point *C*.

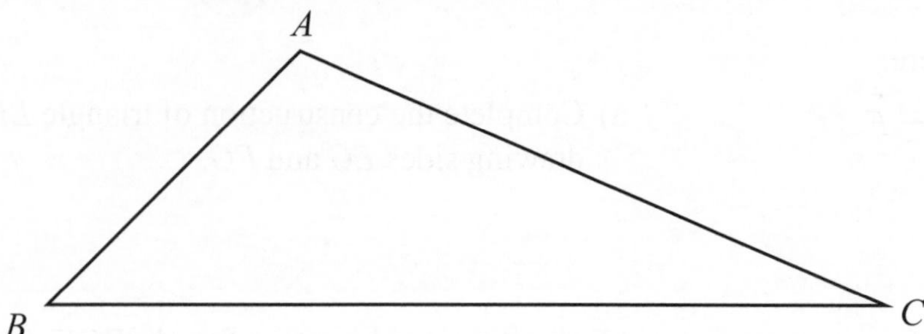

[Total 4 marks]

6 A town council wants to put up a new visitor information board. They think that it should be placed closer to the park than to the library, but also closer to the station than to the park. 

The diagram below shows a scale map of the town centre.
Shade in the region of the town where the board could be placed.

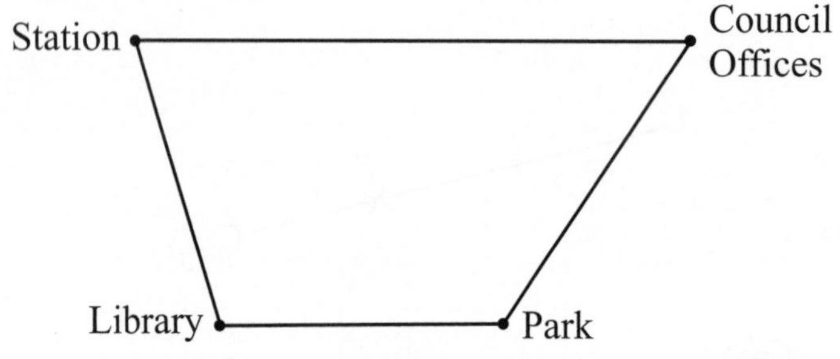

[Total 3 marks]

7 The diagram below shows a sketch of a field *ABCD*. A footpath *AC* runs across the field. 

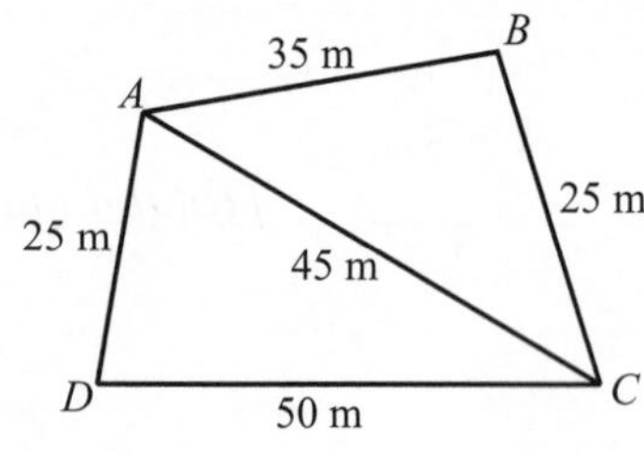

Not drawn accurately

a) Make an accurate scale drawing of the field.
Use a scale of 1 cm : 10 m.

[3]

b) Using your scale drawing, find the length of the line *BD* in the real field.

.... m

[2]

[Total 5 marks]

Score: ___ / **24**

Bearings

1 Two ships leave Dover at the same time.
Ship *A* travels due west for 40 km. Ship *B* travels 60 km on a bearing of 110°. (D)

a) Using a scale of 1 cm = 10 km, draw the journeys of the two ships in the space below and clearly mark their final positions.

[4]

b) Measure the final bearing of Ship *B* from Ship *A*.

.... °
[1]

c) Calculate the final bearing of Ship *A* from Ship *B*.

.... °
[2]

[Total 7 marks]

2 The diagram shows the position of two villages, *A* and *B*. (D)

a) A walker hikes from village *A* on a bearing of 035°.
After an hour's walk he stops when village *B* is directly east of his position.
Mark the walker's position on the diagram with a cross (×) and label it *W*.

[2]

b) Another village, *C*, is on a bearing of 115° from village *A*, and on a bearing of 235° from village *B*. Mark the location of village *C* with a cross (×) and label it *C*.
[3]

c) Use a protractor to measure the bearing that the walker must hike on from his position at *W*, in order to reach village *C*.

.... °
[1]

[Total 6 marks]

Score: ___ / 13

Pythagoras' Theorem

1 The diagram shows a right-angled triangle *ABC*. *AC* is 4 cm long. *BC* is 8 cm long. 

Calculate the length of *AB*.
Give your answer to 2 decimal places.

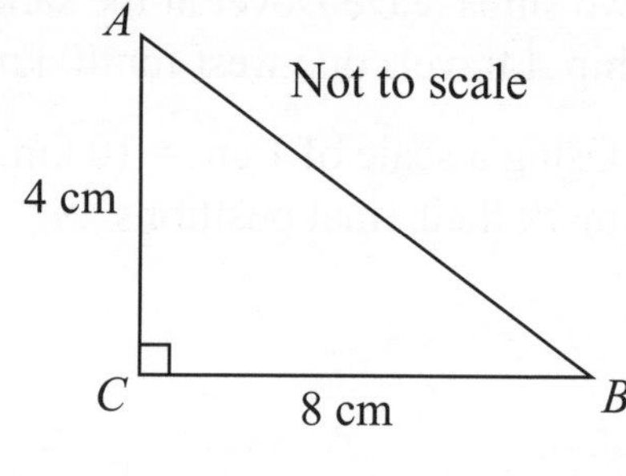

.... cm
[Total 3 marks]

FUNCTIONAL

2 A ladder is 3.5 m long. For safety, when the ladder is leant against a wall, the base should never be less than 2.1 m away from the wall. 

What is the maximum vertical height that the top of the ladder can safely reach to?

.... m
[Total 3 marks]

3 A triangle has a base of 10 cm. Its other two sides are both 13 cm long. 

Calculate the area of the triangle.

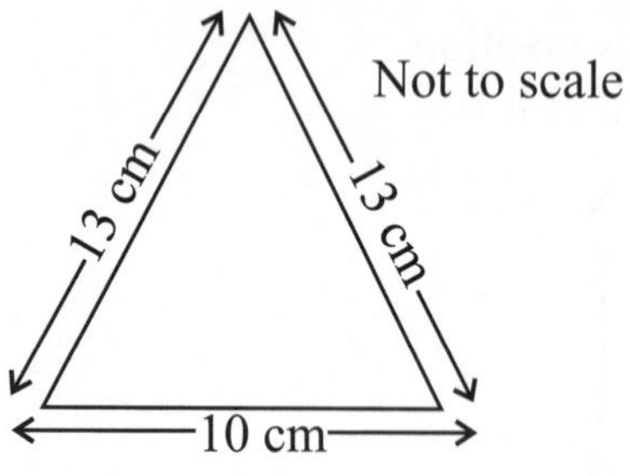

.... cm^2
[Total 4 marks]

4 The diagram shows a kite *ABCD*. *AB* is 28.3 cm long. *BC* is 54.3 cm long. *BE* is 20 cm in length. 

Work out the perimeter of triangle *ABC*. Give your answer to 1 decimal place.

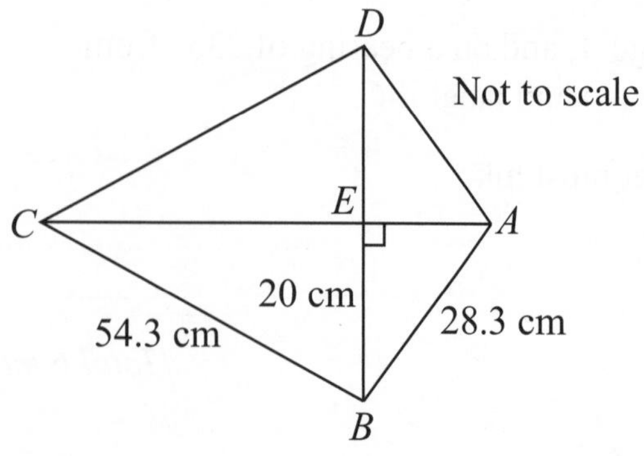

.... cm
[Total 5 marks]

Score: ___ / **15**

Trigonometry — Sin, Cos, Tan

1 The diagram shows a right-angled triangle. 

Find the size of the angle marked x.
Give your answer to 1 decimal place.

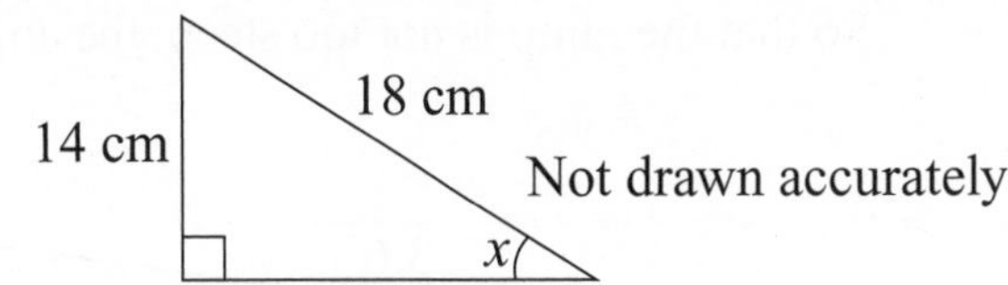

.............................°

[Total 3 marks]

2 The diagram shows a right-angled triangle. 

Find the length of the side marked y.
Give your answer to 3 significant figures.

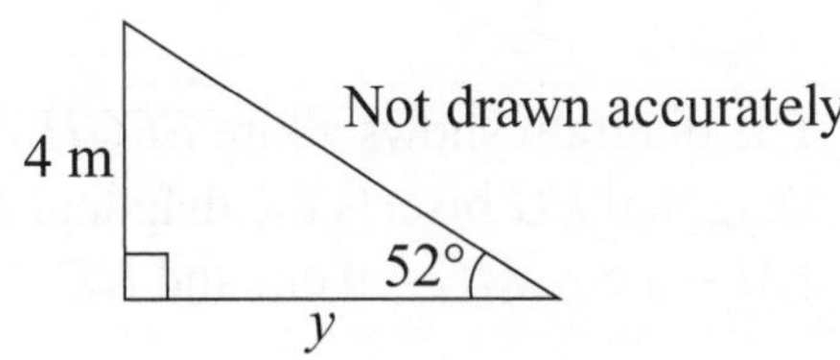

.... m

[Total 3 marks]

3 In the triangle below, $AB = BC = 10$ m and angle $C = 34°$. 

B
Not drawn accurately
10 m 10 m
34°
A C

a) Calculate the length AC.
Give your answer to 2 decimal places.

.... m

[3]

b) Calculate the height of the triangle.
Give your answer to 2 decimal places.

.... m

[3]

[Total 6 marks]

FUNCTIONAL

4 A shopkeeper needs a new access ramp for his shop.
The top of the ramp must be level with the top of the step, which is 12 cm high.
So that the ramp is not too steep, the angle the ramp makes with the ground should be 3.6°.

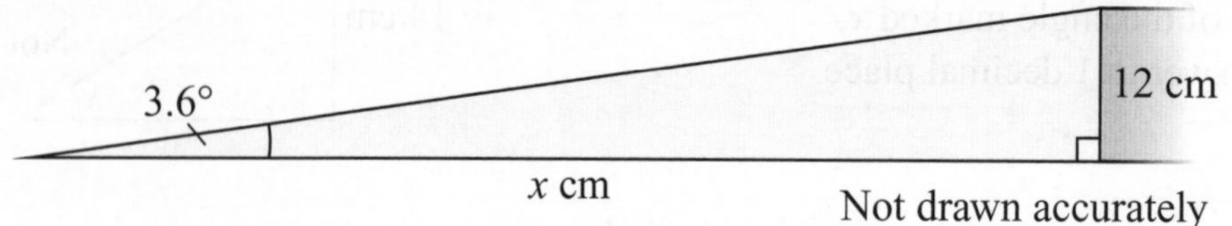

How far away from the bottom of the step should the ramp start?
Give your answer to 3 significant figures.

.... cm

[Total 3 marks]

5 The diagram shows a kite *EFGH*.
Diagonal *EG* bisects the diagonal *HF* at *M*.
EM = 5 cm, *MG* = 9 cm and *HF* = 12 cm.

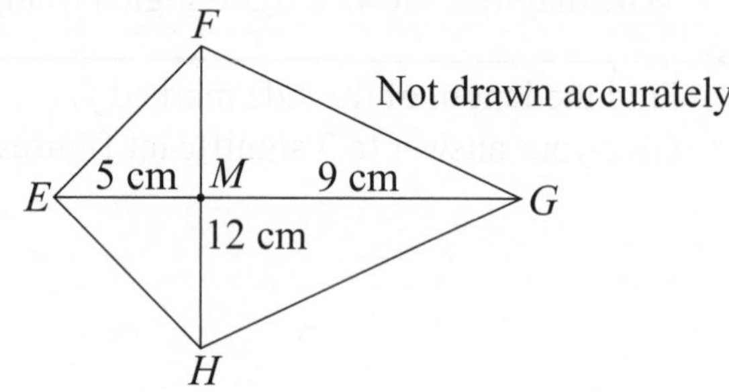

a) Calculate the size of angle *FGM*.
Give your answer to 1 decimal place.

.... °

[3]

b) Calculate the size of angle *FEH*.
Give your answer to 1 decimal place.

.... °

[3]

[Total 6 marks]

6 A regular hexagon is drawn such that all of its vertices are on the circumference of a circle of radius 8.5 cm.

Calculate the distance from the centre of the circle to the centre of one edge of the hexagon.
Give your answer to 2 decimal places.

The sum of internal angles in a polygon = (number of sides – 2) × 180°

.... cm

[Total 5 marks]

Exam Practice Tip

In an exam, it'll help if you start by labelling the sides of a right-angled triangle, opposite (O), adjacent (A) and hypotenuse (H) — these are easy to get muddled up. If you're working out an angle, make sure you check whether it's sensible — if you get an angle of 720° or 0.0072°, it's probably wrong so give it another go.

Score

26

The Sine and Cosine Rules

1 In the triangle below, $AB = 10$ cm, $BC = 7$ cm and angle $ABC = 85°$. 

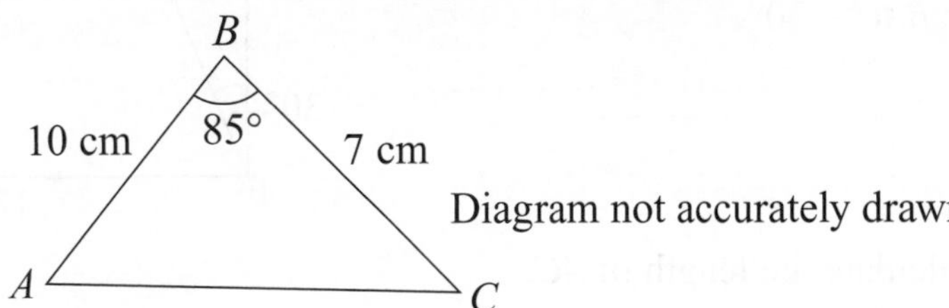

a) Calculate the length of AC.
Give your answer to 3 significant figures.

AC^2 = ...^{2} + ...^{2} – (2 × .... × .... × cos ....°)

$AC = \sqrt{\text{..........} - \text{..........} \times \cos \text{..........}°}$

AC = ...

.... cm
[3]

b) Calculate the area of triangle ABC.
Give your answer to 3 significant figures.

.... cm^2
[2]

[Total 5 marks]

2 The diagram below is a sketch of a metal framework.
Some of the information needed to manufacture the framework has been lost. 

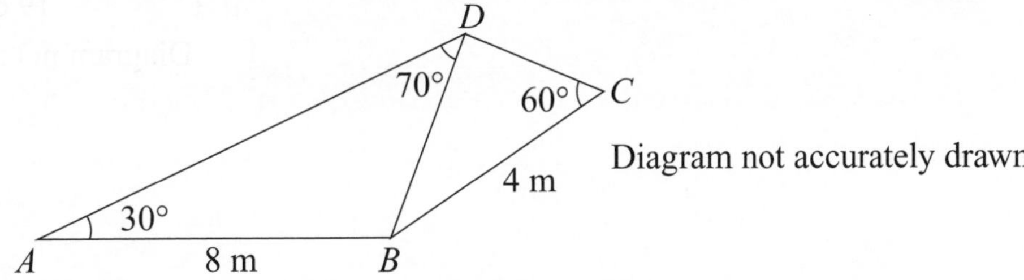

Complete the specification for the framework by calculating:

a) the length of BD.
Give your answer to 3 significant figures.

$\dfrac{BD}{\sin \text{..........}} = \dfrac{\text{..........}}{\sin \text{..........}}$

$BD = \dfrac{\text{..........}}{\sin \text{..........}} \times \sin$ ....

BD = ... m

.... m
[3]

b) the size of angle BDC.
Give your answer to 3 significant figures.

..........................°
[3]

[Total 6 marks]

3 *ABCD* is a trapezium. 

BC is parallel to *AD*.
BC = 5 cm.
AD = 18 cm.
Angle *BAC* = 30°.

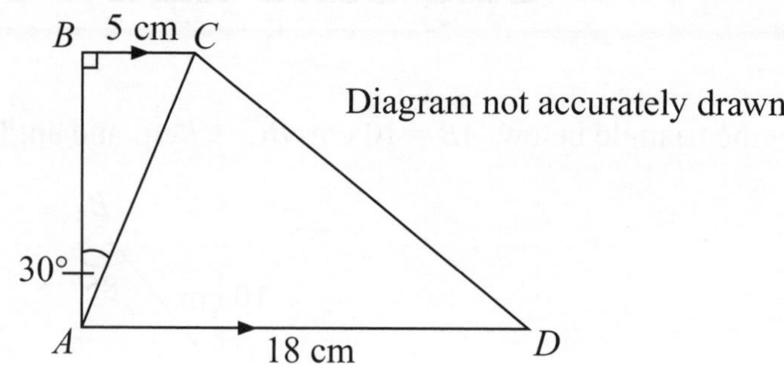

a) Calculate the length of *AC*.

.... cm
[3]

b) Work out the perimeter of triangle *ACD* to the nearest cm.

.... cm
[4]

[Total 7 marks]

4 In the triangle below, *AB* = 12 cm, *BC* = 19 cm and *AC* = 14cm.

Calculate the area of the triangle.

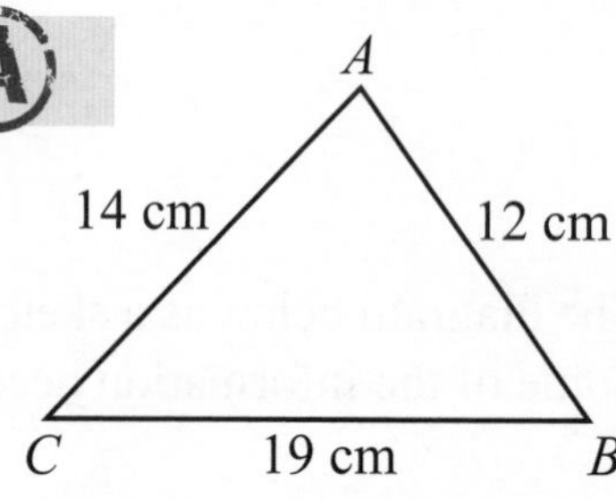

Diagram not accurately drawn

.... cm^2
[Total 5 marks]

*5 *ABCD* is a quadrilateral. 

AB = 55 cm.
DC = 84 cm.
Angle *ABC* = 116°.
Angle *BCD* = 78°.

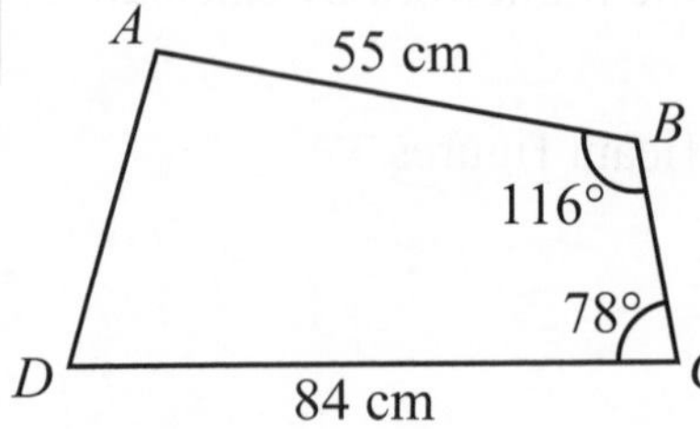

Diagram not accurately drawn

Given that *AC* = 93 cm, work out the area of *ABCD* to 3 significant figures.
Show clearly how you get your answer.

.... cm^2
[Total 8 marks]

Score: ☐
31

3D Pythagoras and Trigonometry

1 The diagram below is a cuboid *ABCDEFGH*. 

The cuboid has sides of length 6 cm, 4 cm and 3 cm.

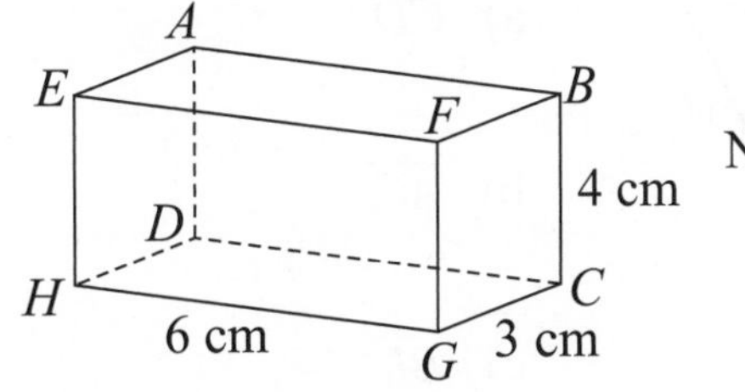

Not to scale

Calculate the length of the diagonal *BH*.
Give your answer to 3 significant figures.

BH^2 = ...^{2} + ...^{2} + ...^{2}

$BH = \sqrt{\text{..............}}$

BH = ...

.... cm
[Total 3 marks]

2 The diagram below is a cuboid *ABCDEFGH*.
It represents an empty box with sides of 2 cm, 5 cm and 8 cm.

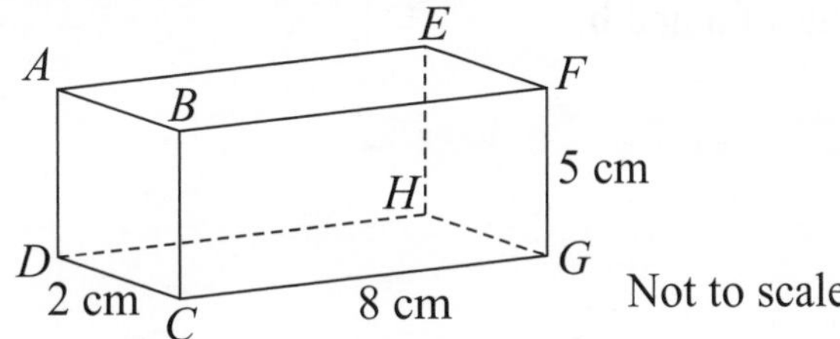

Not to scale

a) Sam is collecting sticks. Work out the length of the longest stick that he can fit into the box. 
Give your answer to 2 significant figures.

.... cm
[3]

b) A straight stick is placed in the box and wedged between points *F* and *D*.
Find the size of the angle the stick makes with the line *DG*.
Give your answer to 2 significant figures.

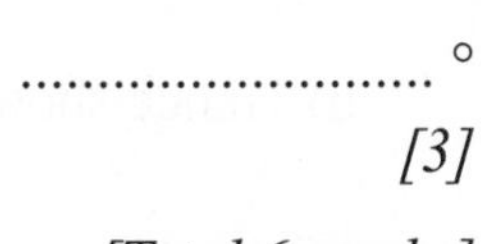

.... °
[3]

[Total 6 marks]

Score: $\frac{\quad}{9}$

Vectors

1 $ABCD$ is a parallelogram. $\overrightarrow{AB} = 2\mathbf{a}$ and $\overrightarrow{AD} = 2\mathbf{d}$.
L is the midpoint of AC, and M is the midpoint of BC.

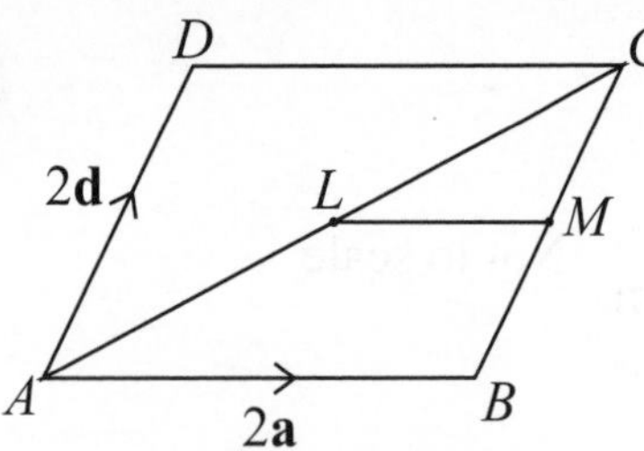

Not drawn accurately

Write in terms of **a** and **d**:

a) $\overrightarrow{CD}$ ....

[1]

b) $\overrightarrow{AC}$ ....

[1]

c) $\overrightarrow{BL}$ ....

[1]

[Total 3 marks]

2 In the diagram, $\overrightarrow{OA} = 2\mathbf{a}$ and $\overrightarrow{OB} = \mathbf{b}$.
M is the midpoint of AB.

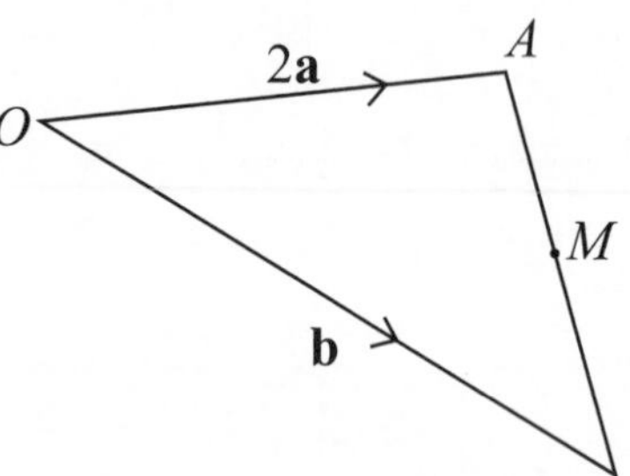

Not drawn accurately

a) Find $\overrightarrow{OM}$ in terms of **a** and **b**. 

$\overrightarrow{OM}$ = $\overrightarrow{......}$ + $\overrightarrow{......}$ = $\overrightarrow{......}$ + $\frac{1}{2}$ $\overrightarrow{......}$

$\overrightarrow{AB}$ = ... + ...

$\overrightarrow{OM}$ = ... + $\frac{1}{2}$(......................) = ...

....

[2]

X is a point on AB such that $AX : XB = 1 : 3$. 

b) Find $\overrightarrow{OX}$ in terms of **a** and **b**.

....

[3]

[Total 5 marks]

3 $ABCD$ is a parallelogram. $\overrightarrow{AB} = 3\mathbf{a}$, and $\overrightarrow{BW} = \mathbf{b}$.

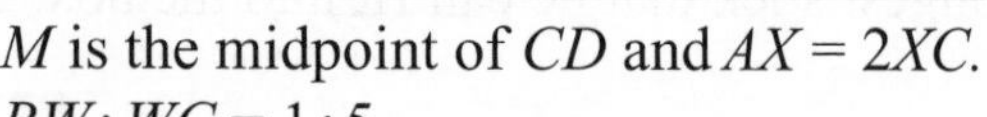

M is the midpoint of CD and $AX = 2XC$.
$BW : WC = 1 : 5$

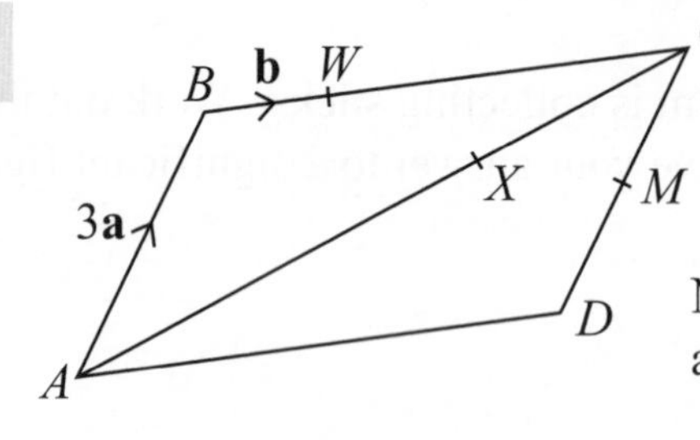

Not drawn accurately

a) Find $\overrightarrow{BX}$ in terms of **a** and **b**.

....

[4]

b) Hence show that B, X and M are three points on a straight line.

[4]

[Total 8 marks]

Score: $\frac{}{16}$

Sampling and Data Collection

1 Leah is doing a questionnaire at her school to find out how popular after school activities are.

a) Design a question for Leah to include in her questionnaire.
You should include suitable response boxes.

[2]

Leah asks pupils at an after school drama club to complete her questionnaire.

b) Write down **one** reason why this might not be a suitable sample.

....

[1]

[Total 3 marks]

2 Mike wants to find out how often people in his year group go to football matches.

He includes the question below in a survey.

How often do you attend football matches?	
Sometimes	A lot
☐	☐

a) Write down **one** thing that is wrong with this question.

....

....

[1]

There are 100 people in Mike's year group.

b) Describe a method he could use to take a random sample of these people.

....

....

[2]

[Total 3 marks]

3 Faye wants to find out how often teenagers buy chocolate bars.

She writes the following question to ask in a survey.

How many chocolate bars have you bought?		
1 – 2	2 – 3	3 – 4
☐	☐	☐

Write down two things that are wrong with the question above.

1. ....

2. ....

[Total 2 marks]

4 The table below shows information on the ages of 800 teenagers. 

Age (years)	13	14	15	16
Number of teenagers	248	192	176	184

Marissa wants to survey a sample of these teenagers, stratified by age.

a) Briefly describe a method she could use to take a sample of 100 of these teenagers, stratified by age.

....

....

[2]

b) Work out how many teenagers aged 14 should be in the sample.

Teenagers aged 14 = (total aged 14 ÷ total teenagers) × size of sample

= (.................... ÷ ....) × ....

= ....

....

[2]

[Total 4 marks]

5 Dougie is investigating the heights of pupils in his school. There are 720 pupils in the school. The table below shows the number of pupils in each year. 

Year	7	8	9	10	11
Number of pupils	167	162	150	125	116

Dougie takes a sample of 75 pupils, stratified by year.

Work out how many pupils from Year 11 are in the sample.

You should answer with a whole number.

....

[Total 2 marks]

6 The table below shows the number of students in two different schools. 

School	Male	Female	Total
Appleborough School	435	487	922
Warringpool High	568	543	1111
Total	1003	1030	2033

Cheng wants to take a sample of 150 students, stratified by school and gender.

Work out how many females from Appleborough School should be in his sample.

....

[Total 2 marks]

Exam Practice Tip

If you're asked about questionnaires in the exam, think about how the question is worded and how suitable the response boxes are. Bias is a pretty common problem too — think about whether the sample is fair. And remember that stratified sampling is about having the same proportions in the sample as in the population.

Score

16

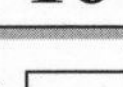

Mean, Median, Mode and Range

1 15 boys and 13 girls took a Maths test. The mean mark for the boys was b.
In the same test the mean mark for the girls was g.
Write down an expression for the mean mark of all 28 pupils.

D

....

[Total 2 marks]

2 Declan is training to take part in a 10 km race.
He runs the same distance every day for 30 days.

C

For the first 20 days, his mean running time was 56.2 minutes.
His mean running time for all 30 days was 54.4 minutes.

Work out Declan's mean running time for the last 10 days of his training.

Total running time for first 20 days = 20 × .... = ...

Total running time for all 30 days = ... × .... = ...

Total running time for last 10 days = ... − .... = ...

Mean running time for last 10 days = ... ÷ ....

.... minutes

[Total 3 marks]

3 Lee has 6 pygmy goats. Their weights, in kg, are listed below.

C

32 23 31 28 36 26

a) Which three weights, from the list above, would have a range which is half the value of the median of the three weights? Write down the range and median with your answer.

.................., ..., ...

range = ..., median = ...

[3]

b) Two of the goats wander off and don't return. The mean weight of the herd is now 27.25 kg. Find the weights of the two goats who wandered off.

.... kg and .... kg

[4]

[Total 7 marks]

Score: ☐ / **12**

 ☐  ☐  ☐

Averages and Spread

1 Liz sells earrings. The prices in pounds of 12 pairs of earrings are given below.

3 4 8 10 11 5 7 4 12 8 9 5

a) Draw an ordered stem and leaf diagram to show this information. You must include a key. 

[3]

b) Liz reduces all her prices by 50p. Will the interquartile range of the new prices be less than, greater than or the same as the interquartile range of the old prices? Give a reason for your answer.

....

....

[1]

[Total 4 marks]

***2** The stem and leaf diagram below shows the amount of rainfall in mm that fell on an island during two different 15 day periods — one in June and the other in November. 

June		November
9 8	0	1 2 2 7 9
5 2	1	2 3 5 5 8
9 8 6 3	2	0 2 2 3 5
8 8 7 4 1 0	3	
3	4	

Key (June): 8 | 0 = 8 mm of rain

Key (November): 0 | 1 = 1 mm of rain

Compare the rainfall in June and November using the median and interquartile ranges.

[Total 6 marks]

***3** Tom gives a puzzle to a sample of boys and girls. The box plots below show information about the time it took the children to finish the puzzle. 

Boys

Girls

20 30 40 50 60 70 80 90

Time (seconds)

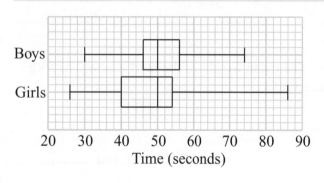

Compare the distribution of the time taken by the boys and the time taken by the girls.

[Total 2 marks]

Score: ____ / **12**

Frequency Tables — Finding Averages

1 The table shows the number of pets owned by each pupil in class 7F. 

Number of pets	Frequency
0	8
1	3
2	5
3	8
4	4
5	1

a) How many pupils are there in class 7F?

.... *[2]*

b) Find the total number of pets owned by pupils in class 7F.

.... *[2]*

c) Work out the mean number of pets per pupil in class 7F.

.... *[2]*

[Total 6 marks]

2 For her GCSE homework, Vanessa collected information about the number of text messages pupils in her school sent one day. She recorded her results in the frequency table below. 

Number of messages	Frequency
0	2
2	4
3	7
5	11
7	6
8	3
10	3

a) How many text messages were sent in total?

.... *[2]*

b) Use the table to calculate:

i) the mean number of text messages sent.

.... *[2]*

ii) the modal number of text messages sent.

.... *[1]*

iii) the median number of text messages sent.

.... *[2]*

[Total 7 marks]

Score: $\frac{\quad}{13}$

Grouped Frequency Tables

1 32 pupils in a class sat an exam in Science.
The distribution of their marks is given in the table below. 

Exam mark	Frequency
$10 < x \leq 20$	2
$20 < x \leq 30$	5
$30 < x \leq 40$	7
$40 < x \leq 50$	8
$50 < x \leq 60$	4
$60 < x \leq 70$	6

Use the table to find:

a) the modal class.

.... *[1]*

b) the group which contains the median.

.... *[1]*

c) an estimate of the mean (give your answer to 3 s.f.).

Tip: add a couple of columns to the table to help you.

.... *[4]*

[Total 6 marks]

2 During a science experiment 10 seeds were planted and their growth measured to the nearest cm after 12 days. The results were recorded in the table below. 

Growth in cm	Number of plants
$0 \leq x \leq 2$	2
$3 \leq x \leq 5$	4
$6 \leq x \leq 8$	3
$9 \leq x \leq 11$	1

a) Use the table to find:

i) the group which contains the median.

.... *[1]*

ii) an estimate of the mean growth.

.... cm *[4]*

b) Explain why you can only find an estimate of the mean.

....

....

[1]

[Total 6 marks]

Score: ___ / **12**

Cumulative Frequency

1 120 pupils in a year group sit an examination at the end of the year. Their results are given in the table below. 

Exam mark (%)	$0 < x \le 20$	$20 < x \le 30$	$30 < x \le 40$	$40 < x \le 50$	$50 < x \le 60$	$60 < x \le 70$	$70 < x \le 80$	$80 < x \le 100$
Frequency	3	10	12	24	42	16	9	4

a) Complete the cumulative frequency table below.

Exam mark (%)	≤ 20	≤ 30	≤ 40	≤ 50	≤ 60	≤ 70	≤ 80	≤ 100
Cumulative Frequency								

[1]

b) Use your table to draw a cumulative frequency graph on the graph paper.

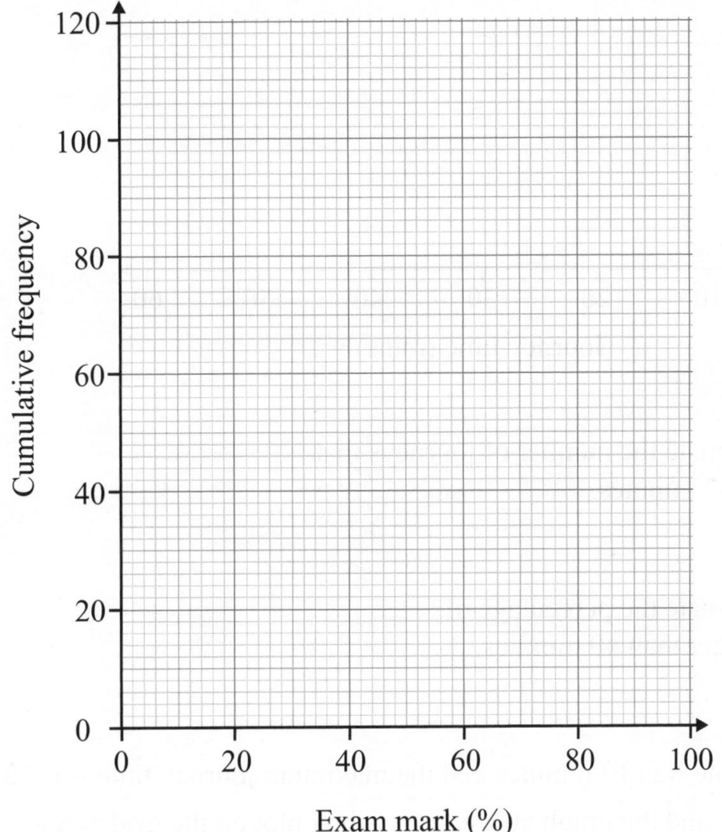

[2]

c) Use your graph to find an estimate for the median.

.... %

[1]

d) Use your graph to find an estimate for the inter-quartile range.

.... %

[2]

[Total 6 marks]

2 The cumulative frequency table below gives information about the length of time it takes to travel between Udderston and Trundle on the main road each morning.

Journey Time (t mins)	$0 < t \le 20$	$0 < t \le 25$	$0 < t \le 30$	$0 < t \le 35$	$0 < t \le 45$	$0 < t \le 60$
Cumulative Frequency	7	22	36	45	49	50

a) On the graph paper below, draw a cumulative frequency graph for the table.

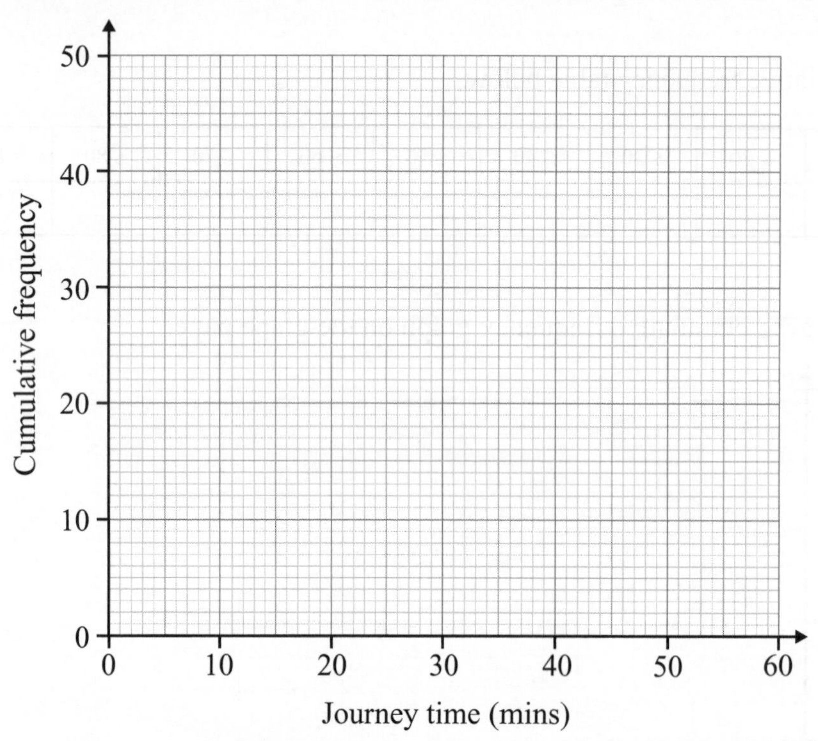

[2]

b) Use your graph to estimate the number of journeys that took between 27 and 47 minutes.

.... journeys
[2]

c) Use your graph to estimate the percentage of journeys that took longer than 40 minutes.

.... %
[2]

The minimum journey time was 12 minutes and the maximum journey time was 52 minutes.

d) Using this information and the graph above, draw a box plot on the grid below to show the journey times between Udderston and Trundle.

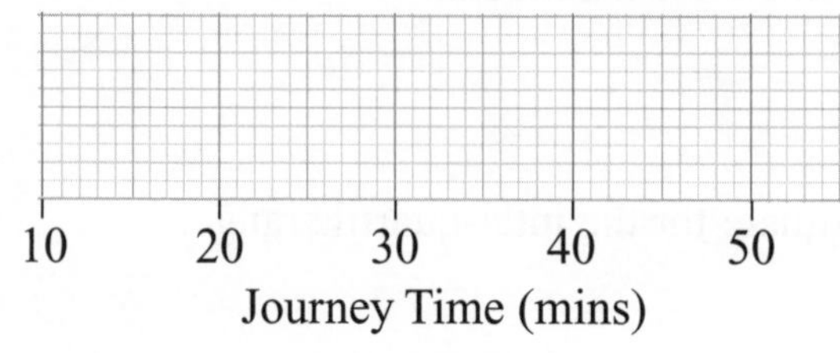

[3]
[Total 9 marks]

Score: $\frac{\quad}{15}$

Histograms and Frequency Density

1 The histogram shows the number of minutes some pupils watched television for one evening. 

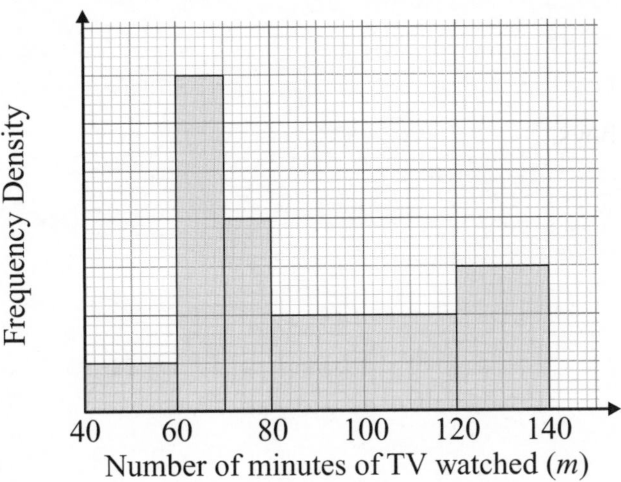

Number of minutes of TV watched (m)	Frequency
$40 \le m < 60$	20
$60 \le m < 70$	
$70 \le m < 80$	
$80 \le m < 120$	
$120 \le m < 140$	

Use the histogram to complete the frequency table.

Start by finding the frequency density for the first interval.

[Total 2 marks]

2 100 Year 11 pupils were each given a potato. The table below gives some information about how long it took the pupils to peel their potato. 

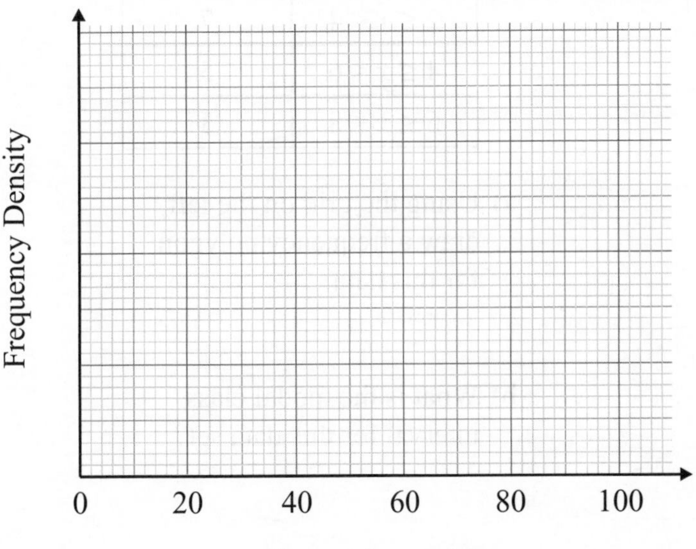

Time, t (s)	Frequency
$0 < t \le 20$	15
$20 < t \le 30$	35
$30 < t \le 40$	30
$40 < t \le 60$	15
$60 < t \le 100$	5

Use the information in the table to draw a histogram on the grid above.

[Total 3 marks]

Score: $\frac{\quad}{5}$

Other Graphs and Charts

1 115 students took part in a sports day. Some took part in swimming, some took part in athletics and the rest took part in football. 

63 of the students were boys.
10 of the students who swam were boys.
32 girls did athletics.
35 of the 41 students who played football were boys.

How many girls took part in swimming?

....

[Total 4 marks]

2 The grouped frequency table below shows the number of hours of homework 30 students did in one week. 

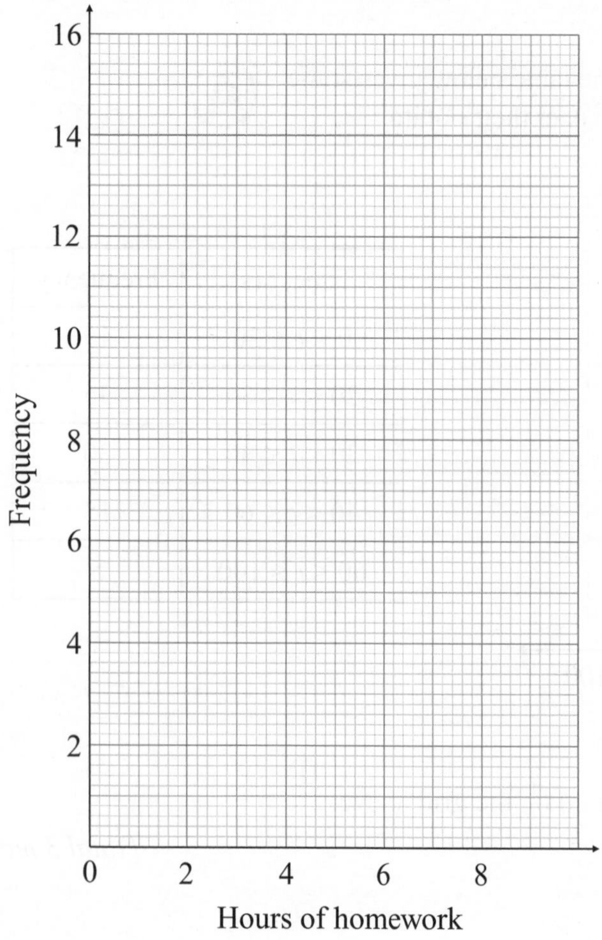

(Blank grid: x-axis "Hours of homework" 0 to 8; y-axis "Frequency" 0 to 16)

Hours of Homework	Frequency
$0 \le x < 2$	15
$2 \le x < 4$	7
$4 \le x < 6$	5
$6 \le x < 8$	3

a) Using the grid on the left, draw a frequency polygon for this data.

[2]

b) What is the modal class interval for this data set?

....

[1]

[Total 3 marks]

Score:  7

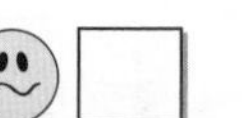  

Scatter Graphs

1 15 pupils in a class study both Spanish and Italian.
Their end of year exam results are shown on the scatter graph below.

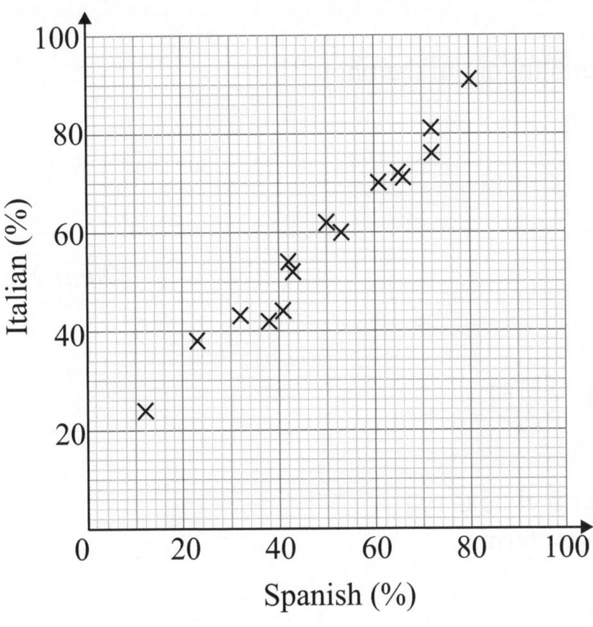

a) Describe the strength and type of correlation shown on this graph.

.... *[2]*

b) Draw a line of best fit for the data. *[1]*

c) Ahmed was absent for his Spanish exam but scored 66% on his Italian exam. Estimate the mark he might have got in Spanish.

.... % *[2]*

[Total 5 marks]

2 A furniture company is looking at how effective their advertising is.
They are comparing how much they spent on advertising in random months with their total sales value for that month. This information is shown on the graph below.

The table shows the amount spent on advertising and the value of sales for three more months.

Amount spent on advertising (thousands of pounds)	0.75	0.15	1.85
Sales (thousands of pounds)	105	60	170

200
150
100
50
Sales (thousands of pounds)
0
0.5
1
1.5
2
Amount spent on advertising (thousands of pounds)

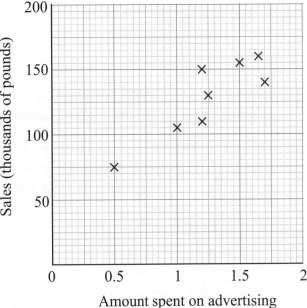

a) Plot the information from the table on the scatter graph. *[1]*

b) Describe the relationship between the amount spent on advertising and the value of sales.

.... *[1]*

c) Use your graph to estimate how much the company would need to spend on advertising in order to sell £125 000 worth of furniture in one month.

£ .... *[3]*

[Total 5 marks]

Score: /10

Probability Basics

1 Amelie takes some photos of her sister.
The probability that her sister will be blinking in a photo is $\frac{2}{5}$

Amelie picks one photo at random.
What is the probability that her sister is not blinking in the photo?

....

[Total 2 marks]

2 There are 10 counters in a bag.
Four of the counters are blue and the rest are red.
One counter is picked out at random.

a) Work out the probability that the counter picked is red.
Give your answer as a fraction in its lowest terms.

....

[2]

b) What is the probability that the counter picked is green?

....

[1]

[Total 3 marks]

3 Arthur has stripy, spotty and plain socks in his drawer.
He picks a sock from the drawer at random.

The probability that he picks a plain sock is 0.4.
He is twice as likely to pick a stripy sock than a spotty sock.
What is the probability that he picks a spotty sock? Give your answer as a decimal.

let P(spotty sock) = y

then P(stripy sock) = ... y

.... + y + ... = 1

.... = 0.6

y = ...

....

[Total 4 marks]

Score: /9

Listing Outcomes and Expected Frequency

1 Alvar has a fair six sided dice and a set of five cards numbered 2, 4, 6, 8 and 10. 
He rolls the dice and chooses a card at random.
Alvar adds the number on the dice to the number on the card to calculate his total score.

a) Complete the table below to show all of the possible scores.

Cards

Dice		2	4	6	8	10
	1				9	11
	2			8	10	12
	3			9	11	13
	4		8	10	12	14
	5	7	9	11	13	15
	6	8	10	12	14	16

[2]

b) Find the probability that Alvar will score exactly 9.

....

[2]

Alvar decides to play a game with the dice and cards against his friends Zynah and Colin.
If the total score is less than 8 Colin will win, if the total score is more than 11 Alvar will win.
Otherwise Zynah will win.

c) Find the probability that Zynah will win the game.

....

[2]

[Total 6 marks]

2 Shaun is playing the game 'hook-a-duck'. 

There is a number on the bottom of each rubber duck.
The winning numbers and the probability of each being chosen are given in the table below.

Winning number	2	5	7	8	10
Probability	0.02	0.36	0.23	0.21	0.08

a) Work out the probability that Shaun will hook a duck with a number 2 or 8.

....

[2]

b) Shaun plays the game 36 times. Estimate how many times he does **not** win.

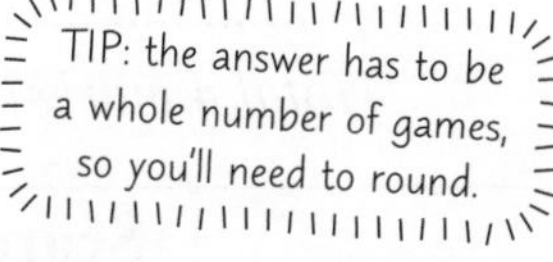

TIP: the answer has to be
a whole number of games,
so you'll need to round.

....

[4]

[Total 6 marks]

Score: ___ / **12**

The AND / OR Rules

1 Here is a 5-sided spinner. 
The spinner is biased.

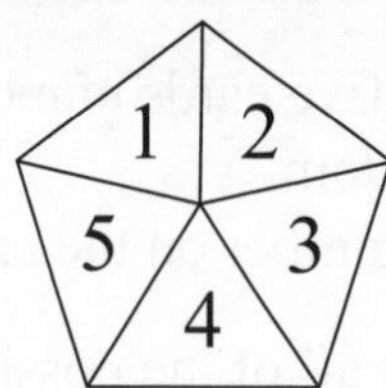

The probability that the spinner will land on the numbers 1 to 4 is given in this table.

Number	1	2	3	4	5
Probability	0.3	0.15	0.2	0.25	

I spin the spinner once.

a) Work out the probability the spinner will not land on 2.

....

[2]

b) Work out the probability the spinner will land on an odd number.

....

[3]

c) Work out the probability that the spinner will land on 5.

....

[2]

I spin the spinner twice.

d) Work out the probability that the spinner will land on 3 both times.

....

[2]

[Total 9 marks]

2 Rebecca buys a bag of beads to make a necklace.
The bag contains 8 brown beads and 12 orange beads.
She picks three beads from the bag and puts them onto a string.

Work out the probability that she puts 2 orange beads and one brown bead onto her string, in **any** order.

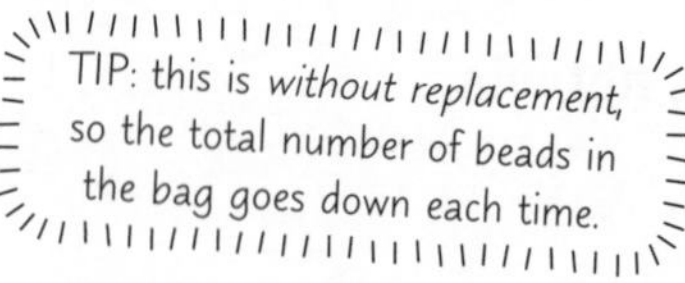

TIP: this is without replacement, so the total number of beads in the bag goes down each time.

....

[Total 4 marks]

Exam Practice Tip

All you need to remember here is if you're being asked the probability of Thing One AND Thing Two happening you MULTIPLY, and if you're being asked the probability of Thing One OR Thing Two happening you ADD. Careful with your adding and multiplying if your probabilities are fractions — it's an easy way to slip up.

Score

13

Tree Diagrams

1 Jo and Heather are meeting for coffee.
The probability that Jo will wear burgundy trousers is $\frac{2}{5}$.
There is a one in four chance that Heather will wear burgundy trousers.
The two events are independent.

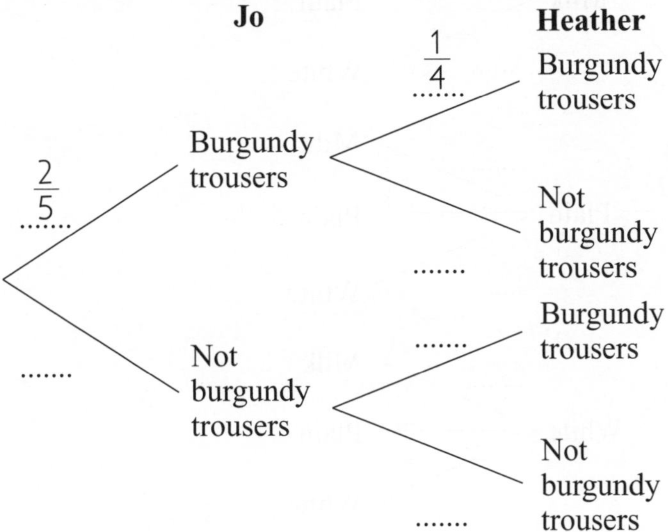

a) Complete the tree diagram above. *[2]*

b) What is the probability that neither of them wear burgundy trousers?

Probability neither wear burgundy trousers = $\frac{3}{5} \times \frac{\ldots}{\ldots} = \frac{\ldots}{\ldots}$ ....

[2]

[Total 4 marks]

2 A couple are both carriers of a recessive gene that causes a hereditary disease.
If they have a child, the probability that the child will suffer from the disease is 0.25.
The couple plan to have two children.

If the couple have two children, find the probability that at least one of them will have the disease.

....

[Total 4 marks]

3 A box of chocolates contains 12 chocolates.
5 of the chocolates are milk chocolate, 4 are plain chocolate and 3 are white chocolate.
Two chocolates are chosen at random without replacement.

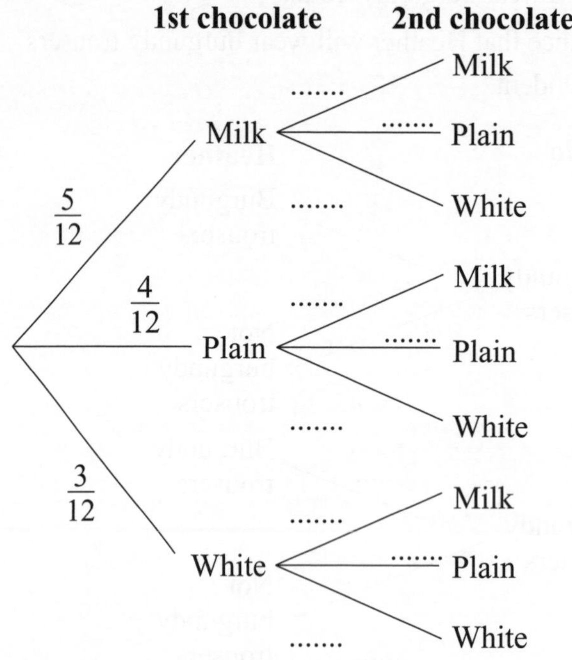

a) Complete the tree diagram above.

[2]

b) Calculate the probability that one milk chocolate and one white chocolate are chosen.

....

[2]

c) Work out the probability that at least one plain chocolate is chosen.

....

[3]

[Total 7 marks]

Score: $\frac{\quad}{15}$

Relative Frequency

1 Suda has a six sided dice. The sides are numbered 1 to 6. 

Suda rolls the dice 50 times and records the results in the table below.

Number	1	2	3	4	5	6
Relative Frequency	0.32	0.12	0.24	0.14	0.06	0.12

a) How many times did she roll a 6?

....

[2]

b) Is Suda's dice fair? Explain your answer.

....

[2]

c) She rolls the dice another 50 times. Should she expect the same results? Explain your answer.

....

[1]

[Total 5 marks]

2 Eimear has a bag containing a large number of counters.
Each counter is numbered either 1, 2, 3, 4 or 5. 

She selects one counter from the bag, makes a note of its number, and then puts it back in the bag.
Eimear does this 100 times. She records her results in the table below.

Number on counter	1	2	3	4	5
Frequency	23	25	22	21	9
Relative Frequency					

a) Complete the table, giving the relative frequencies of the number of times each counter is selected.

[2]

b) Elvin says that he thinks that the bag contains the same number of counters with each number.
Do you agree? Give a reason for your answer.

....

[1]

c) Using Eimear's results, estimate the probability of selecting an odd number when **one** counter is picked from the bag.

....

[2]

[Total 5 marks]

Score: ___ / **10**

Candidate Surname | Candidate Forename(s)

Centre Number | Candidate Number | Candidate Signature

GCSE

Mathematics Higher Tier

Paper 1 (Non-Calculator)

Practice Paper

You must have:
Pen, pencil, eraser, ruler, protractor, pair of compasses.
You may use tracing paper.

You are **not allowed** to use a calculator.

Instructions to candidates

- Use **black** ink to write your answers.
- Write your name and other details in the spaces provided above.
- Answer **all** questions in the spaces provided.
- In calculations, show clearly how you worked out your answers.
- Do all rough work on the paper.

Information for candidates

- The marks available are given in brackets at the end of each question.
- You may get marks for method, even if your answer is incorrect.
- There are 22 questions in this paper. There are no blank pages.
- There are 100 marks available for this paper.
- In questions labelled with an asterisk (*), you will be assessed on the quality of your written communication — take particular care here with spelling, punctuation and the quality of explanations.

Get the answers — on video and in print

Your free Online Edition of this book includes a link to step-by-step video solutions for this Exam Paper, plus worked solutions you can print out.
There's more info about how to get your Online Edition at the front of this book.

Answer ALL the questions.

Write your answers in the spaces provided.

You must show all of your working.

1 Here is a pattern made of equilateral triangles.

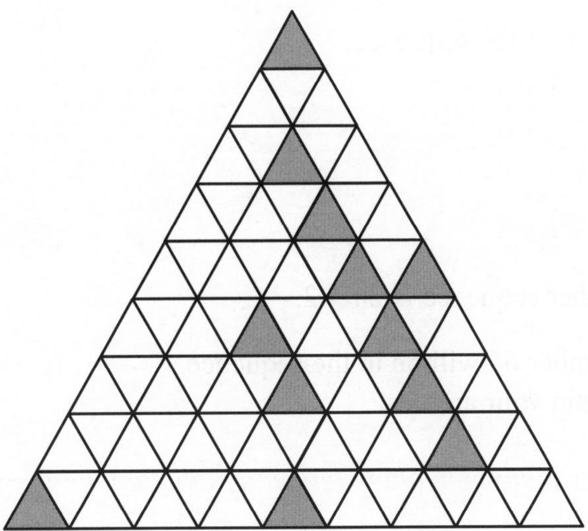

Shade 12 more triangles to make a pattern with rotational symmetry of order 3.

[Total 3 marks]

2 In a class of 26 children, 12 are boys and the rest are girls.

(a) Work out the ratio of boys to girls.
Give your answer in its simplest form.

....

[2]

In another class the ratio of boys to girls is 2 : 3.
There are 25 children in the class.

(b) Work out how many girls are in the class.

.... girls

[2]

[Total 4 marks]

3 (a) Here are the first 5 terms in a sequence.

2 13 24 35 46

(i) Write an expression for the nth term of this sequence.

....

(ii) Find the 8th term of the sequence.

....

[3]

(b) The nth term of another sequence is $2n + 2$.

Rita says that the number 65 will be in the sequence.
Is she correct? Explain your answer.

....

....

....

....

[2]

[Total 5 marks]

---

4 A regular polygon has 7 sides.

(a) Write down the sum of the exterior angles of the polygon.

..................................°

[1]

(b) Calculate the sum of the interior angles of the polygon.

..................................°

[2]

[Total 3 marks]

***5** Michael and Jojo are going out for a steak dinner.
Their three favourite restaurants are advertising the following special offers.

<u>The Big Grill</u> STEAK - £16 each Buy 1 get the second half price	<u>Steak 'a' Lot</u> STEAK - £18 each Buy 2 and get 20% off the total price.	<u>Danny's Steak House</u> STEAK - £21 each Buy 2 and get a third off the total price.

Which restaurant should Michael and Jojo go to for the best deal on steak?
Show all of your working.

....

[Total 5 marks]

---

6 Work out $3\frac{3}{7} - 2\frac{1}{5}$

....

[Total 3 marks]

7 A large supermarket chain is planning to open a new store in a town called Digton. Residents of Digton are asked to complete a questionnaire to give their views on this idea.

Here is one of the questions from the questionnaire:

'There is nowhere in Digton that sells a good range of products — so Digton needs a new supermarket. Do you agree?'

(a) Write down one criticism of this question.

....

....

[1]

(b) Suggest a more suitable question that could be used instead.

....

....

[1]

Another question on the questionnaire is:

'How far are you willing to travel to buy your food shopping each week?'

☐ Not far ☐ Quite far ☐ Very far

(c) Write down one criticism of this question.

....

....

[1]

(d) Rewrite the question with more suitable response options.

....

....

[2]

[Total 5 marks]

---

8 (a) Write 56^2 as a product of its prime factors.

....

[2]

(b) Find the highest common factor of 56 and 72.

....

[1]

[Total 3 marks]

---

9 A chocolate manufacturer trials a new shape of box for one of its products.

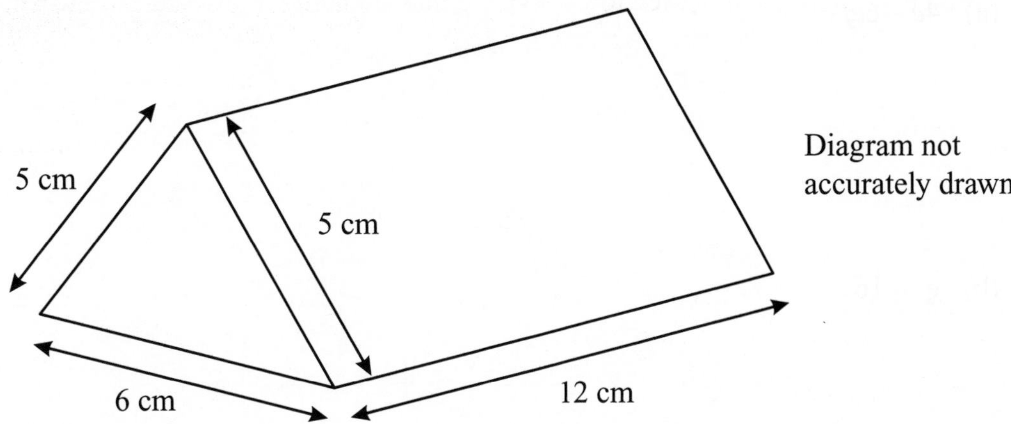

(a) Find the surface area of the box.

.... cm^2

[3]

(b) Find the volume of the box.

.... cm^3

[2]

[Total 5 marks]

---

10 Rearrange the equations below to make b the subject in each case.

(a) $a = \frac{1}{2}bc^2$

[2]

(b) $12 = \frac{bx + 8}{by - 4}$

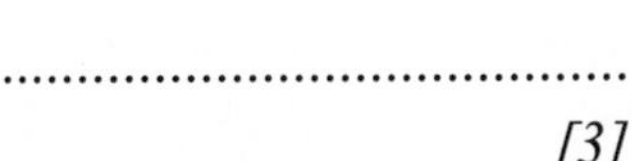

[3]

[Total 5 marks]

---

11 Fully factorise the following expressions.

(a) $4e - 6ef$

....

[1]

(b) $g^2 - 16$

....

[1]

[Total 2 marks]

---

12 (a) Simplify

(i) $m^4 \times m^3$

....

(ii) $(8n^6)^{\frac{1}{3}}$

....

[3]

(b) Expand and simplify $(p - 3)(p + 5)$

....

[2]

(c) Solve $8(2q - 4) + 5(q + 11) = 65$

$q =$ ....

[2]

[Total 7 marks]

---

13 In the diagram below, shape **B** is a transformation of shape **A**.

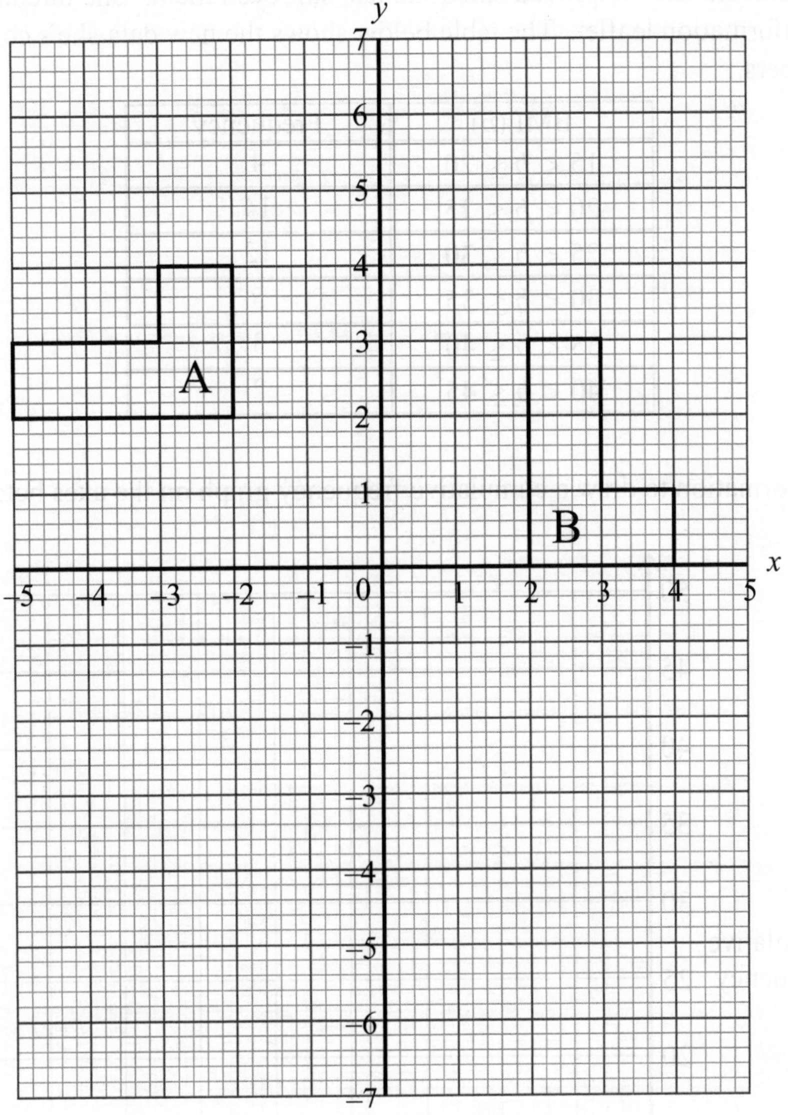

(a) Describe fully the transformation that maps shape **A** onto shape **B**.

....

....

.... *[3]*

(b) Enlarge shape **B** by a scale factor of $-\frac{3}{2}$ from the centre (2, –1).
Label the enlargement **C**.

[3]

[Total 6 marks]

14 Megan is the manager of a health club. She wants to know if the BMIs (Body Mass Indexes) of the female members have improved since she last surveyed them. She intends to publish her findings in an information leaflet. The table below shows the new data she's collected from the 40 female members.

BMI (b)	Frequency
$15 < b \leq 20$	4
$20 < b \leq 25$	14
$25 < b \leq 30$	12
$30 < b \leq 35$	5
$35 < b \leq 40$	3
$40 < b \leq 45$	2

(a) Use this information to draw a cumulative frequency graph on the axes below.

[2]

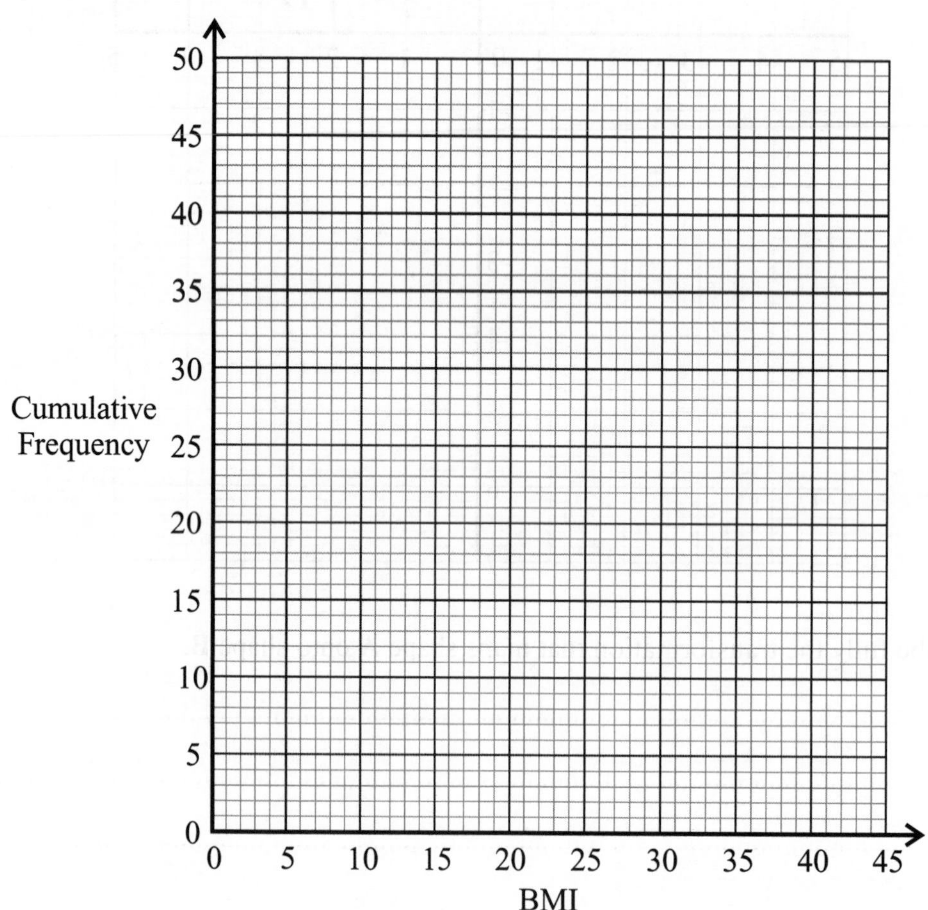

(b) Estimate the median BMI.

....

[1]

(c) Estimate the interquartile range (IQR).

....

[2]

*(d) Megan also wants to include a comparison of the BMIs of the male and female members of the health club in her information leaflet.

A box plot giving information on the BMIs of the male health club members is shown below.

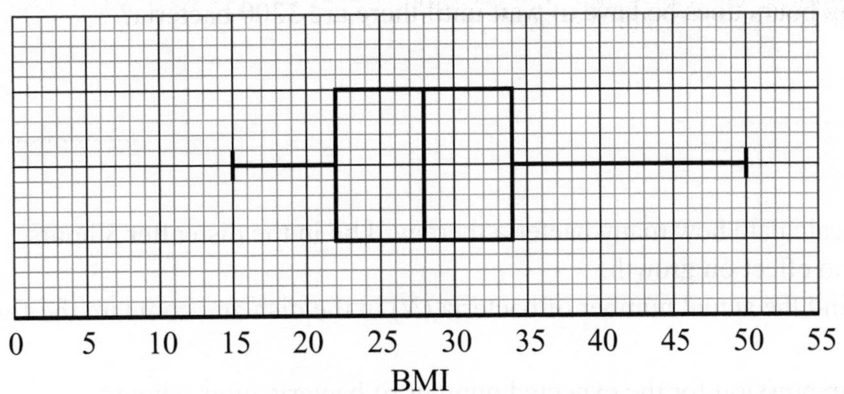

Compare the BMIs of the women to the BMIs of the men.

....

....

....

[2]

[Total 7 marks]

---

15 Simplify these algebraic fractions as much as possible.

(a) $\dfrac{4x + 10}{6x + 14}$

....

[2]

(b) $\dfrac{x^2 - 2x - 15}{x^2 + 10x + 21}$

....

[3]

[Total 5 marks]

16 John is growing some bacteria in a laboratory. To begin with there are 200 bacteria and the number of bacteria doubles every hour. He wants to run a test that could inhibit their growth.

(a) John needs around 3200 bacteria before he can run a successful test.
How many hours does he have to wait until there are 3200 bacteria?

.... hours
[2]

John needs to calculate how many bacteria there will be in the dish after 8 hours, if his test has no effect on growth.
He will then find the actual number of bacteria (N) in the dish and compare the figures.

(b) Write an expression for the expected number of bacteria after n hours.

....
[1]

(c) Work out the expected number of bacteria after 8 hours.
Give your answer in standard form.

....
[2]

[Total 5 marks]

---

17 The diagram below shows the rectangle *ABCD*.

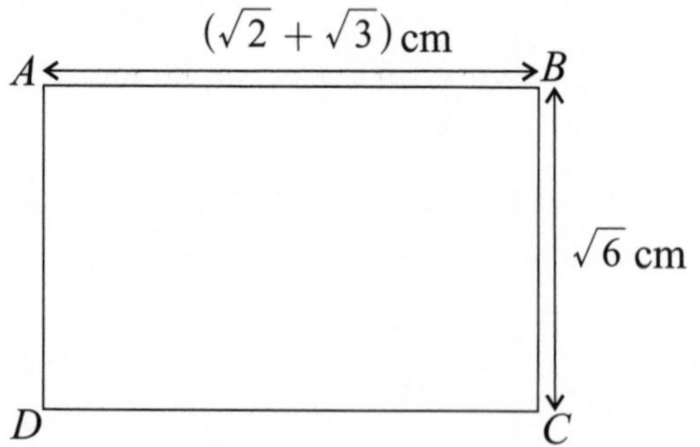

Diagram not accurately drawn

Calculate the area of the rectangle, giving your answer in the form $(a\sqrt{3} + b\sqrt{2})$ cm^2.

.... cm^2

[Total 3 marks]

---

18 In the diagram below, O is the centre of the circle. The angle a is 36°.

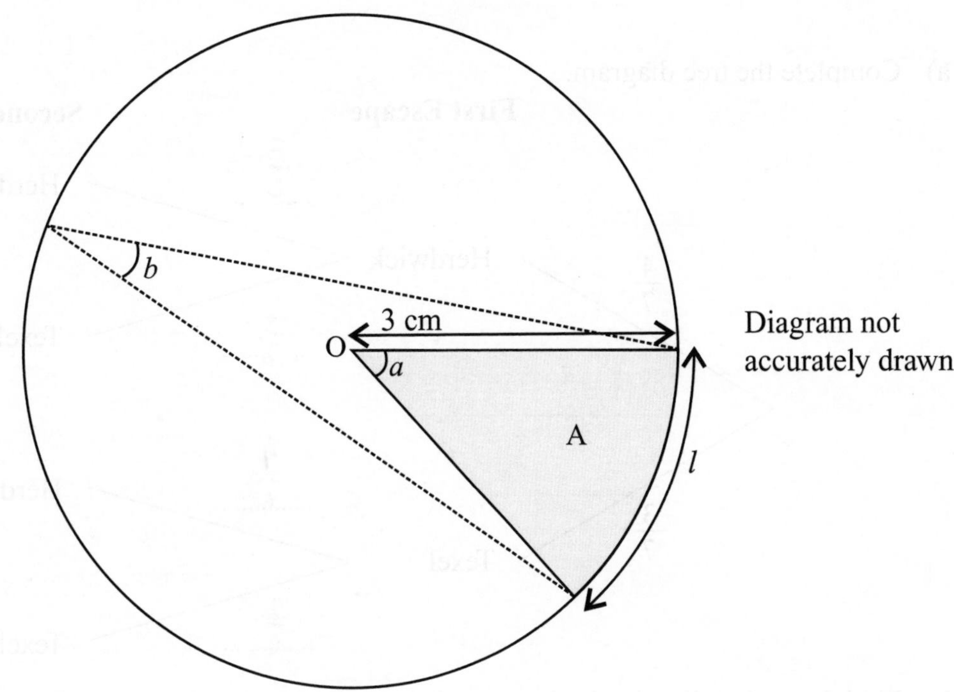

(a) What is the size of angle b?

.... °

[1]

(b) Calculate the area of the minor sector A.
Leave your answer in terms of π.

.... cm^2

[3]

(c) Calculate the length of the minor arc, l, in terms of π.
Give your answer as a fraction in its lowest terms.

.... cm

[3]

[Total 7 marks]

19 A field contains 4 Herdwick sheep and 3 Texel sheep. One random sheep escapes from the field. Later on, another random sheep escapes.

(a) Complete the tree diagram.

[2]

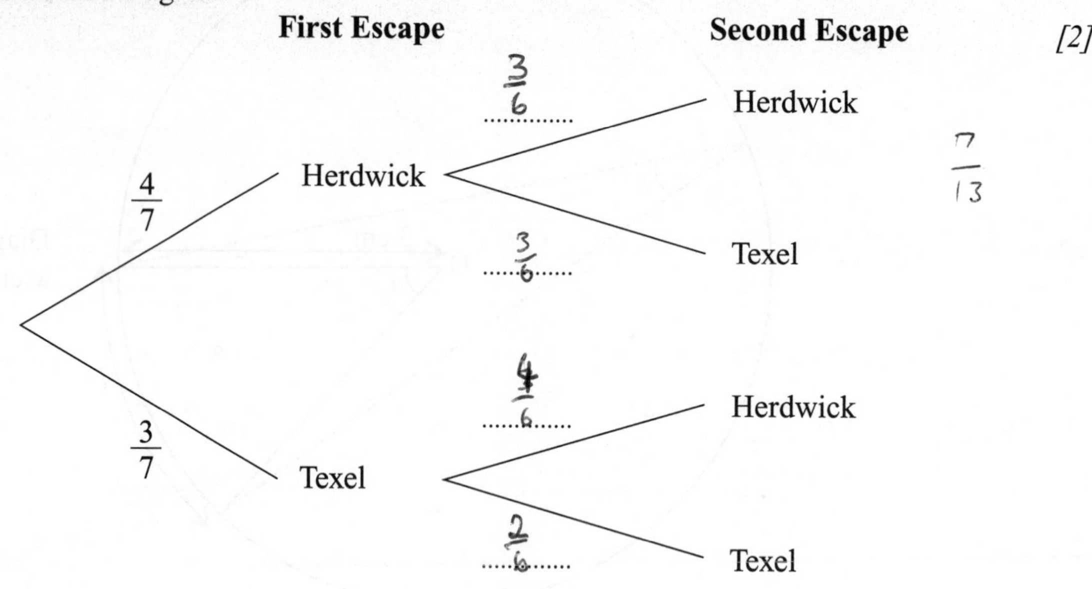

(b) Find the probability that both escaped sheep are Herdwicks

....

[2]

(c) Find the probability that a Herdwick and a Texel sheep escaped, in either order.

....

[2]

[Total 6 marks]

---

20 Solve the simultaneous equations

$$y^2 + 4x = 17$$
$$y = x - 5$$

[Total 3 marks]

21 Write $x^2 + 6x - 8$ in the form $(x + a)^2 + b$

....

[Total 3 marks]

22

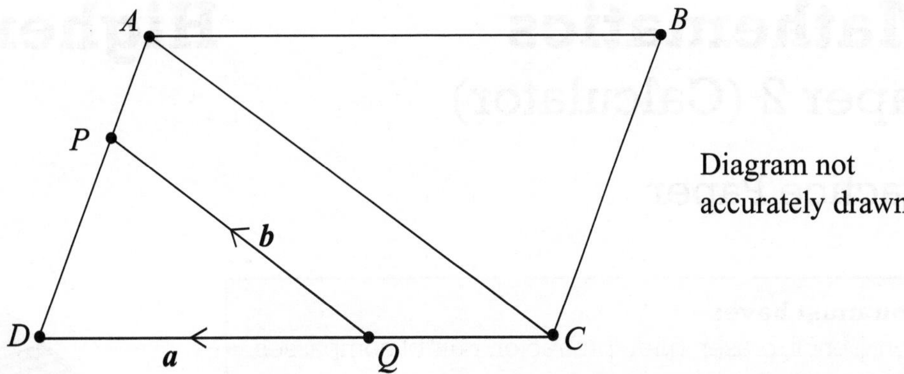

ABCD is a parallelogram.

$\overrightarrow{QP} = \boldsymbol{b}$ and $\overrightarrow{QD} = \boldsymbol{a}$.

Triangles *PQD* and *ACD* are similar.

$AD : PD = 5 : 3$

(a) Find $\overrightarrow{CA}$ in terms of $\boldsymbol{a}$ and $\boldsymbol{b}$.

....

[1]

R is a point on *AC* so that $5\overrightarrow{AR} = 2\overrightarrow{AC}$.

(b) Show that $\overrightarrow{PR}$ is parallel to $\overrightarrow{DQ}$.

[4]

[Total 5 marks]

[TOTAL FOR PAPER = 100 MARKS]

Candidate Surname | Candidate Forename(s)

Centre Number | Candidate Number | Candidate Signature

GCSE

Mathematics — Higher Tier

Paper 2 (Calculator)

Practice Paper

You must have:
Pen, pencil, eraser, ruler, protractor, pair of compasses.
You may use tracing paper.

You **may use** a calculator.

Instructions to candidates

- Use **black** ink to write your answers.
- Write your name and other details in the spaces provided above.
- Answer **all** questions in the spaces provided.
- In calculations, show clearly how you worked out your answers.
- Do all rough work on the paper.
- Unless a question tells you otherwise, take the value of π to be 3.142, or use the π button on your calculator.

Information for candidates

- The marks available are given in brackets at the end of each question.
- You may get marks for method, even if your answer is incorrect.
- There are 21 questions in this paper. There are no blank pages.
- There are 100 marks available for this paper.
- In questions labelled with an asterisk (*), you will be assessed on the quality of your written communication — take particular care here with spelling, punctuation and the quality of explanations.

Get the answers — on video and in print

Your free Online Edition of this book includes a link to step-by-step video solutions for this Exam Paper, plus worked solutions you can print out.
There's more info about how to get your Online Edition at the front of this book.

Answer ALL the questions.

Write your answers in the spaces provided.

You must show all of your working.

1 A painter wants to calculate the cost of painting the four outside walls of a warehouse.
The diagram below gives the dimensions of the warehouse.

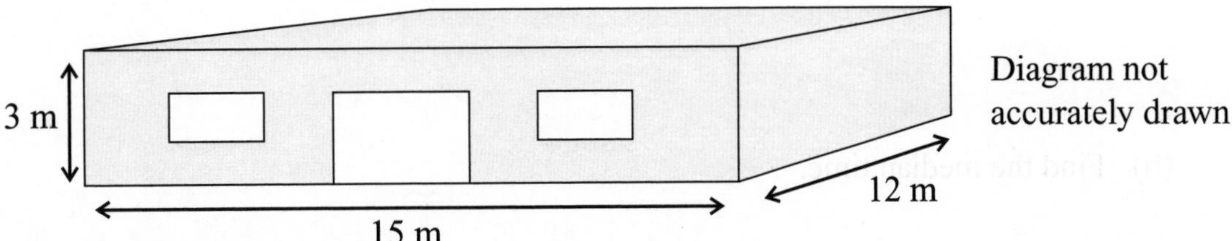

There are 5 windows in the warehouse that each measure 2 m by 1 m and a door that measures 3 m by 2.5 m.

The paint covers 13 m² per litre.
The paint can be bought in tins that contain 5 litres or 2.5 litres.

5 litre tins cost £20.99
2.5 litre tins cost £12.99

Calculate the cheapest price for painting the warehouse. You must show all your working.

£ ....

[Total 6 marks]

2 Here are the times, in seconds, that it took 18 scouts to tie a knot.

12	6	7	23	8	15	19	39	31
7	15	16	9	11	7	28	9	25

(a) In the space below, draw an ordered stem and leaf diagram to represent this data.

[3]

(b) Find the median time.

.... seconds

[1]

[Total 4 marks]

---

3 Mrs Thompson is on holiday in Spain and wants to buy a luxury ham that's a speciality of the region.

In the UK, the ham costs £35.20 per lb.
A shop in Spain is selling the ham for €75.60 per kilo.
The exchange rate is £1 = €1.16 and 1 kg ≈ 2.2 lb.

If Mrs Thompson wants to buy 5 lb of ham, how much would she save **in pounds** by buying the ham in Spain rather than the UK?

£ ....

[Total 4 marks]

---

4 Alice walks to the garage to pick up her car.
Her journey is shown on the distance-time graph below.

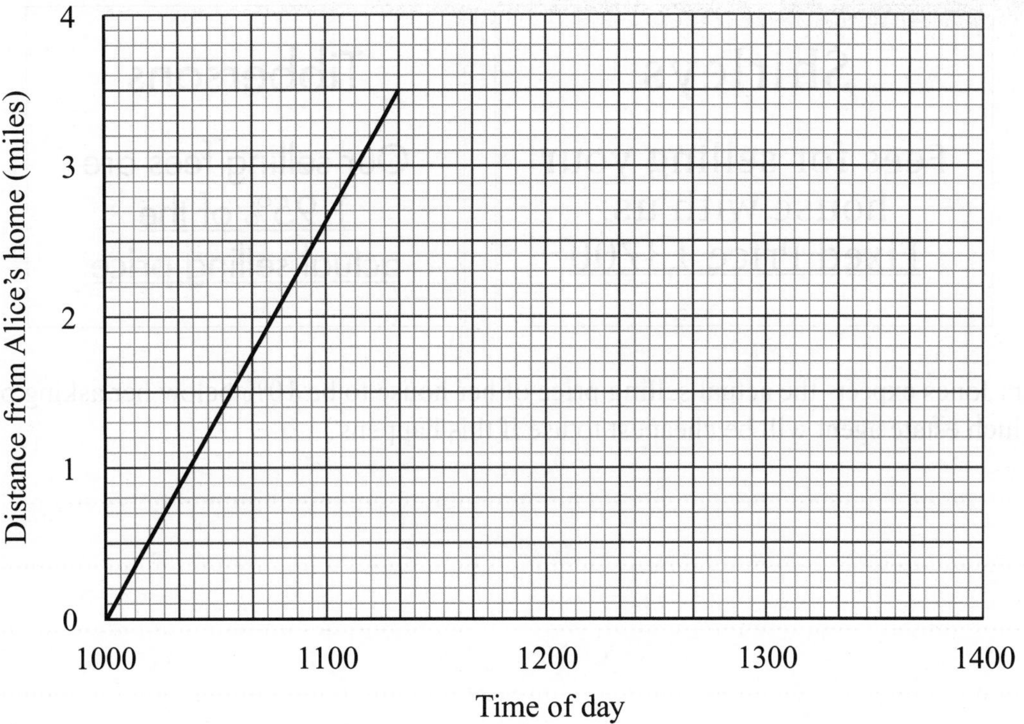

(a) How far is it from Alice's house to the garage?

.... miles

[1]

(b) At what speed does she walk to the garage?

.... mph

[2]

Alice spends 20 minutes at the garage, and then drives home at a speed of 21 mph.

(c) Complete the graph to show the time that Alice spends at the garage and her return journey.

[3]

(d) How long was Alice away from home for in total?

....

[1]

[Total 7 marks]

5 Mrs Jones is trying to sell her house. She decides to advertise her house with an estate agent, with an asking price of £190 000. She asks two estate agents what fees they will charge.

Shirleys	Tibbersons
Fees for selling your house with us: <u>Fixed Price £3700</u>	Our selling fees are <u>1.95% of the actual selling price</u>

*(a) Mrs Jones expects the actual selling price of her house to be 10% below her asking price. Which estate agent will be cheapest to use if this happens?

....

....

....

....

[3]

(b) Mrs Jones finds a house she wants to buy. It has an asking price of £212 500. She is told that the asking price was dropped by 15% six months ago.

What was the price of the house before the asking price was dropped?

£ ....

[3]

[Total 6 marks]

6 Two children play a game. Each round, Eva throws an ordinary unbiased 6-sided dice, and Finn spins a fair 3-sided spinner, labelled 1 to 3, twice and adds his scores together.

To win a round they have to score 6.

(a) Who is most likely to win a round? You must show your working.

....

[2]

(b) Eva and Finn decide to change the rules to increase their chances of winning a round. To win now, the score has to be 5 or more. They play 54 games in total.

Estimate the number of games in which Eva and Finn both score 5 or more.

....

[3]

[Total 5 marks]

---

7 The equation $x^3 - x - 4 = 0$ has a solution between 1 and 2.

Use trial and improvement to find this solution.
Give your answer correct to one decimal place.
You must show **ALL** of your working.

$x =$ ....

[Total 4 marks]

---

8 Reena inherits £4500. She decides to place the money in a savings account, and is considering two different accounts.

Account 1 pays a simple interest rate of 5% per year.
Account 2 pays a compound interest rate of 3.5%, compounded yearly.

(a) How much money will each account have in it after 1 year?

Account 1: £ .... Account 2: £ ....

[2]

(b) Reena wants to invest her money for 10 years.

In which account will her savings grow the most in this time?
Show your working clearly.

....

[3]

[Total 5 marks]

---

9 In February 2010, the UK population was estimated to be 62 000 000 people.

The UK national debt is the money that the UK government owes to people who have bought government bonds. In February 2010, the debt was calculated to be £8.494×10^{11}.

Use this information to estimate the national debt per person in the UK in February 2010.
Give your answer in standard form.

£ ....

[Total 2 marks]

10 The table below gives information about the heights of the children in Class A.

Height in cm (h)	Frequency
$130 \leq h < 140$	5
$140 \leq h < 150$	10
$150 \leq h < 160$	14
$160 \leq h < 170$	8
$170 \leq h < 180$	3

(a) Calculate an estimate for the mean height of the children in Class A.

.... cm

[4]

*(b) Below are two frequency polygons showing the heights of the children in Classes A and B.

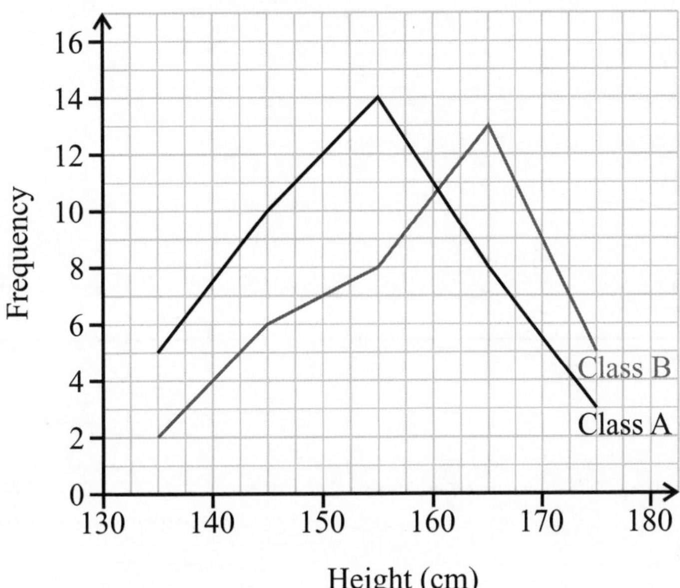

Compare the heights in the two classes.

....

....

....

....

[3]

[Total 7 marks]

11 The diagram below shows a trapezium. FG is parallel to EH.
EH is 15.5 cm, EF is 4.8 cm and FG is 10 cm.

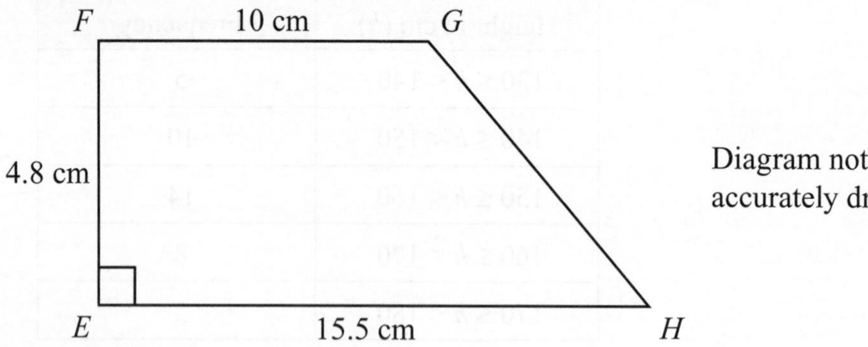

Diagram not accurately drawn

(a) Calculate the length of GH.

.... cm

[3]

(b) Calculate the size of angle EHG.
Give your answer correct to 1 decimal place.

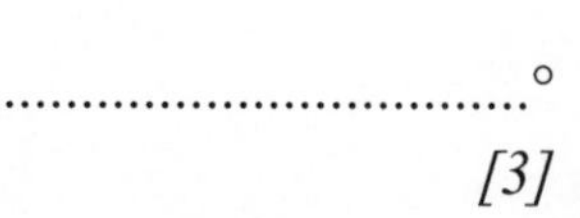

....................................°

[3]

[Total 6 marks]

---

12 (a) Factorise fully

(i) $3y - 6y^2z$

....

(ii) $6x^2 - 8x - 8$

....

[3]

(b) Solve the equation $x^2 - 8x + 3 = 0$
Give your answer in surd form.

....

[3]

[Total 6 marks]

13 On the grid below, shade the region that satisfies all three of these inequalities:

$x \leq 3$ $\quad$ $y > -4$ $\quad$ $y \leq x + 2$

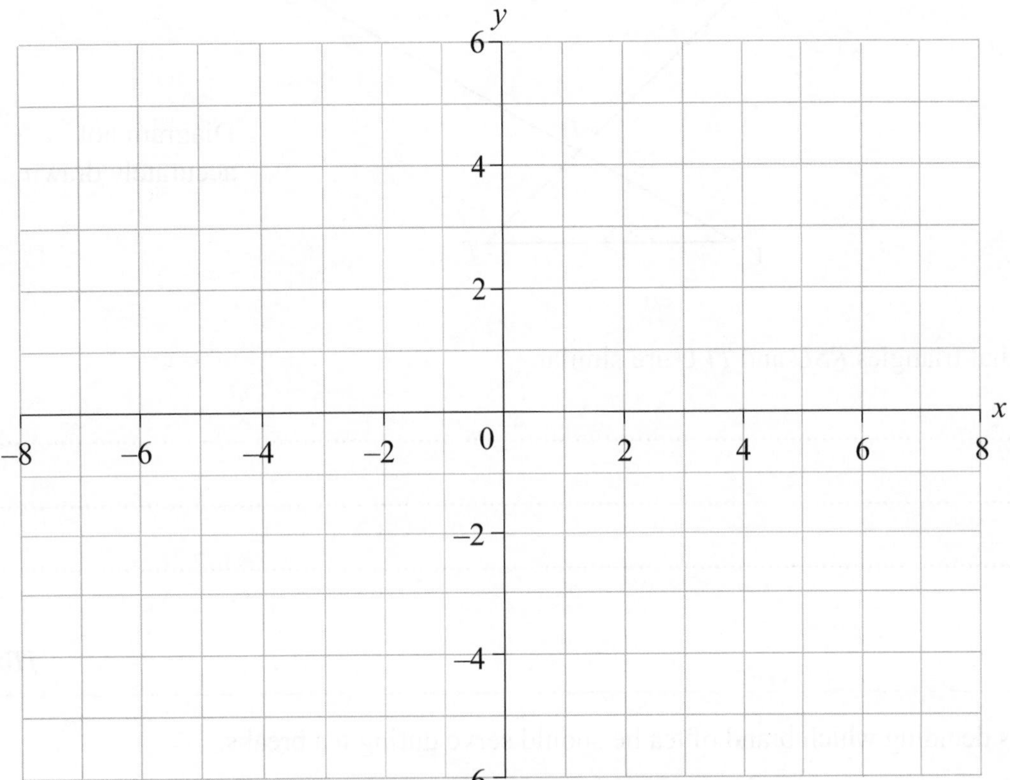

[Total 4 marks]

---

14 A sweet shop sells cylindrical tubs of sherbet.
The cylindrical tubs have an internal diameter of 3.8 cm and are 4.9 cm tall.

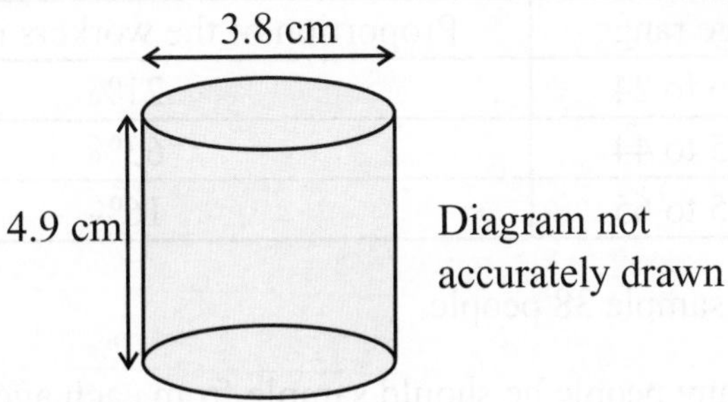

1 cm³ of sherbet weighs 0.63 g.

Calculate the weight, in grams, of sherbet in a full tub.
Give your answer correct to 2 decimal places.

.... g

[Total 3 marks]

15 *RUT* and *SUV* are straight lines that intersect at *U*.

RS and *VT* are parallel.

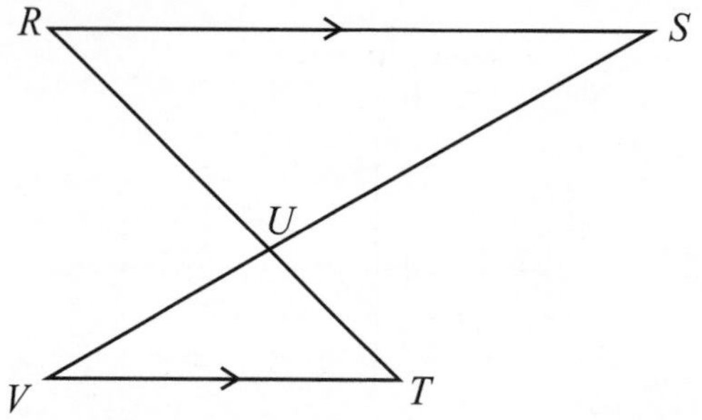

Diagram not accurately drawn

Show that triangles *RSU* and *TVU* are similar.

....

....

....

[Total 3 marks]

---

16 Aaron is deciding which brand of tea he should serve during tea breaks.

He wants to take a sample of workers in his company and ask them which brand they prefer.

He decides to use a stratified sample to proportionally represent the age distribution of workers within the company.

(a) The table below shows the age distribution of workers in the company.

Age range	Proportion of the workers in that range
16 to 24	21%
25 to 44	63%
45 to 65	16%

Aaron decides to sample 38 people.

Calculate how many people he should sample from each age range.

[3]

(b) Suggest one problem of using a stratified sample in this case.

....

....

[1]

[Total 4 marks]

***17** Jim has to deliver a load of metal rods on his truck.
Each rod is cut so that it weighs 80 kg (correct to the nearest 5 kg).

The maximum load that the truck can take is 1900 kg, to the nearest 100 kg.

What is the greatest number of rods that Jim can put onto his truck while being sure that it is loaded within safe limits? Explain your reasoning clearly.

....

[Total 4 marks]

---

18 The diagram below shows pyramid *PQRST*.

PR is 8.5 cm and the diagonal *RT* is 10 cm.

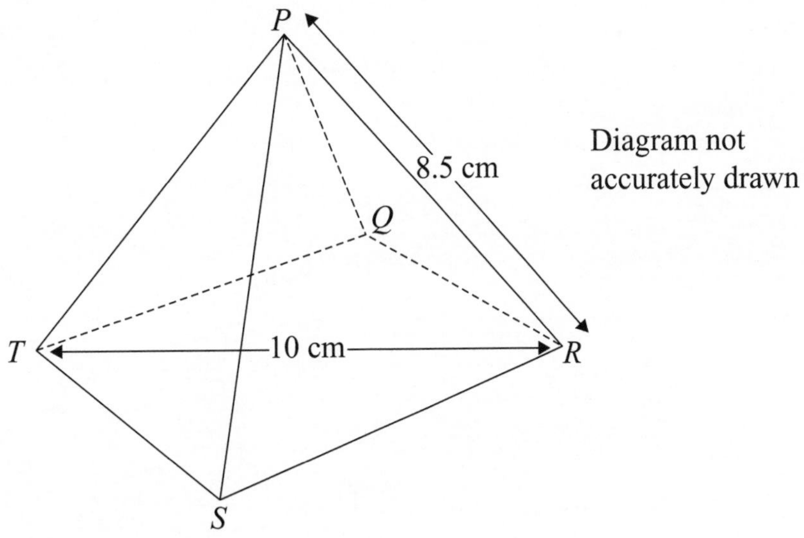

The plane *PRT* has an area of 35 cm².

Calculate the size of angle *PRT*. Give your answer correct to 1 decimal place.

.... °

[Total 3 marks]

---

19 A company is testing an air pressure gauge that is based on a gas-filled ball.

The air pressure is inversely proportional to the cube of the diameter of the ball.
When the air pressure, p, is 60 bars, the diameter of the ball, d, is 2 cm.

(a) Write down a formula connecting p and d.

....

[3]

(b) What diameter will the ball be when the pressure is 100 bars?
Give your answer correct to 2 decimal places.

.... cm

[2]

[Total 5 marks]

***20** Prove that the squares of any two consecutive multiples of 3 always add up to a multiple of 9.

[Total 5 marks]

---

21 The height, h metres, of a stone shot by a catapult is related to its horizontal distance from the catapult, d metres, as described by the equation $h = 2d - 0.02d^2$.

(a) Complete this table of values for $h = 2d - 0.02d^2$.

[2]

d	0	20	40	50	60	80	100
h	0		48		48	32	0

(b) Draw the graph of $h = 2d - 0.02d^2$ on the grid.

[2]

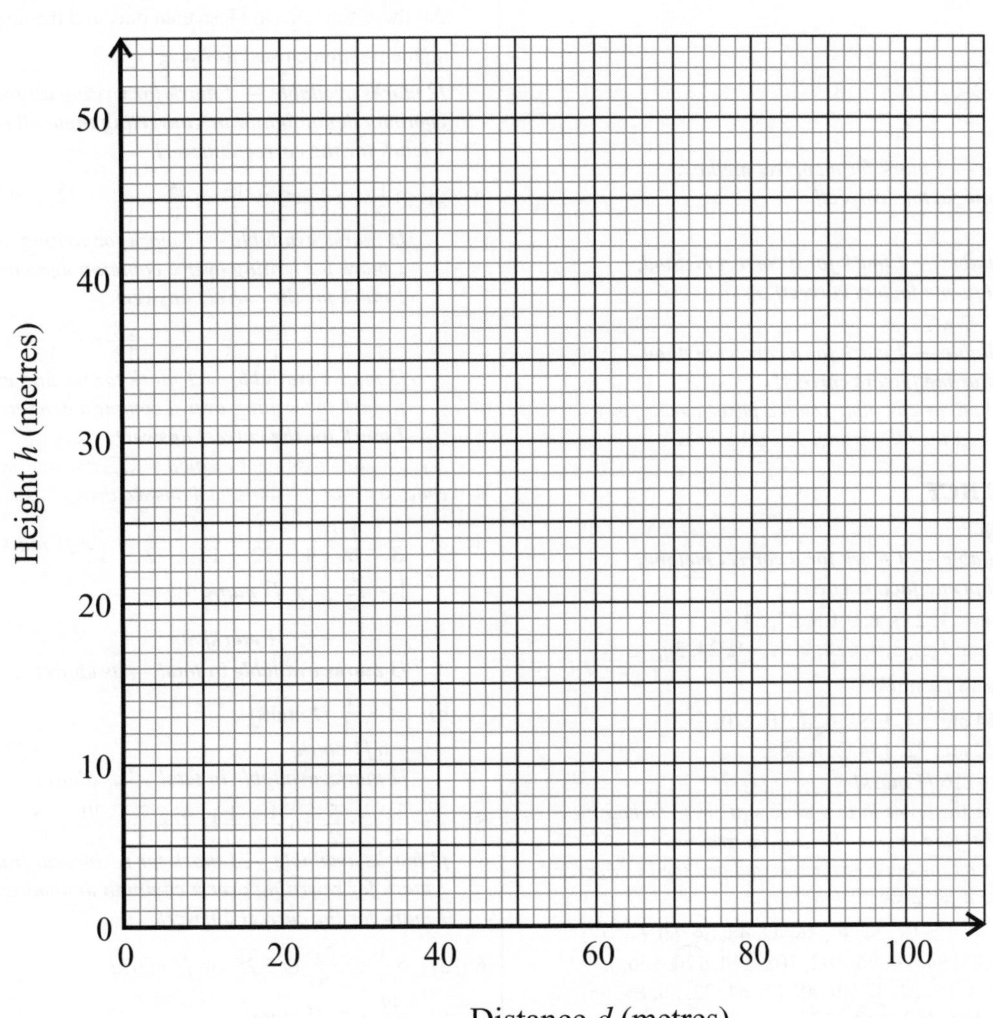

(c) The catapult shoots a stone up a hill with a gradient of 1 in 10.
By drawing an appropriate line on the graph, find the horizontal distance travelled by the stone before it hits the hill.

.... m

[3]

[Total 7 marks]

[TOTAL FOR PAPER = 100 MARKS]

Answers

Section One — Numbers

Page 4: Primes and Prime Factors

1 Take $a = 2$ and $b = 3$
   a) $2 + 3 = 5$ ***[1 mark]***
   b) $2 \times 3 = 6$ ***[1 mark]***
   c) $2^2 + 3^2 = 4 + 9 = 13$ ***[1 mark]***

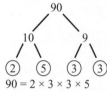

2 90 → 10 and 9; 10 → (2) and (5); 9 → (3) and (3)
   $90 = 2 \times 3 \times 3 \times 5$
   [2 marks available — 1 mark for a correct method, 1 mark for all prime factors correct]

3 a) $2 \times 3 \times 5 \times 7$
   [2 marks available — 1 mark for a correct method, 1 mark for all prime factors correct]
   b) $3 \times 3 \times 5 \times 5 \times 7 \times 7$
   [2 marks available — 1 mark for a correct method, 1 mark for all prime factors correct]
   "A correct method" here is either using a factor tree or just repeatedly dividing the factors until you get primes.

Page 5: LCM and HCF

1 a) $2 \times 2 \times 2 \times 3 \times 3$
   [2 marks available — 1 mark for a correct method, 1 mark for all prime factors correct]
   b) Factors of 54 are: 1, 2, 3, 6, 9, (18), 27, 54
   Factors of 72 are: 1, 2, 3, 4, 6, 8, 9, 12, (18), 24, 36, 72
   So the HCF is 18 ***[1 mark]***
   c) Multiples of 54 are: 54, 108, 162, (216), 270, ...
   Multiples of 72 are: 72, 144, (216), 288, ...
   So the LCM is 216 ***[1 mark]***

In Q1-Q3, you could use the prime factors to go straight to finding the LCM/HCF, but there's a good chance of making a mistake. It's generally safer to list all the multiples/factors and find the LCM/HCF that way, even if it takes a bit longer.

2 Multiples of 6 are: 6, 12, 18, 24, 30, 36, 42, 48, 54, 60, 66, 72, 78, 84, 90, 96, 102, 108, 114, (120), 126, ...
   Multiples of 8 are: 8, 16, 24, 32, 40, 48, 56, 64, 72, 80, 88, 96, 104, 112, (120), 128, ...
   Multiples of 10 are: 10, 20, 30, 40, 50, 60, 70, 80, 90, 100, 110, (120), 130, ...
   So the LCM is 120
   [2 marks available — 1 mark for a correct method, 1 mark for LCM correct]

3 Multiples of 35 are: 35, 70, 105, 140, 175, 210, 245, 280, 315, 350, (385), 420, ...
   Multiples of 55 are: 55, 110, 165, 220, 275, 330, (385), 440, ...
   So the LCM is 385, which is the minimum number of jars he needs.
   So this is $385 \div 35 = 11$ packs
   [3 marks available — 1 mark for a correct method to find LCM, 1 mark for LCM correct, 1 mark for correct number of packs]

4 The first car takes 30 seconds to complete a circuit, the second car takes 70 seconds to complete a circuit.
   Multiples of 30 are: 30, 60, 90, 120, 150, 180, (210), 240, ...
   Multiples of 70 are: 70, 140, (210), 280, ...
   So it will be 210 seconds or 3.5 minutes until they are side by side on the start line.
   [2 marks available — 1 mark for a correct method, 1 mark for the correct answer]

Pages 6-7: Fractions

1 a) $\frac{12}{60}$ ***[1 mark]***$= \frac{1}{5}$ ***[1 mark]***
   [2 marks available in total — as above]
   b) $\frac{22}{33}$ ***[1 mark]***$= \frac{2}{3}$ ***[1 mark]***
   [2 marks available in total — as above]

2 $\frac{5}{6} = \frac{100}{120}$ $\frac{3}{4} = \frac{90}{120}$ $\frac{7}{8} = \frac{105}{120}$ $\frac{4}{5} = \frac{96}{120}$
   All these fractions are less than one, and the largest is $\frac{105}{120}$, so the fraction closest to 1 is $\frac{7}{8}$
   [2 marks available — 1 mark for writing all fractions over a common denominator or converting them all to decimals, 1 mark for the correct answer]

3 a) $3\frac{1}{2} + 2\frac{3}{5} = \frac{7}{2} + \frac{13}{5} = \frac{35}{10} + \frac{26}{10} = \frac{35 + 26}{10} = \frac{61}{10}$ or $6\frac{1}{10}$
   [3 marks available — 1 mark for writing as improper fractions, 1 mark for writing over a common denominator, 1 mark for the correct answer]
   b) $3\frac{3}{4} - 2\frac{1}{3} = \frac{15}{4} - \frac{7}{3} = \frac{45}{12} - \frac{28}{12} = \frac{45 - 28}{12} = \frac{17}{12}$ or $1\frac{5}{12}$
   [3 marks available — 1 mark for writing as improper fractions, 1 mark for writing over a common denominator, 1 mark for the correct answer]
   If you've used a different method in Q3, but still shown your working, and ended up with the same final answer, then you still get full marks.

4 a) $\frac{1}{3} + \frac{1}{6} + \frac{1}{4} = \frac{4}{12} + \frac{2}{12} + \frac{3}{12} = \frac{9}{12}$ ***[1 mark]***
   $1 - \frac{9}{12} = \frac{3}{12}$ ***[1 mark]***
   $= \frac{1}{4}$ ***[1 mark]***
   [3 marks available in total — as above]
   b) $24 \times \frac{1}{4}$ ***[1 mark]***
   $= 6$ ***[1 mark]***
   [2 marks available in total — as above]

5 $a = \frac{3}{4}$, $b = \frac{5}{2}$, so $\frac{1}{a} + \frac{1}{b} = \frac{4}{3} + \frac{2}{5} = \frac{20}{15} + \frac{6}{15} = \frac{26}{15}$ or $1\frac{11}{15}$
   [3 marks available — 1 mark for reciprocal fractions, 1 mark for rewriting over a common denominator, 1 mark for the correct answer]

6 a) $5\frac{1}{4}$ or $\frac{21}{4}$ or 5.25 km ***[1 mark]***
   b) $\frac{49}{32}$ km^2 ***[1 mark]***

7 a) $1\frac{2}{3} \times \frac{9}{10} = \frac{5}{3} \times \frac{9}{10} = \frac{5 \times 9}{3 \times 10} = \frac{45}{30} = \frac{3}{2}$
   [3 marks available — 1 mark for multiplying the two fractions together, 1 mark for an equivalent fraction, 1 mark for the correct final answer]
   b) $3\frac{1}{7} \times 1\frac{1}{7} = \frac{22}{7} \times \frac{8}{7} = \frac{22 \times 8}{7 \times 7}$ ***[1 mark]***
   $= \frac{176}{49}$ ***[1 mark]***
   [2 marks available in total — as above]

8 a) $\frac{3}{8} \div \frac{9}{10} = \frac{3}{8} \times \frac{10}{9} = \frac{3 \times 10}{8 \times 9} = \frac{30}{72} = \frac{5}{12}$
   [3 marks available — 1 mark for taking the reciprocal and multiplying the two fractions together, 1 mark for an equivalent fraction, 1 mark for the correct final answer]
   b) $3\frac{1}{2} \div 1\frac{3}{4} = \frac{7}{2} \div \frac{7}{4} = \frac{7}{2} \times \frac{4}{7} = \frac{7 \times 4}{2 \times 7} = \frac{28}{14} = 2$
   [3 marks available — 1 mark for taking the reciprocal and multiplying the two fractions together, 1 mark for an equivalent fraction, 1 mark for the correct final answer]

Page 8: Decimals

1 a) 23.912 *[1 mark]*
b) 2 391 200 *[1 mark]*
c) 5600 *[1 mark]*

2 a) 16.388 *[1 mark]*
b) 163.88 *[1 mark]*
c) 0.0034 *[1 mark]*

3 $0.725 = \frac{725}{1000} = \frac{29}{40}$
[2 marks available — 1 mark for turning into an equivalent fraction, 1 mark for the correct final answer]

4 Multiply 2.40 by 10 to get rid of the decimal point, and divide 320 by 10.

$$\begin{array}{r} 32 \\ \times\, 24 \\ \hline 128 \\ +\,640 \\ \hline 768 \end{array}$$

$768 \times 10 \div 10 = £768$
[3 marks available — 1 mark for 2.40 × 340, 1 mark for a correct method of multiplication, 1 mark for the correct final answer]
You could use any method of non-calculator multiplication to get the second mark for this question.

Page 9: Fractions and Recurring Decimals

1 $10 \div 11 = 0.\dot{9}\dot{0}$ *[1 mark]*

2 Convert to an equivalent fraction with all nines on the bottom
$\frac{7}{33} = \frac{21}{99}$ *[1 mark]*
Then the number on the top tells you the recurring part,
so $\frac{7}{33} = 0.\dot{2}\dot{1}$ *[1 mark]*
[2 marks available in total — as above]
The first mark could also be obtained by using a division method.

3 a) Let $r = 0.\dot{7}$, so $10r = 7.\dot{7}$ *[1 mark]*
$10r - r = 7.\dot{7} - 0.\dot{7}$
$9r = 7$ *[1 mark]*
$r = \frac{7}{9}$ *[1 mark]*
[3 marks available in total — as above]
b) Let $r = 0.\dot{2}\dot{6}$, so $100r = 26.\dot{2}\dot{6}$ *[1 mark]*
$100r - r = 26.\dot{2}\dot{6} - 0.\dot{2}\dot{6}$
$99r = 26$ *[1 mark]*
$r = \frac{26}{99}$ *[1 mark]*
[3 marks available in total — as above]
c) Let $r = 1.\dot{3}\dot{6}$, so $100r = 136.\dot{3}\dot{6}$ *[1 mark]*
$100r - r = 136.\dot{3}\dot{6} - 1.\dot{3}\dot{6}$
$99r = 135$ *[1 mark]*
$r = \frac{135}{99}$ *[1 mark]*
$r = \frac{15}{11}$ or $1\frac{4}{11}$ *[1 mark]*
[4 marks available in total — as above]

4 Let $10r = 5.\dot{9}\dot{0}$, so $1000r = 590.\dot{9}\dot{0}$ *[1 mark]*
$990r = 585$ *[1 mark]*
$r = \frac{585}{990} = \frac{13}{22}$ *[1 mark]*
[3 marks available in total — as above]

Pages 10-12: Percentages

1 a) $(36 \div 80) \times 100$ *[1 mark]*
$= 45\%$ *[1 mark]*
[2 marks available in total — as above]
b) $(75 \div 600) \times 100$ *[1 mark]*
$= 12.5\%$ *[1 mark]*
[2 marks available in total — as above]

2 Number of male micro pigs = 40 – 24 = 16 *[1 mark]*
Fraction male $= \frac{16}{40} = \frac{2}{5}$ *[1 mark]*
So percentage male = 40% *[1 mark]*
[3 marks available in total — as above]

3 a) 16% of teachers liked white chocolate best
$(1 \div 4) \times 100 = 25\%$ of boys liked white chocolate best
$(7 \div 35) \times 100 = 20\%$ of girls liked white chocolate best
Therefore the boys had the highest percentage of people who liked white chocolate best.
[3 marks available — 1 mark for calculating percentage of boys, 1 mark for calculating percentage of girls, 1 mark for boys as answer]
b) Number of teachers who liked white chocolate best
$= 0.16 \times 25 = 4$
Number of boys who liked white chocolate best
$= 0.25 \times 36 = 9$
Number of girls who liked white chocolate best
$= 7$
Total number of people = 25 + 36 + 35 = 96
$(4 + 9 + 7) \div 96 \times 100 = 20 \div 96 \times 100 = 20.83... = 20.8\%$
[4 marks available — 1 mark for calculating the number of teachers and boys who liked white chocolate best, 1 mark for finding the total number of people surveyed, 1 mark for calculating percentage of total, 1 mark for correct answer]

4 $3.2\% = 3.2 \div 100 = 0.032$
3.2% of £2000 = 0.032 × £2000 = £64
2 × £64 = £128
[3 marks available — 1 mark for a correct method to find 3.2% of £2000, 1 mark for multiplying this by 2, 1 mark for correct answer]

5 £32 010 – £9440 = £22 570 *[1 mark]*
20% = 20 ÷ 100 = 0.2
20% of £22 570 = 0.2 × £22 570 = £4514 *[1 mark]*
£45 000 – £32 010 = £12 990 *[1 mark]*
40% = 40 ÷ 100 = 0.4
40% of £12 990 = 0.4 × £12 990 = £5196 *[1 mark]*
£4514 + £5196 = £9710
(£9710 ÷ £45 000) × 100 *[1 mark]*
= 21.57... = 21.6% *[1 mark]*
[6 marks available in total — as above]

6 20% = 20 ÷ 100 = 0.2
0.2 × £927 = £185.40 *[1 mark]*
£927 + £185.40 *[1 mark]*
= £1112.40 *[1 mark]*
[3 marks available in total — as above]

7 £15 714 = 108%
£15 714 ÷ 108 = £145.50 = 1% *[1 mark]*
£145.50 × 100 = 100% *[1 mark]*
= £14 550 *[1 mark]*
[3 marks available in total — as above]

8 a) 36 – 30 = 6 *[1 mark]*
$\frac{6}{30} \times 100$ *[1 mark]*
= 20% *[1 mark]*
[3 marks available in total — as above]
b) 135 cm = 112.5%
135 cm ÷ 112.5 = 1.2 cm = 1% *[1 mark]*
1.2 cm × 100 *[1 mark]*
= 120 cm = 100% *[1 mark]*
[3 marks available in total — as above]

9 a) 18 500 – 12 600 = £5900 *[1 mark]*
$\frac{5900}{18\,500} \times 100$ *[1 mark]*
= 31.891... = 31.9% *[1 mark]*
[3 marks available in total — as above]
b) $\frac{11\,549}{70}$ *[1 mark]*
= 164.9857...
164.9857... × 100 *[1 mark]*
= £16 498.57... = £16 499 *[1 mark]*
[3 marks available in total — as above]

10 £7.15 = 65%
£7.15 ÷ 65 = £0.11 = 1% ***[1 mark]***
£0.11 × 100 ***[1 mark]***
= £11 = 100% ***[1 mark]***
3% = 3 ÷ 100 = 0.03
0.03 × £11 ***[1 mark]***
= £0.33, so the price increase is 33p ***[1 mark]***
[5 marks available in total — as above]

Pages 13-14: Compound Growth and Decay

1 a) Population after 15 years = $2000 \times \left(1 - \frac{8}{100}\right)^{15}$ ***[1 mark]***
$= 2000 \times (0.92)^{15}$ ***[1 mark]***
= 572.59...
573 fish. ***[1 mark]***
[3 marks available in total — as above]
It'll take more than 15 years for the population to get down to 572 fish, so you need to round up (the population hasn't dropped to 572 yet so there are still 573).

b) Three quarters of initial population = $2000 \times \frac{3}{4} = 1500$
$2000 \times 0.92 = 1840$
$2000 \times 0.92^2 = 1692.8$
$2000 \times 0.92^3 = 1557.376$
$2000 \times 0.92^4 = 1432.78592 < 1500$
Population is less than $\frac{3}{4}$ of the initial population after 4 years.
[2 marks available — 1 mark for calculating 2000 × 0.92^n for n > 1, 1 mark for correct answer]

2 Approximate value of Alun's car
$= £10\,500 \times \left(1 - \frac{22}{100}\right)^9 = £1122.12$ (to 2 d.p.)
Two thirds of the car's current approximate value
$= \frac{2}{3} \times £1122.12 = £748.08$
Cost of repairs needed:

Exhaust (full replacement)		£290
Brakes: new pads × 4	£39 × 4 =	£156
new discs × 4	£59 × 4 =	£236
Tyres (full set)		£95
Suspension coil		£98
New seat belt		£62
	Total cost:	£937

The cost of the repairs (£937) is greater than two thirds of the approximate value of the car (£748.08), so Alun should scrap his car.
[4 marks available — 1 mark for £748.08, 1 mark for summing the repair costs, 1 mark for £937, 1 mark for final answer with justification]
You need to write your working and answer clearly to get the marks for this question (the asterisk next to the question number means you're being marked for your 'quality of written communication', not just your maths). Say what you're doing at each step and then give a reason for your answer in a sentence at the end.

3 $£120\,000 \times \left(1 + \frac{15}{100}\right)^5 = £241\,362.86... = £241\,000$ (to nearest £1000)
[3 marks available — 1 mark for using correct formula, 2 marks for correct answer to nearest £1000, otherwise 1 mark for an unrounded answer]

4 a) $£10\,000 \times \left(1 + \frac{5.5}{100}\right)^3 = £11\,742.41375 = £11\,742.41$ (to 2 d.p.)
£11 742.41 – £10 000 = £1742.41
[3 marks available — 1 mark for using correct formula, 1 mark for correct account balance, and 1 mark for correct final answer]

b) From part a) he will not have reached his target after 3 years with the Compound Collectors Account, so after 4 and 5 years he will have:
$£10\,000 \times \left(1 + \frac{5.5}{100}\right)^4 = £12\,388.246...$ and
$£10\,000 \times \left(1 + \frac{5.5}{100}\right)^5 = £13\,069.600... > £13\,000$
With the Compound Collectors Account he'll reach his target in 5 years.
Annual interest with the Simple Savers Account is:
$£10\,000 \times \frac{5.9}{100} = £590$
After 5 years Rich will have 5 × £590 = £2950 of interest, so he'll have £10 000 + £2950 = £12 950 in total.
Rich will not have reached his target of £13 000 after 5 years with the Simple Savers Account, so the Compound Collectors Account will get him to his target faster.
[3 marks available — 1 mark for calculating how long it will take him to reach his target with one of the accounts, 1 mark for finding how much he will have from the other account in this time, or for calculating how long it will take him to reach his target with the other account, and 1 mark for comparing the time for the two accounts, concluding that the Compound Collectors Account is faster]

5 Let r be the interest rate.
$£2704 = £2500 \times \left(1 + \frac{r}{100}\right)^2$ ***[1 mark]***
$\frac{£2704}{£2500} = \left(1 + \frac{r}{100}\right)^2$
$1 + \frac{r}{100} = \sqrt{\frac{£2704}{£2500}} = 1.04$ ***[1 mark]***
interest rate = 4% ***[1 mark]***
[3 marks available in total — as above]

Pages 15-17: Ratios and Proportion

1 96 ÷ (5 + 6 + 6 + 7) = 96 ÷ 24 ***[1 mark]***
= 4
Longest piece is 7 × 4 cm ***[1 mark]***
= 28 cm ***[1 mark]***
[3 marks available in total — as above]

2 a) $3\frac{3}{4} : 1\frac{1}{2}$ ***[1 mark]***
$= 4 \times 3\frac{3}{4} : 4 \times 1\frac{1}{2} = 15 : 6$ ***[1 mark]***
$= 5 : 2$ ***[1 mark]***
[3 marks available in total — as above]

b) 1355 ml ÷ 5 = 271 ml ***[1 mark]***
271 ml × 2 = 542 ml ***[1 mark]***
[2 marks available in total — as above]
If your answer to part a) was incorrect, but your answer to part b) was correct for your incorrect ratio, you still get the marks for part b).

3 Susan, Edmund, Peter and Lucy shared the money in the ratio 1 : 2 : 6 : 3
[1 mark for 1 : 2 : 6 : 3 or any four numbers in that ratio, in any order]
120 ÷ (1 + 2 + 6 + 3) = 10 ***[1 mark]***
Lucy got £10 × 3 = £30 ***[1 mark]***
[3 marks available in total — as above]
You could answer this question using a formula — if you let x be the amount of money that Susan gets, then x + 2x + 6x + 3x = £120.

4 $\frac{1}{3}$ of £21 000 = $\frac{1}{3}$ × £21 000 = £21 000 ÷ 3
= £7000 on staff training & new exhibits ***[1 mark]***
£7000 ÷ (2 + 5) = £7000 ÷ 7 = £1000 ***[1 mark]***
£1000 × 5 = £5000 on new exhibits ***[1 mark]***
[3 marks available in total — as above]

5 2928 ÷ (3 + 5) = 2928 ÷ 8 = 366 ***[1 mark]***
number of second class passengers = 366 × 5 = 1830
number of first class passengers = 366 × 3 = 1098
[1 mark for both]
second class ticket takings = 1830 × £190 = £347 700 ***[1 mark]***
first class ticket takings = £666 120 – £347 700 = £318 420 ***[1 mark]***
price of a first class ticket = £318 420 ÷ 1098 = £290 ***[1 mark]***
[5 marks available in total — as above]

6 Cost for 1 litre of petrol = £31.25 ÷ 25 = £1.25 ***[1 mark]***
Cost for 52 litres of petrol = £1.25 × 52 = £65 ***[1 mark]***
[2 marks available in total — as above]

7 a) $\frac{18}{12} = \frac{3}{2}$ ***[1 mark]***
$\frac{3}{2} \times 150\text{g} = 225$ g ***[1 mark]***
[2 marks available in total — as above]

b) 300 ÷ 75 = 4 ***[1 mark]***
4 × 12 flapjacks = 48 flapjacks ***[1 mark]***
[2 marks available in total — as above]

8 Cost of 1 glass slipper = £86.25 ÷ 23 = £3.75 ***[1 mark]***
Cost of 35 glass slippers = £3.75 × 35 = £131.25 ***[1 mark]***
[2 marks available in total — as above]

9 Time for 1 person = 3 × 12 = 36 hours ***[1 mark]***
Time for 9 people = 36 ÷ 9 = 4 hours ***[1 mark]***
[2 marks available in total — as above]

10 a) Food for 1 person for 6 × 250 = 1500 days ***[1 mark]***
Food for 300 people for 1500 ÷ 300 = 5 days ***[1 mark]***
[2 marks available in total — as above]

b) Food for 1 day for 250 × 6 = 1500 people ***[1 mark]***
Food for 15 days for 1500 ÷ 15 = 100 people ***[1 mark]***
[2 marks available in total — as above]

11 Belgian chocolates are €7 ÷ 350 = €0.02 per gram. ***[1 mark]***
English chocolates are £12.99 ÷ 500 = £0.02598 per gram ***[1 mark]***
= 1.22 × 0.02598
= €0.0316956 per gram ***[1 mark]***

The Belgian chocolates are cheaper per gram (by about €0.01), so they are better value for money. ***[1 mark]***
[4 marks available in total — as above]

You multiply by 1.22 because there's €1.22 to every £1.
You could divide the price in euros for the Belgian chocolates by 1.22 instead, and then compare the prices in pounds.

Page 18: Rounding Numbers and Estimating

1 a) $\frac{197.8}{\sqrt{0.01+0.23}} = \frac{197.8}{\sqrt{0.24}} = \frac{197.8}{0.489897948...} = 403.757559...$
[2 marks available — 1 mark for some correct working, 1 mark for answer correct to 4 decimal places,]

b) 404 ***[1 mark]***
In questions 1 and 2, if you get part a) wrong but round your wrong answer correctly in part b) you'll still get the mark for part b).

2 a) $\sqrt{\frac{12.71+137.936}{\cos 50° \times 13.2^2}} = \sqrt{\frac{150.646}{0.642787609... \times 174.24}}$
$= \sqrt{1.34506182...}$
$= 1.1597680...$
[2 marks available — 1 mark for some correct working, 1 mark for answer correct to 4 decimal places]

b) 1.16 ***[1 mark]***

3 $\frac{215.7 \times 48.8}{460} \approx \frac{200 \times 50}{500} = \frac{200}{10} = 20$
[2 marks available — 1 mark for rounding at least one number to 1 significant figure, 1 mark for an answer between 20 and 22]

4 $\sqrt{\frac{2321}{19.673 \times 3.81}} \approx \sqrt{\frac{2000}{20 \times 4}}$
[1 mark for rounding at least two numbers to 1 s.f.]
$= \sqrt{\frac{100}{4}} = \sqrt{25}$ ***[1 mark for either expression]***
= 5 ***[1 mark]***
[3 marks available in total — as above]

Page 19: Bounds

1 a) 54.05 cm ***[1 mark]***

b) lower bound for the width of the paper = 23.55 cm ***[1 mark]***
lower bound for the perimeter = (54.05 cm × 2) + (23.55 cm × 2)
= 155.2 cm [***1 mark]***
[2 marks available in total — as above]

2 upper bound for x = 57.5 mm ***[1 mark]***
upper bound for y = 32.5 mm ***[1 mark]***
upper bound for area = 57.5 mm × 32.5 mm = 1868.75 mm^2
= 1870 mm^2 to 3 s.f. ***[1 mark]***
[3 marks available in total — as above]

3 lower bound for distance = 99.5 m
upper bound for time = 12.55 s ***[1 mark for both]***
lower bound for speed = $\frac{99.5}{12.55}$ m/s
= 7.928... m/s ***[1 mark]***
lower bound for speed to 2 s.f. = 7.9 m/s
lower bound for speed to 1 s.f. = 8 m/s

upper bound for distance = 100.5 m
lower bound for time = 12.45 s ***[1 mark for both]***
upper bound for speed = $\frac{100.5}{12.45}$ m/s
= 8.072... m/s ***[1 mark]***
upper bound for speed to 2 s.f. = 8.1 m/s
upper bound for speed to 1 s.f. = 8 m/s

The lower bound to 2 s.f. does not equal the upper bound to 2 s.f., but the lower bound to 1 s.f. does equal the upper bound to 1 s.f. So Dan's speed is 8 m/s to 1 significant figure.
[1 mark for comparing bounds to reach correct answer to 1 s.f.]
[5 marks available in total — as above]

Page 20: Standard Form

1 a) 12500 = 1.25 × 10^4 ***[1 mark]***
b) 0.0064 = 6.4 × 10^{-3} ***[1 mark]***
c) 8.6 = 8.6 × 10^0 ***[1 mark]***

2 a) A = 4.834 × 10^9 = 4 834 000 000 ***[1 mark]***
b) $B \times C = (2.7 \times 10^5) \times (5.81 \times 10^3) = (2.7 \times 5.81) \times (10^5 \times 10^3)$
= 15.687 × 10^8 ***[1 mark]***
= 1.5687 × 10^9 ***[1 mark]***
[2 marks available in total — as above]
c) C, B, A (5.81 × 10^3, 2.7 × 10^5, 4.834 × 10^9) ***[1 mark]***

3 time (s) = distance (miles) ÷ speed (miles/s)
= (9.3 × 10^7) ÷ (1.86 × 10^5) seconds ***[1 mark]***
= (9.3 ÷ 1.86) × (10^7 ÷ 10^5) seconds ***[1 mark]***
= 5 × 10^2 seconds ***[1 mark]***
[3 marks available in total — as above]

4 a) number of tablets = dose (grams) ÷ dose per tablet (grams)
= (4 × 10^{-4}) ÷ (8 × 10^{-5}) ***[1 mark]***
= (4 ÷ 8) × (10^{-4} ÷ 10^{-5})
= 0.5 × 10^1 ***[1 mark]***
= 5 ***[1 mark]***
[3 marks available in total — as above]

b) new dose = 4 × 10^{-4} grams + 6 × 10^{-5} grams ***[1 mark]***
= 4 × 10^{-4} grams + 0.6 × 10^{-4} grams ***[1 mark]***
= (4 + 0.6) × 10^{-4} grams
= 4.6 × 10^{-4} grams per day ***[1 mark]***
[3 marks available in total — as above]

Section Two — Algebra

Page 21: Sequences

1 The first term in this sequence is (3 × 1) + 2 = 5
The second term in this sequence is (3 × 2) + 2 = 8
The third term in this sequence is (3 × 3) + 2 = 11
So the first 3 terms in this sequence are 5, 8 and 11.
[2 marks available — 1 mark for first term correct, 1 mark for both second and third terms correct]

2 a) 3 8 13 18
+5 +5 +5
The common difference is 5, so the next two terms in the sequence will be 18 + 5 = 23 and 23 + 5 = 28. ***[1 mark]***

b) The common difference is 5 so $5n$ is in the formula.

$5n$: 5 10 15 20
↓−2 ↓−2 ↓−2 ↓−2
term: 3 8 13 18

You have to subtract 2 to get to the term, so the expression for the nth term is $5n - 2$.
[2 marks available — 2 marks for correct expression, otherwise 1 mark for finding 5n.]

You could also have found the nth term using the equation nth term = dn + (a − d), where d is the common difference (in this case 5) and a is the first term (in this case 3).

c) Substituting $n = 30$ into the expression for the nth term: $5n - 2 = (5 \times 30) - 2 = 148$. ***[1 mark]***

3 a) 3 7 11 15 19 (+4 +4 +4 +4)

The common difference is 4 so $4n$ is in the formula.

$4n$: 4 8 12 16 20
↓−1 ↓−1 ↓−1 ↓−1 ↓−1
term: 3 7 11 15 19

You have to subtract 1 to get to the term, so the expression for the nth term is $4n - 1$.
[2 marks available — 2 marks for correct expression, otherwise 1 mark for finding 4n.]

b) All multiples of 4 are even numbers, and an even number minus 1 is always an odd number. So all the terms in this sequence will be odd numbers. ***[1 mark]***
502 is an even number, so 502 cannot be in the sequence. ***[1 mark]***
[2 marks available in total — as above]

This question has a star by it, which means you'll be assessed on the quality of your written communication. So you don't lose marks, make sure you present your answer in a clear and logical way and show all of your working or reasoning.

Pages 22-23: Powers and Roots

1 a) $a^5 \times a^{-3} = a^{5+(-3)} = a^2$ ***[1 mark]***

b) $x^7 \div x = x^{7-1} = x^6$ ***[1 mark]***

c) $(d^9)^2 = d^{9\times 2} = d^{18}$ ***[1 mark]***
so $\frac{(d^9)^2}{d^4} = \frac{d^{18}}{d^4} = d^{18-4} = d^{14}$ ***[1 mark]***
[2 marks available in total — as above]

2 a) $3^0 = 1$ ***[1 mark]***

b) $5^{-2} = \frac{1}{5^2} = \frac{1}{25}$ or 0.04 ***[1 mark]***

c) $8^{\frac{4}{3}} = (8^{\frac{1}{3}})^4 = (2)^4 = 16$
[2 marks available — 1 mark for correct working, 1 mark for the correct final answer.]

3 $y^{-3} = \frac{1}{y^3}$, $y^1 = y$, $y^0 = 1$, $y^{\frac{1}{3}} = \sqrt[3]{y}$,
so the correct order is... y^{-3} y^0 $y^{\frac{1}{3}}$ y^1 y^3
[2 marks available — 2 marks for all 5 in the correct order, otherwise 1 mark for any 4 in the correct relative order.]

If you can't identify which term is the smallest just by looking at them, try substituting a value for y into all the expressions and working out the answer. Then it'll be easy to tell which is the smallest.

4 a) $3a^3 \times 2ab^2 = (3 \times 2) \times (a^3 \times a) \times b^2 = 6a^4b^2$
[2 marks available — 1 mark for correct working, 1 mark for the correct answer.]

b) $\frac{4a^5b^3}{2ab^2} = (4 \div 2) \times (a^5 \div a) \times (b^3 \div b^2) = 2a^4b$
[2 marks available — 1 mark for correct working, 1 mark for the correct answer.]

5 a) $\frac{1}{100} = \frac{1}{10^2} = 10^{-2}$, so $k = -2$ ***[1 mark]***

b) $\sqrt{9} = 9^{\frac{1}{2}}$, so $k = \frac{1}{2}$ or 0.5 ***[1 mark]***

c) $(3^4)^2 = 3^{4\times 2} = 3^8$ and $\frac{3^5}{3^{11}} = 3^{5-11} = 3^{-6}$ ***[1 mark]***
so $(3^4)^2 \times \frac{3^5}{3^{11}} = 3^8 \times 3^{-6} = 3^2$ and $k = 2$ ***[1 mark]***
[2 marks available in total — as above]

6 $(9a^4)^{\frac{1}{2}} = \sqrt{9a^4} = 3a^2$ ***[1 mark]***
$\frac{2ab^2}{6a^3b} = \frac{2}{6} \times \frac{a}{a^3} \times \frac{b^2}{b} = \frac{1}{3} \times \frac{1}{a^2} \times b = \frac{b}{3a^2}$ ***[1 mark]***
so $(9a^4)^{\frac{1}{2}} \times \frac{2ab^2}{6a^3b} = 3a^2 \times \frac{b}{3a^2} = b$ ***[1 mark]***
[3 marks available in total — as above]

7 $64^{\frac{1}{3}} = \sqrt[3]{64} = 4$ ***[1 mark]***
$4^{-2} = \frac{1}{4^2} = \frac{1}{16}$ ***[1 mark]***
so $64^{\frac{1}{3}} \times 4^{-2} = 4 \times \frac{1}{16} = \frac{4}{16} = \frac{1}{4}$ or 0.25 ***[1 mark]***
[3 marks available in total — as above]

Page 24: Algebra Basics

1 a) $w \times w \times w \times w \times w = w^5$ ***[1 mark]***

b) $4k - 2j + 5k - 8j = 4k + 5k - 2j - 8j = 9k - 10j$
[2 marks available — 2 marks for correct expression, otherwise 1 mark for one term correct.]

c) $2de + 3e - 2d + 4de - 3d^2 = 2de + 4de + 3e - 2d - 3d^2$
$= 6de + 3e - 2d - 3d^2$
[2 marks available — 1 mark for 6de, 1 mark for 3e − 2d − 3d²]

2 a) $2a \times 5b = (2 \times 5) \times a \times b = 10ab$ ***[1 mark]***

b) $x^2 + 15x - 7x - x^2 + x = x^2 - x^2 + 15x - 7x + x = 9x$
[2 marks available — 1 mark for cancelling the x²s, 1 mark for the correct answer.]

c) $3p^2 + pq + 2p^2q - 3pq + p^2 = 3p^2 + p^2 + pq - 3pq + 2p^2q$
$= 4p^2 - 2pq + 2p^2q$
[2 marks available — 2 marks for correct expression, otherwise 1 mark for one term correct.]

3 The perimeter of the rectangle is $2x + 3 + 2x + 3 + 5y - 8 + 5y - 8$
$= 4x + 10y - 10$ ***[1 mark]*** So $4x + 10y - 10 = 7y - 2x$. ***[1 mark]***
This rearranges to give $6x + 3y = 10$ ***[1 mark]***
[3 marks available in total — as above]

Page 25: Multiplying Out Brackets

1 a) $3(x - 1) = (3 \times x) + (3 \times -1) = 3x - 3$ ***[1 mark]***

b) $4a(a + 2b) = (4a \times a) + (4a \times 2b) = 4a^2 + 8ab$ ***[1 mark]***

c) $8p^2(3 - 2p) - 2p(p - 3)$
$= [(8p^2 \times 3) + (8p^2 \times -2p)] - [(2p \times p) + (2p \times -3)]$
$= 24p^2 - 16p^3 - 2p^2 + 6p$ ***[1 mark]***
$= 22p^2 - 16p^3 + 6p$ ***[1 mark]***
[2 marks available in total — as above]

2 a) $(2t - 5)(3t + 4) = (2t \times 3t) + (2t \times 4) + (-5 \times 3t) + (-5 \times 4)$
$= 6t^2 + 8t - 15t - 20$ ***[1 mark]***
$= 6t^2 - 7t - 20$ ***[1 mark]***
[2 marks available in total — as above]

b) $(x + 3)^2 = (x + 3)(x + 3)$
$= (x \times x) + (x \times 3) + (3 \times x) + (3 \times 3)$
$= x^2 + 3x + 3x + 9$ ***[1 mark]***
$= x^2 + 6x + 9$ ***[1 mark]***
[2 marks available in total — as above]

3 $a = 4(3b - 1) + 6(5 - 2b)$
$a = (4 \times 3b) + (4 \times -1) + (6 \times 5) + (6 \times -2b)$
$a = 12b - 4 + 30 - 12b$
$a = 26$
[2 marks available — 1 mark for correctly expanding the brackets, 1 mark for simplifying to a = 26.]

4 Area = ½ × base × height
$= \frac{1}{2} \times (3x + 5) \times (2x - 4) = \frac{1}{2}(3x + 5)(2x - 4)$ ***[1 mark]***
$= \frac{1}{2} \times [(3x \times 2x) + (3x \times -4) + (5 \times 2x) + (5 \times -4)]$
$= \frac{1}{2} \times (6x^2 - 12x + 10x - 20)$
$= \frac{1}{2} \times (6x^2 - 2x - 20)$ ***[1 mark]***
$= 3x^2 - x - 10$ ***[1 mark]***
[3 marks available in total — as above]
You could also have multiplied (2x − 4) by ½ first of all. The area would then just be (3x + 5)(x −2), which is a bit simpler to multiply out.

Page 26: Factorising

1 $4a^2 - 24ab = 4(a^2 - 6ab)$ ***[1 mark]***
$= 4a(a - 6b)$ ***[1 mark]***
[2 marks available in total — as above]

2 a) $6x + 3 = 3(2x + 1)$ ***[1 mark]***
b) $7y - 21y^2 = 7(y - 3y^2)$ ***[1 mark]***
$= 7y(1 - 3y)$ ***[1 mark]***
[2 marks available in total — as above]
c) $2v^3w + 8v^2w^2 = 2(v^3w + 4v^2w^2)$ ***[1 mark]***
$= 2v^2w(v + 4w)$ ***[1 mark]***
[2 marks available in total — as above]

3 a) $x^2 - 16 = x^2 - 4^2 = (x + 4)(x - 4)$ ***[1 mark]***
b) $9n^2 - 4m^2 = (3n)^2 - (2m)^2$ ***[1 mark]***
$= (3n + 2m)(3n - 2m)$ ***[1 mark]***
[2 marks available in total — as above]

Page 27: Manipulating Surds

1 $(2 + \sqrt{3})(5 - \sqrt{3}) = (2 \times 5) + (2 \times -\sqrt{3}) + (\sqrt{3} \times 5) + (\sqrt{3} \times -\sqrt{3})$
$= 10 - 2\sqrt{3} + 5\sqrt{3} - 3$
$= 7 + 3\sqrt{3}$
[2 marks available — 1 mark for correct working, 1 mark for the correct answer.]

2 $(\sqrt{2} - 4)^2 = 2 - 4\sqrt{2} - 4\sqrt{2} + 16 = 18 - 8\sqrt{2}$
So $\frac{(\sqrt{2} - 4)^2}{\sqrt{2}} = \frac{18 - 8\sqrt{2}}{\sqrt{2}} = \frac{\sqrt{2}(18 - 8\sqrt{2})}{2} = \frac{18\sqrt{2} - 16}{2}$
$= 9\sqrt{2} - 8$
[3 marks available — 1 mark for correctly expanding $(\sqrt{2} - 4)^2$, 1 mark for rationalising the denominator, 1 mark for the correct answer.]

3 $\sqrt{27} = \sqrt{9} \times \sqrt{3} = 3\sqrt{3}$
So $\frac{(\sqrt{27} + 6)}{\sqrt{3}} = \frac{(3\sqrt{3} + 6)}{\sqrt{3}} = \frac{\sqrt{3}(3\sqrt{3} + 6)}{3} = \frac{9 + 6\sqrt{3}}{3}$
$= 3 + 2\sqrt{3}$, so $a = 3$ and $b = 2$.
[3 marks available — 1 mark for correctly simplifying $\sqrt{27}$, 1 mark for rationalising the denominator, 1 mark for the correct answer.]

4 Using the formula for the area of a trapezium, A (from the formula sheet):
$A = \frac{1}{2}(a + b)h = \frac{1}{2}(4\sqrt{5} + 6\sqrt{5}) \times 2\sqrt{10}$ ***[1 mark]***
$= \frac{1}{2}(10\sqrt{5}) \times 2\sqrt{10}$ ***[1 mark]***
$= \frac{1}{2}(10\sqrt{5}) \times 2(\sqrt{5} \times \sqrt{2})$ ***[1 mark]***
$= 10 \times \sqrt{5} \times \sqrt{5} \times \sqrt{2}$
$= 50\sqrt{2}$ cm² ***[1 mark]***
[4 marks available in total — as above]
You could have split the trapezium up into a rectangle and a triangle and found the area of each separately, then added them together.

Pages 28-29: Solving Equations

1 a) $40 - 3x = 17x$, $40 = 17x + 3x$, $40 = 20x$, $x = \frac{40}{20} = 2$
[2 marks available — 1 mark for adding 3x to both sides, 1 mark for the correct answer]
b) $2y - 5 = 3y - 12$, $12 - 5 = 3y - 2y$, $y = 7$
[2 marks available — 1 mark for adding 12 and subtracting 2y from each side, 1 mark for the correct answer]
c) $2r - 6 = 3(3 - r)$, $2r - 6 = 9 - 3r$, $2r + 3r = 9 + 6$, $5r = 15$, $r = \frac{15}{5} = 3$
[3 marks available — 1 mark for expanding out the bracket, 1 mark for adding 6 and 3r to both sides, 1 mark for the correct answer]

2 a) $9b - 7 = 2(3b + 1)$, $9b - 7 = 6b + 2$, $9b - 6b = 2 + 7$, $3b = 9$
$b = \frac{9}{3} = 3$
[3 marks available — 1 mark for expanding out the bracket, 1 mark for adding 7 and subtracting 6b from each side, 1 mark for the correct answer]
b) $\frac{28 - z}{4} = 5$, $28 - z = 20$, $z = 28 - 20$, $z = 8$
[2 marks available — 1 mark for multiplying both sides by 4, 1 mark for correct answer]

3 $\frac{5}{4}(2c - 1) = 3c - 2$
$5(2c - 1) = 4(3c - 2)$ ***[1 mark]***
$(5 \times 2c) + (5 \times -1) = (4 \times 3c) + (4 \times -2)$
$10c - 5 = 12c - 8$
$12c - 10c = 8 - 5$ ***[1 mark]***
$2c = 3$
$c = \frac{3}{2}$ or 1.5 ***[1 mark]***
[3 marks available in total — as above]

4 $\frac{8 - 2x}{3} + \frac{2x + 4}{9} = 12$
$\frac{9(8 - 2x)}{3} + \frac{9(2x + 4)}{9} = 108$
$3(8 - 2x) + (2x + 4) = 108$ ***[1 mark]***
$24 - 6x + 2x + 4 = 108$
$6x - 2x = 24 + 4 - 108$ ***[1 mark]***
$4x = -80$ ***[1 mark]***
$x = -20$ ***[1 mark]***
[4 marks available in total — as above]

5 The perimeter is $(2x - 2) + (x + 1) + (22 - x) + (3x + 2)$, so...
$(2x - 2) + (x + 1) + (22 - x) + (3x + 2) = 58$ ***[1 mark]***
$2x - 2 + x + 1 + 22 - x + 3x + 2 = 58$
$2x + x - x + 3x = 58 + 2 - 1 - 22 - 2$ ***[1 mark]***
$5x = 35$
$x = 7$ ***[1 mark]***
[3 marks available in total — as above]

6 The amount of money Liam has is given by $17.80 + 4.20h$, where h is the number of hours Liam has worked.
$17.80 + 4.20h = 190$ ***[1 mark]***
$4.20h = 190 - 17.80$ ***[1 mark]***
$4.20h = 172.20$
$h = 41$ ***[1 mark]***
So Liam will have to work 41 hours to have enough money.
[3 marks available in total — as above]

Pages 30-31: Formulas

1 a) $y = \frac{x - 2}{3}$, so $3y = x - 2$ and $x = 3y + 2$
[2 marks available — 1 mark for multiplying both sides by 3, 1 mark for the correct answer.]
b) When $y = 5$, $x = (3 \times 5) + 2 = 15 + 2 = 17$
[2 marks available — 1 mark for correct substitution, 1 mark for the correct answer.]

2 a) $V = \frac{1}{3}Ah$, so $3V = Ah$ and $h = \frac{3V}{A}$
[2 marks available — 1 mark for multiplying both sides by 3, 1 mark for the correct answer.]
b) When $V = 18$ and $A = 12$, $h = \frac{3 \times 18}{12} = \frac{54}{12} = 4.5$ cm
[2 marks available — 1 mark for correct substitution, 1 mark for the correct answer.]

3 a) $F = \frac{9}{5}C + 32$, so $\frac{9}{5}C = F - 32$ and $C = \frac{5}{9}(F - 32)$
[2 marks available — 1 mark for subtracting 32 from each side, 1 mark for the correct answer.]

b) When $F = 41$, $C = \frac{5}{9}(41 - 32) = \frac{5}{9}(9) = 5$ °C
[2 marks available — 1 mark for correct substitution, 1 mark for the correct answer.]

4 $s = \frac{1}{2}gt^2$, so $gt^2 = 2s$ ***[1 mark]***, $t^2 = \frac{2s}{g}$ ***[1 mark]***,
$t = \sqrt{\frac{2s}{g}}$ ***[1 mark]***
[3 marks available in total — as above]

5 a) $a + y = \frac{b - y}{a}$, so...
$a(a + y) = b - y$ ***[1 mark]***, $a^2 + ay = b - y$,
$ay + y = b - a^2$ ***[1 mark]***, $y(a + 1) = b - a^2$ ***[1 mark]***,
$y = \frac{b - a^2}{a + 1}$ ***[1 mark]***
[4 marks available in total — as above]

b) When $a = 3$ and $b = 6$, $y = \frac{6 - 3^2}{3 + 1} = -\frac{3}{4}$ or -0.75
[2 marks available — 1 mark for correct substitution, 1 mark for the correct answer.]

6 $x = \sqrt{\frac{(1+n)}{(1-n)}}$, so $x^2 = \frac{(1+n)}{(1-n)}$ ***[1 mark]***, $x^2(1 - n) = 1 + n$,
$x^2 - x^2n = 1 + n$ ***[1 mark]***, $x^2 - 1 = n + x^2n$ ***[1 mark]***,
$x^2 - 1 = n(1 + x^2)$ ***[1 mark]***,
$n = \frac{x^2 - 1}{1 + x^2}$ ***[1 mark]***
[5 marks available in total — as above]

7 a) The amount that Peter paid is given by $\frac{2}{3}T$
The amount that Marek paid is $4.5 + 0.5d$
If Marek paid twice as much as Peter, then $4.5 + 0.5d = 2 \times \frac{2}{3}T$,
so $4.5 + 0.5d = \frac{4T}{3}$ ***[1 mark]***

b) $4.5 + 0.5d = \frac{4T}{3}$, so $0.5d = \frac{4T}{3} - 4.5$ and
$d = 2(\frac{4T}{3} - 4.5) = \frac{8T}{3} - 9$
When $T = 22.5$, $d = \frac{8 \times 22.5}{3} - 9 = 51$ miles
[3 marks available — 1 mark for correctly rearranging the equation, 1 mark for correctly substituting T = 22.5, 1 mark for the correct answer.]

Pages 32-33: Factorising Quadratics

1 $(x + 3)(x + 6)$
[2 marks available — 1 mark for correct numbers in brackets, 1 mark for correct signs]
The brackets can be either way around — $(x + 6)(x + 3)$ is also correct.

2 $(y + 1)(y - 5)$
[2 marks available — 1 mark for correct numbers in brackets, 1 mark for correct signs]

3 a) $(x - 4)(x + 8)$
[2 marks available — 1 mark for correct numbers in brackets, 1 mark for correct signs]

b) $(3x + 2)(x - 2)$
[2 marks available — 1 mark for correct numbers in brackets, 1 mark for correct signs]

4 a) $(x - 4)(x - 5)$
[2 marks available — 1 mark for correct numbers in brackets, 1 mark for correct signs]

b) $x - 4 = 0$ or $x - 5 = 0$
$x = 4$ or $x = 5$
[1 mark for both solutions correct]

5 $x^2 + 4x - 12 = 0$
$(x + 6)(x - 2) = 0$
[1 mark for correct numbers in brackets, 1 mark for correct signs]
$x + 6 = 0$ or $x - 2 = 0$
$x = -6$ or $x = 2$
[1 mark for both solutions]
[3 marks available in total — as above]

6 a) $(2x - 7)(x + 4)$
[2 marks available — 1 mark for correct numbers in brackets, 1 mark for correct signs]

b) $(2x - 7)(x + 4) = (2x - 7)^2$ ***[1 mark]***
$(2x - 7)(x + 4) - (2x - 7)^2 = 0$
$(2x - 7)((x + 4) - (2x - 7)) = 0$ ***[1 mark]***
$2x - 7 = 0$ or $x + 4 - 2x + 7 = 0$ ***[1 mark]***
$x = 3.5$ or $-x + 11 = 0$
$x = 3.5$ or $x = 11$
[1 mark for both solutions]
[4 marks available in total — as above]

7 a) $(5x - 9)(x - 2)$
[2 marks available — 1 mark for correct numbers in brackets, 1 mark for correct signs]

b) Replacing x with $(x - 1)$ in the factorised expression from a)...
$5(x - 1)^2 - 19(x - 1) + 18 = (5(x - 1) - 9)((x - 1) - 2)$ ***[1 mark]***
$= (5x - 5 - 9)(x - 1 - 2)$
$= (5x - 14)(x - 3)$ ***[1 mark]***
[2 marks available in total — as above]

8 a) The area of the square is $(x + 3)(x + 3) = x^2 + 6x + 9$. ***[1 mark]***
The area of the triangle is $\frac{1}{2}(2x + 2)(x + 3)$
$= \frac{1}{2}(2x^2 + 6x + 2x + 6) = \frac{1}{2}(2x^2 + 8x + 6)$
$= x^2 + 4x + 3$ ***[1 mark]***
So the area of the whole shape is $x^2 + 6x + 9 + x^2 + 4x + 3$
$= 2x^2 + 10x + 12$ ***[1 mark]***
$2x^2 + 10x + 12 = 60$, so $2x^2 + 10x - 48 = 0$ ***[1 mark]***
[4 marks available in total — as above]

b) $2x^2 + 10x - 48 = 0$
$(2x - 6)(x + 8) = 0$ ***[1 mark]***
$2x - 6 = 0$ or $x + 8 = 0$
$x = 3$ or $x = -8$
[1 mark for both solutions]
A length can't have a negative value so the answer must be $x = 3$ ***[1 mark]***
[3 marks available in total — as above]

Page 34: The Quadratic Formula

1 a = 1, b = 5 and c = 3
$$x = \frac{-5 \pm \sqrt{5^2 - 4 \times 1 \times 3}}{2 \times 1} = \frac{-5 \pm \sqrt{13}}{2}$$
$x = -0.70$ or $x = -4.30$
[3 marks available — 1 mark for correct substitution, 1 mark for each correct solution]

2 a = 1, b = 6 and c = –3
$$x = \frac{-6 \pm \sqrt{6^2 - 4 \times 1 \times -3}}{2 \times 1} = \frac{-6 \pm \sqrt{48}}{2}$$
$x = 0.46$ or $x = -6.46$
[3 marks available — 1 mark for correct substitution, 1 mark for each correct solution]

3 a = 2, b = –7 and c = 2
$$x = \frac{-(-7) \pm \sqrt{(-7)^2 - 4 \times 2 \times 2}}{2 \times 2} = \frac{7 \pm \sqrt{33}}{4}$$
$x = 3.19$ or $x = 0.31$
[3 marks available — 1 mark for correct substitution, 1 mark for each correct solution]

4 a = 3, b = –2 and c = –4
$$x = \frac{-(-2) \pm \sqrt{(-2)^2 - 4 \times 3 \times -4}}{2 \times 3} = \frac{2 \pm \sqrt{52}}{6}$$
$$x = \frac{1 + \sqrt{13}}{3} \text{ or } x = \frac{1 - \sqrt{13}}{3}$$
[3 marks available — 1 mark for correct substitution, 1 mark for each correct solution]

Page 35: Completing the Square

1 $8 \div 2 = 4$, so $a = 4$ and the bit in brackets is $(x + 4)^2$. ***[1 mark]***
Expanding the brackets: $(x + 4)^2 = x^2 + 8x + 16$. ***[1 mark]***
To complete the square: $17 - 16 = 1$, so $b = 1$. ***[1 mark]***
$a = 4$ and $b = 1$
[3 marks available in total — as above]

2 $-6 \div 2 = -3$, so $a = -3$ and the bit in brackets is $(x - 3)^2$.
Expanding the brackets: $(x - 3)^2 = x^2 - 6x + 9$. ***[1 mark]***
To complete the square: $3 - 9 = -6$, so $b = -6$. ***[1 mark]***
$x^2 - 6x + 3 = (x - 3)^2 - 6$ ***[1 mark]***
[3 marks available in total — as above]

3 $(x + 2)^2 - 9 = x^2 + 4x + 4 - 9$ ***[1 mark]*** $= x^2 + 4x - 5$
$a = 4$ and $b = -5$ ***[1 mark]***
[2 marks available in total — as above]

4 a) $-10 \div 2 = -5$, so $p = -5$ and the bit in brackets is $(x - 5)^2$. ***[1 mark]***
Expanding the brackets: $(x - 5)^2 = x^2 - 10x + 25$. ***[1 mark]***
To complete the square: $-5 - 25 = -30$, so $q = -30$. ***[1 mark]***
$p = -5$ and $q = -30$
[3 marks available in total — as above]

b) $(x - 5)^2 - 30 = 0$, so $(x - 5)^2 = 30$ and $x - 5 = \pm\sqrt{30}$
So $x = 5 + \sqrt{30}$ or $x = 5 - \sqrt{30}$
[2 marks available — 1 mark for each correct solution]

Page 36: Algebraic Fractions

1 a) $\dfrac{3x - 12}{x^2 - 16} = \dfrac{3(x - 4)}{(x + 4)(x - 4)} = \dfrac{3}{x + 4}$
[3 marks available — 1 mark for correctly factorising the denominator, 1 mark for correctly factorising the numerator, 1 mark for the correct answer]

b) $\dfrac{x^2 - 4}{x^2 + 8x + 12} = \dfrac{(x + 2)(x - 2)}{(x + 2)(x + 6)} = \dfrac{x - 2}{x + 6}$
[3 marks available — 1 mark for correctly factorising the denominator, 1 mark for correctly factorising the numerator, 1 mark for the correct answer]

2 $\dfrac{4x^2 + 10x - 6}{16x^2 - 4} = \dfrac{(4x - 2)(x + 3)}{(4x - 2)(4x + 2)} = \dfrac{x + 3}{4x + 2}$
[3 marks available — 1 mark for correctly factorising the denominator, 1 mark for correctly factorising the numerator, 1 mark for the correct answer]

3 a) $\dfrac{x^2}{3x} \times \dfrac{6}{x + 1} = \dfrac{6x^2}{3x(x + 1)} = \dfrac{2x}{x + 1}$
[2 marks available — 1 mark for correct multiplication, 1 mark for the correct answer]

b) $\dfrac{10x}{3 + x} \div \dfrac{4}{5(3 + x)} = \dfrac{10x}{3 + x} \times \dfrac{5(3 + x)}{4} = \dfrac{50x(3 + x)}{4(3 + x)} = \dfrac{50x}{4} = \dfrac{25x}{2}$
[3 marks available — 1 mark for converting to a multiplication, 1 mark for correct multiplication, 1 mark for correct answer]

4 $\dfrac{2}{3} + \dfrac{m - 2n}{m + 3n} = \dfrac{2(m + 3n)}{3(m + 3n)} + \dfrac{3(m - 2n)}{3(m + 3n)} = \dfrac{2(m + 3n) + 3(m - 2n)}{3(m + 3n)}$
$= \dfrac{2m + 6n + 3m - 6n}{3(m + 3n)} = \dfrac{5m}{3(m + 3n)}$
[3 marks available — 1 mark for finding the common denominator, 1 mark for a correct method for addition, 1 mark for the correct final answer]

5 $\dfrac{1}{x - 5} + \dfrac{2}{x - 2} = \dfrac{x - 2}{(x - 5)(x - 2)} + \dfrac{2(x - 5)}{(x - 5)(x - 2)} = \dfrac{(x - 2) + 2(x - 5)}{(x - 5)(x - 2)}$
$= \dfrac{x - 2 + 2x - 10}{(x - 5)(x - 2)} = \dfrac{3x - 12}{(x - 5)(x - 2)}$
[3 marks available — 1 mark for finding the common denominator, 1 mark for a correct method for addition, 1 mark for the correct final answer]

Page 37: Inequalities

1 $-2 \leq x < 4$ ***[1 mark]***
You know the first sign is ≤ because the circle above the number line is coloured in, so −2 is included. The second sign is < because the circle above the number line is not coloured in, so 4 is not included.

2 $-3, -2, -1, 0, 1$
[2 marks available — 2 marks for all five numbers correct, otherwise 1 mark for four correct numbers]

3 $9 < 2p \leq 18$, so $4.5 < p \leq 9$ ***[1 mark]***
$p = 5, 6, 7, 8$ or 9 ***[2 marks for all five numbers correct, otherwise 1 mark for four correct numbers]***
[3 marks available in total — as above]

4 a) $4q - 5 < 23$, so $4q < 28$ ***[1 mark]*** and $q < 7$ ***[1 mark]***
[2 marks available in total — as above]

b) $\dfrac{2x}{5} \leq 3$, so $2x \leq 15$ ***[1 mark]*** and $x \leq 7.5$ ***[1 mark]***
[2 marks available in total — as above]

c) $4x + 1 > x - 5$, so $3x > -6$ ***[1 mark]*** and $x > -2$ ***[1 mark]***
[2 marks available in total — as above]

5 a) $5 - 3x > 7 - x$, so $-2 > 2x$ ***[1 mark]*** and $x < -1$ ***[1 mark]***
[2 marks available in total — as above]

b) −4 −3 −2 −1 0 1 2 3 4 ***[1 mark]***
The circle shouldn't be coloured in — if it was it'd be x ≤ −1.

Page 38: Graphical Inequalities

1 a)

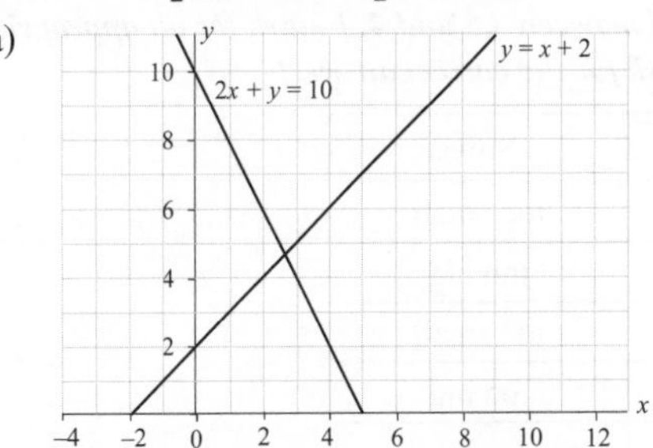

[2 marks available — 1 mark for correctly drawing 2x + y = 10, 1 mark for correctly drawing y = x + 2]

b)

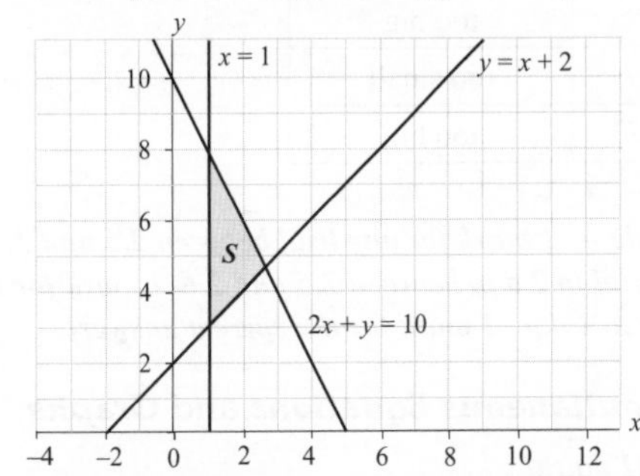

[2 marks available — 1 mark for correctly drawing x = 1, 1 mark for shading the correct area]

2

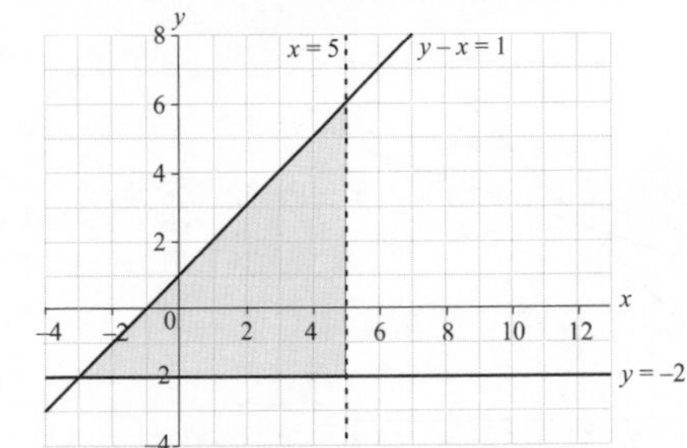

[4 marks available — 1 mark for drawing each line correctly, 1 mark for shading the correct area]

3 $y \geq 2$ ***[1 mark]***, $x + y \leq 8$ ***[1 mark]*** and $y \leq x$ ***[1 mark]***
[3 marks available in total — as above]

Page 39: Trial and Improvement

1

x	$x^3 + 4x$	Notes
2	16	too small
3	39	too big
2.5	25.625	too big
2.3	21.367	too small
2.4	23.424	too small
2.45	24.506...	too big

$x = 2.4$

[4 marks available — 1 mark for any trial between 2 and 3, 1 mark for any trial between 2 and 2.5, 1 mark for an appropriate trial to 2 d.p., 1 mark for the correct answer]

2

x	$x^2(x + 1)$	Notes
3	36	too small
4	80	too big
3.5	55.125	too small
3.7	64.343	too big
3.6	59.616	too small
3.65	61.949...	too small

$x = 3.7$

[4 marks available — 1 mark for any trial between 3 and 4, 1 mark for any trial between 3.5 and 4, 1 mark for an appropriate trial to 2 d.p., 1 mark for the correct answer]

3

x	4^x	Notes
2	16	too small
3	64	too big
2.5	32	too small
2.7	42.224...	too big
2.6	36.758...	too big
2.55	34.296...	too big
2.53	33.358...	too big
2.52	32.899...	too small
2.525	33.128...	too big

$x = 2.52$

[4 marks available — 1 mark for any trial between 2.5 and 3, 1 mark for any trial to 2 d.p. between 2.5 and 2.6, 1 mark for an appropriate trial to 3 d.p., 1 mark for the correct answer]

Pages 40-41: Simultaneous Equations and Graphs

1 $x = 3$ and $y = 4$ ***[1 mark]***

These are the x and y coordinates of the point where the two lines cross.

2 a) $x = 1, y = 2$ ***[1 mark]***

b)

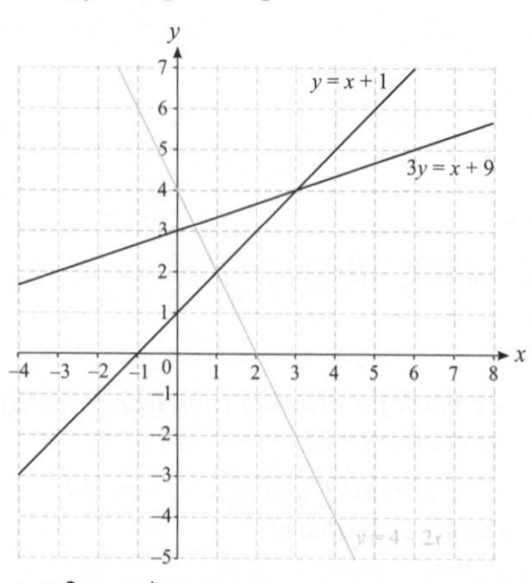

$x = 3, y = 4$

[2 marks available — 1 mark for correctly drawing the line 3y = x + 9, 1 mark for the correct answer]

3

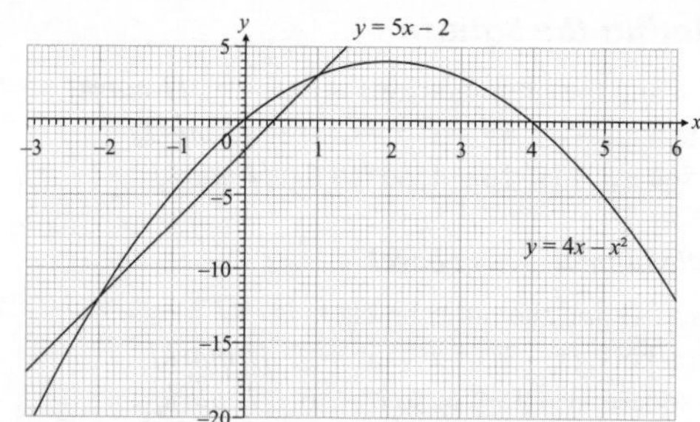

$x = 1, y = 3$ and $x = -2, y = -12$

[3 marks available — 1 mark for correctly drawing the line y = 5x – 2, 1 mark for each correct solution]

4

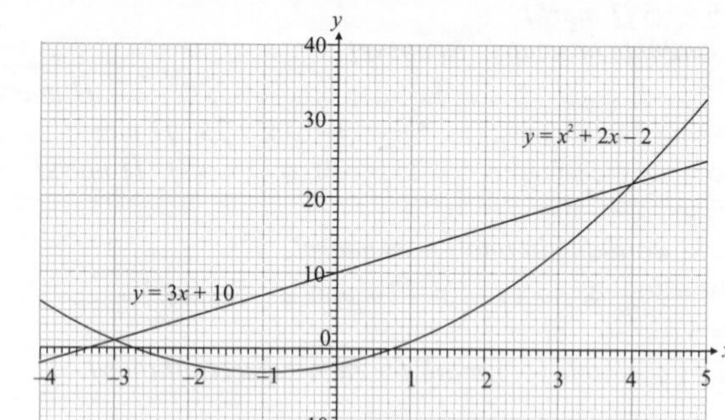

$x = -3, y = 1$ and $x = 4, y = 22$

[3 marks available — 1 mark for correctly drawing the line y = 3x + 10, 1 mark for each correct solution]

5 At the points where the graphs cross, $\frac{6}{x-2} = 2 - 5x$, so $(x - 2)(2 - 5x) = 6$. ***[1 mark]***

The x values at the points where the two graphs cross are 0.5 and 4 so the solutions of the equation $(2 - 5x)(x - 2) = 6$ are $x = 0.5$ ***[1 mark]*** and $x = 4$ ***[1 mark]***

[3 marks available in total — as above]

6

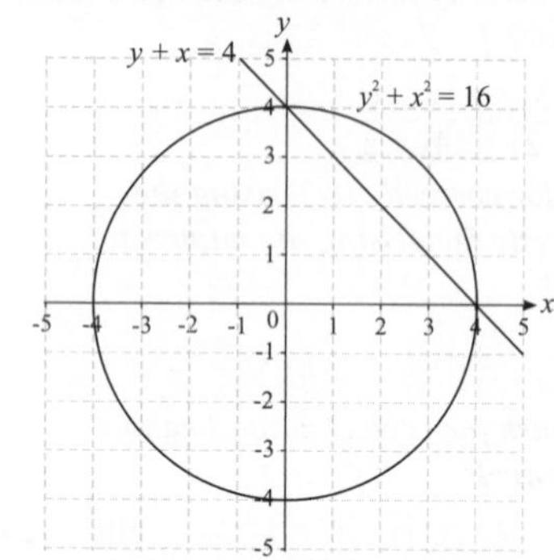

$x = 0, y = 4$ and $x = 4, y = 0$

[3 marks available — 1 mark for correctly drawing the line y + x = 4, 1 mark for each correct solution]

Page 42: Simultaneous Equations

1 $x + 3y = 11 \xrightarrow{\times 3} 3x + 9y = 33$ ***[1 mark]***

$3x + 9y = 33$
$3x + y = 9 -$
$8y = 24$
$y = 3$ ***[1 mark]***

$x + 3y = 11$
$x + (3 \times 3) = 11$
$x = 11 - 9$
$x = 2$ ***[1 mark]***

[3 marks available in total — as above]

2 $2x + 3y = 12 \xrightarrow{\times 5} 10x + 15y = 60$ ***[1 mark]***

$5x + 4y = 9 \xrightarrow{\times 2} 10x + 8y = 18$ ***[1 mark]***

$10x + 15y = 60$
$10x + 8y = 18 -$
$7y = 42$
$y = 6$ ***[1 mark]***

$2x + 3y = 12$
$2x = 12 - (3 \times 6)$
$2x = -6$
$x = -3$ ***[1 mark]***

[4 marks available in total — as above]

3 Let f be the number of chocolate frogs and m be the number of sugar mice.
$4f + 3m = £3.69$ and $6f + 2m = £3.96$ ***[1 mark]***
$4f + 3m = £3.69 \xrightarrow{\times 2} 8f + 6m = £7.38$
$6f + 2m = £3.96 \xrightarrow{\times 3} 18f + 6m = £11.88$
$18f + 6m = £11.88$ $\quad$ $4f + 3m = £3.69$
$8f + 6m = £7.38$ – $\quad$ $3m = £3.69 - (4 \times 0.45)$
$10f = £4.50$ $\quad$ $3m = £1.89$
$f = £0.45$ ***[1 mark]*** $\quad$ $m = £0.63$ ***[1 mark]***
So a bag with 2 chocolate frogs and 5 sugar mice would cost
$(2 \times 0.45) + (5 \times 0.63) = £4.05$ ***[1 mark]***
[4 marks available in total — as above]

4 $x^2 + y = 4$, so $y = 4 - x^2$
$4x - 1 = 4 - x^2$ ***[1 mark]***
$x^2 + 4x - 5 = 0$ ***[1 mark]***
$(x + 5)(x - 1) = 0$ ***[1 mark]***
$x = -5$ or $x = 1$ ***[1 mark]***
When $x = 1$, $y = (4 \times 1) - 1 = 3$
When $x = -5$, $y = (4 \times -5) - 1 = -21$
So the solutions are $x = 1, y = 3$ and $x = -5, y = -21$ ***[1 mark]***
[5 marks available in total — as above]

5 $y = x + 6$, so $2x^2 + (x + 6)^2 = 51$ ***[1 mark]***
$2x^2 + x^2 + 12x + 36 = 51$
$3x^2 + 12x - 15 = 0$ ***[1 mark]***
$(3x - 3)(x + 5) = 0$ ***[1 mark]***
$x = 1$ or $x = -5$ ***[1 mark]***
When $x = 1$, $y = 1 + 6 = 7$
When $x = -5$, $y = -5 + 6 = 1$
So the solutions are $x = 1, y = 7$ ***[1 mark]*** and $x = -5, y = 1$ ***[1 mark]***
[6 marks available in total — as above]

Pages 43-44: Direct and Inverse Proportion

1 a) $y \propto x$, so $y = kx$ ***[1 mark]***
When $y = 27$ and $x = 9$, $27 = k \times 9$, so $k = 27 \div 9 = 3$ ***[1 mark]***
So $y = 3x$ ***[1 mark]***
[3 marks available in total — as above]
b) $y = 3x$ so when $x = 8$, $y = 3 \times 8 = 24$ ***[1 mark]***

2 $m \propto \frac{1}{n}$, so $m = \frac{k}{n}$ ***[1 mark]***
When $m = 3$ and $n = 12$, $3 = \frac{k}{12}$, so $k = 3 \times 12 = 36$ ***[1 mark]***
So $m = \frac{36}{n}$ ***[1 mark]***
When n = 4, $m = \frac{36}{4} = 9$ ***[1 mark]***
[4 marks available in total — as above]

3 a) $c \propto \frac{1}{d^2}$, so $c = \frac{k}{d^2}$ ***[1 mark]***
When $c = 2$ and $d = 3$, $2 = \frac{k}{3^2}$, so $k = 2 \times 3^2 = 18$ ***[1 mark]***
So $c = \frac{18}{d^2}$ ***[1 mark]***
[3 marks available in total — as above]
b) $c = \frac{18}{d^2}$ so when $c = 0.5$, $0.5 = \frac{18}{d^2}$, $d = \pm\sqrt{\frac{18}{0.5}}$ ***[1 mark]***
$= \pm 6$ ***[1 mark]***
[2 marks available in total — as above]

4 a) $A \propto \sqrt{T}$, so $A = k\sqrt{T}$ ***[1 mark]***
When $T = 36$ and $A = 4$, $4 = k\sqrt{36}$, so $k = 4 \div \sqrt{36} = \frac{2}{3}$ ***[1 mark]***
So $A = \frac{2}{3}\sqrt{T}$ ***[1 mark]***
[3 marks available in total — as above]
b) If T halves, $\sqrt{T}$ will be divided by $\sqrt{2}$.
A is directly proportional to $\sqrt{T}$, so the value of A must also be divided by $\sqrt{2}$. ***[1 mark]***

5 $y \propto \frac{1}{x^3}$, so $y = \frac{k}{x^3}$ ***[1 mark]***
When $y = 1.5$ and $x = 8$, $1.5 = \frac{k}{8^3}$, so $k = 1.5 \times 8^3 = 768$ ***[1 mark]***
So $y = \frac{768}{x^3}$ ***[1 mark]***
When $x = 2$, $y = \frac{768}{2^3} = 96$ ***[1 mark]***
[4 marks available in total — as above]

6 $p \propto \sqrt[3]{q}$, so $p = k\sqrt[3]{q}$ ***[1 mark]***
When $p = 15$ and $q = 27$, $15 = k\sqrt[3]{27}$, so $k = 15 \div \sqrt[3]{27} = 5$ ***[1 mark]***
So $p = 5\sqrt[3]{q}$ ***[1 mark]***
When $p = 20$, $20 = 5\sqrt[3]{q}$, so $q = (20 \div 5)^3 = 64$ ***[1 mark]***
[4 marks available in total — as above]

7 a) $x \propto M$, so $x = kM$ ***[1 mark]***
When $M = 40$ and $x = 2$, $2 = k \times 40$, so $k = 2 \div 40 = \frac{1}{20}$ ***[1 mark]***
So $x = \frac{1}{20}M$ or $M = 20x$ ***[1 mark]***
[3 marks available in total — as above]
b) $x = \frac{1}{20}M$ so when $M = 55$, $x = \frac{1}{20} \times 55 = 2.75$ cm ***[1 mark]***

8 $h \propto S^2$, so $h = kS^2$ ***[1 mark]***
When $h = 35$ and $S = 50$, $35 = k \times 50^2$,
so $k = 35 \div 50^2 = 0.014$ ***[1 mark]***
So $h = 0.014S^2$ ***[1 mark]***
$h = 0.014S^2$ so when $S = 40$, $h = 0.014 \times 40^2 = 22.4$ ***[1 mark]***
[4 marks available in total — as above]

Page 45: Proof

1 m and n are integers. $2m + 1$ represents any odd number. $2n$ represents any even number. So an odd number times an even number is given by $(2m + 1) \times 2n$. ***[1 mark]***
$(2m + 1) \times 2n = 4mn + 2n$
$= 2(2mn + n) = 2x$ (where $x = 2mn + n$). ***[1 mark]***
Any integer multiplied by 2 is an even number, so $2x$ must be even and therefore any odd number multiplied by any even number is always an even number. ***[1 mark]***
[3 marks available in total — as above]

2 n is an integer. $2n$ represents any even number, so the sum of 3 consecutive even numbers will be given by
$2n + (2n + 2) + (2n + 4)$. ***[1 mark]***
$2n + (2n + 2) + (2n + 4) = 6n + 6 = 6(n + 1)$
$= 6x$ (where $x = n + 1$). ***[1 mark]***
Any integer multiplied by 6 is a multiple of 6, so $6x$ must be a multiple of 6 and therefore the sum of any 3 consecutive even numbers will be a multiple of 6. ***[1 mark]***
[3 marks available in total — as above]

3 n is an integer. $2n$ represents any even number, so the difference between the squares of two consecutive even numbers will be given by $(2n + 2)^2 - (2n)^2$. ***[1 mark]***
$(2n + 2)^2 - (2n)^2 = (4n^2 + 8n + 4) - 4n^2 = 8n + 4 = 4(2n + 1)$
$= 4x$ (where $x = 2n + 1$) ***[1 mark]***
Any integer multiplied by 4 is a multiple of 4, so $4x$ must be a multiple of 4 and therefore the difference between the squares of two consecutive even numbers will always be a multiple of 4. ***[1 mark]***
[3 marks available in total — as above]

4 $(3n + 2)^2 - (n + 2)^2 = (3n + 2)(3n + 2) - (n + 2)(n + 2)$
$= (9n^2 + 12n + 4) - (n^2 + 4n + 4)$ ***[1 mark]***
$= 9n^2 + 12n + 4 - n^2 - 4n - 4$ ***[1 mark]***
$= 8n^2 + 8n$
$= 8n(n + 1)$ ***[1 mark]***
[3 marks available in total — as above]

5 $(2n - 1)^2 + 8(2n - 1) = (2n - 1)(2n - 1) + 8(2n - 1)$
$= (4n^2 - 4n + 1) + (16n - 8)$ ***[1 mark]***
$= 4n^2 - 4n + 1 + 16n - 8$
$= 4n^2 + 12n - 7$ ***[1 mark]***
$= 4n^2 + 12n - 8 + 1$ ***[1 mark]***
$= 2(2n^2 + 6n - 4) + 1$ ***[1 mark]***
$= 2x + 1$ (where $x = 2n^2 + 6n - 4$) ***[1 mark]***
An integer multiplied by 2 is always even, so $2x$ will always be even and $2x + 1$ will always be odd. Therefore, $(2n - 1)^2 + 8(2n - 1)$ will always be odd. ***[1 mark]***
[6 marks available in total — as above]

Section Three — Graphs

Pages 46-48: Straight-Line Graphs

1 a)

x	–2	–1	0	1	2
y	–1	1	3	5	7

[2 marks available — 2 marks for all correct answers, otherwise 1 mark for two correct answers]

b)

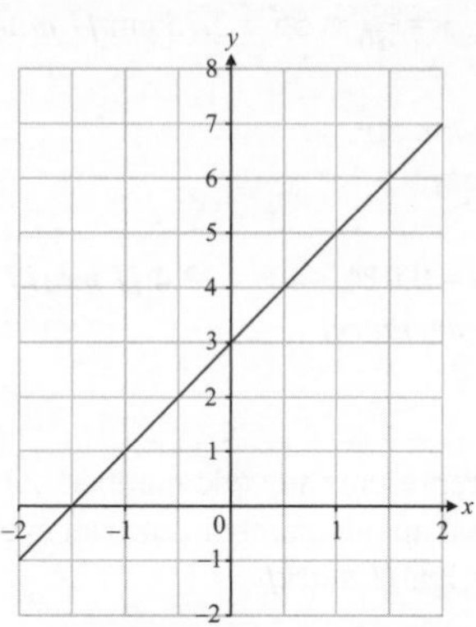

[2 marks available — 2 marks for a correct straight line passing through (–2, –1), otherwise 1 mark for a line with the correct gradient or with at least 3 points plotted correctly]

c) $y = 6$ ***[1 mark]***

d) $x = -0.5$ ***[1 mark]***

2

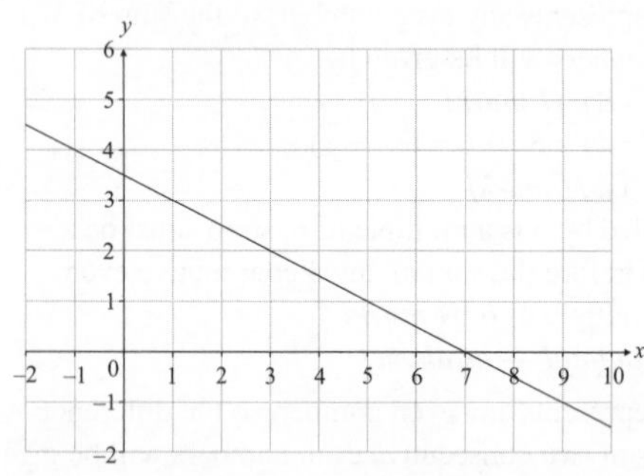

[3 marks available — 1 mark for plotting any point on the line (e.g. (0, 3.5)), 1 mark for plotting a second correct point (e.g. (7, 0)), 1 mark for the correct line extending between x = –2 and x = 10]

To draw these graphs, you could either create a table of values and plot the points, or you could set y = 0 and x = 0 and join up the points.

3 a) $\left(\frac{(6+(-4))}{2}, \frac{(2+1)}{2}, \frac{(1+3)}{2}\right)$ ***[1 mark]***

$= (1, 1.5, 2)$ ***[1 mark]***

[2 marks available in total — as above]

b) $\frac{(6+a)}{2} = 3$

$a = 6 - 6$

$a = 0$

$\frac{2+b}{2} = 5$

$b = 10 - 2$

$b = 8$

[3 marks available — 1 mark for a correct method and 1 mark for each correct a and b value]

4 a) Using $y = mx + c$, where m is the gradient, and c is the y-intercept:

$m = \frac{(7-(-3))}{(5-0)}$

$m = 2$ ***[1 mark]***

When $x = 0$, $y = -3$, so $c = -3$ ***[1 mark]***

So, $y = 2x - 3$ ***[1 mark]***

[3 marks available in total — as above]

b) Using gradient from part a), $m = 2$

When $x = 2$, $y = 10$, so

$10 = (2 \times 2) + c$ ***[1 mark]***

i.e. $c = 6$ ***[1 mark]***

So, $y = 2x + 6$ ***[1 mark]***

[3 marks available in total — as above]

5 $3x + 4 = 2x + 6$ ***[1 mark]***

$x = 2$ ***[1 mark]***

so, $y = 10$ and point M is $(2, 10)$ ***[1 mark]***

gradient of perpendicular line $= \frac{-1}{2} = -0.5$,

so, $y = -0.5x + c$ ***[1 mark]***

$10 = -0.5 \times 2 + c$, so $c = 10 + 1 = 11$

$y = -0.5x + 11$ ***[1 mark]***

[5 marks available in total — as above]

Pages 49-50: Quadratic Graphs

1 a)

x	–4	–3	–2	–1	0	1	2
y	3	–2	–5	–6	–5	–2	3

[2 marks available — 2 marks for all answers correct, otherwise 1 mark for only one correct answer]

b)

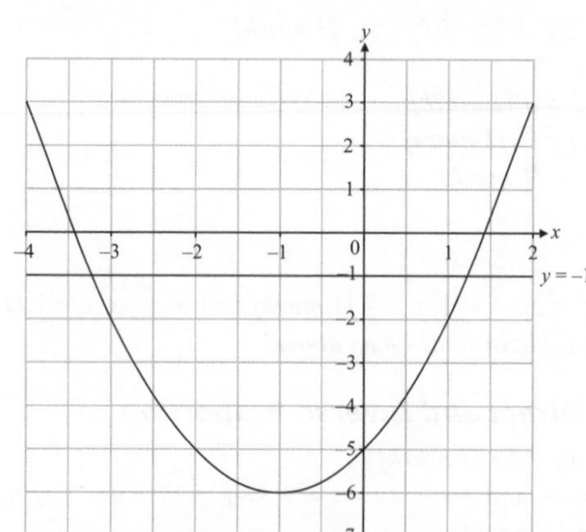

[2 marks available — 1 mark for plotting at least five points correctly, 1 mark for a smooth curve through these points]

c) $x \approx -3.2$ and $x \approx 1.2$

[2 marks available — 1 mark for drawing the line y = –1, 1 mark for estimating both a solution between –3 and –3.4 and a solution between 1 and 1.4]

2 a) $x = 1$ and $x = 2$ ***[1 mark]***

b) Using the line $y = 6$, the graphs intersect at $(-1, 6)$ and $(4, 6)$. So, the solutions are $x = -1$ and 4.

[2 marks available — 1 mark for drawing the line y = 6, 1 mark for both correct answers]

3 a)

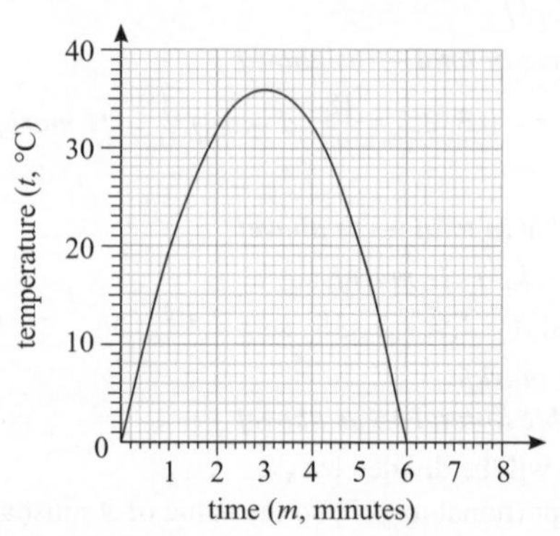

[2 marks available — 1 mark for plotting correct values and 1 mark for a smooth curve through these points]

b) 36 °C ***[1 mark for anything from 35 °C to 37 °C]***

Pages 51-53: Harder Graphs

1 a)

x	2.5	3	3.5	4
y	–5.375	–5	–2.125	4

[2 marks available — 2 marks for all answers correct, otherwise 1 mark for two correct answers]

b)

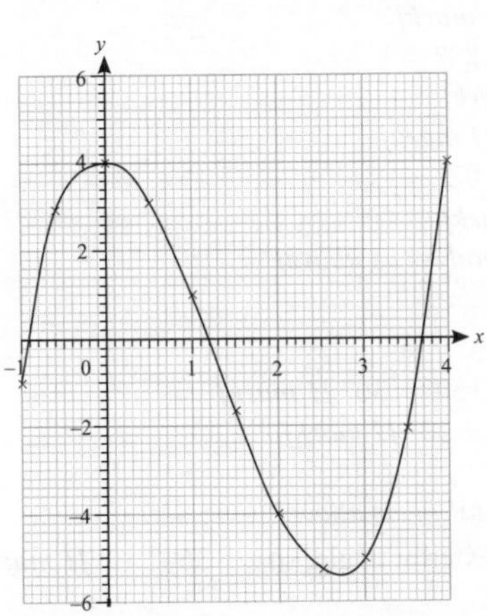

[2 marks available — 1 mark for plotting correct points, 1 mark for joining them with a smooth curve]

c) Reading off the graph, where the line intersects the x-axis, $x = -0.9$, $x = 1.2$ and $x = 3.7$ ***[1 mark]***

You'll still get the mark if your answers are within 0.1 of the answer.

2 $x = 310°$ (accept $308° - 312°$) ***[1 mark]***

3 a) F ***[1 mark]***

b) A ***[1 mark]***

c) E ***[1 mark]***

4 a)

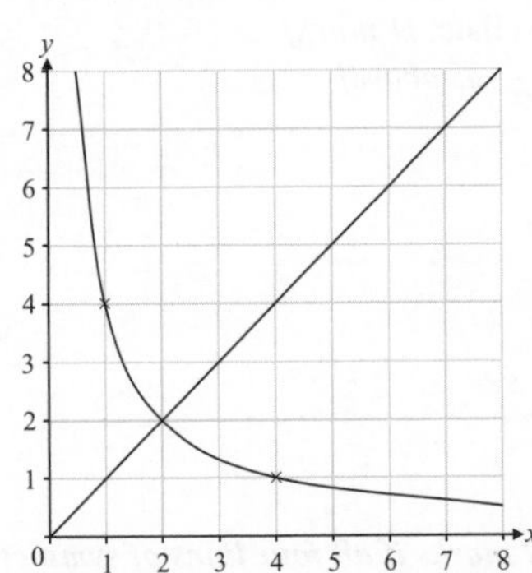

[2 marks available — 1 mark for a curve passing through (4, 1) and approaching y = 0 asymptotically, 1 mark for a curve passing through (1, 4) and approaching x = 0 asymptotically]

b) By plotting $y = x$ and reading off where it intersects the curve (see graph above), the coordinates are (2, 2) ***[1 mark]***

You could also find the values of x and y by substituting y = x into $y = \frac{4}{x}$.

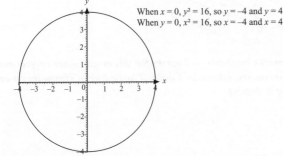

5

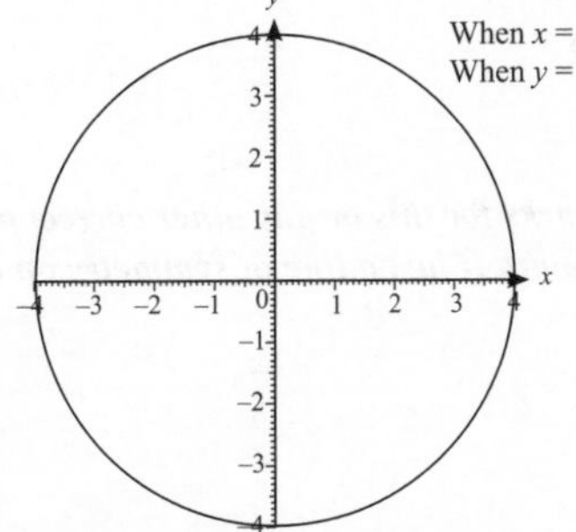

When $x = 0$, $y^2 = 16$, so $y = -4$ and $y = 4$
When $y = 0$, $x^2 = 16$, so $x = -4$ and $x = 4$

[2 marks available — 1 mark for complete circle with correct centre point, 1 mark for radius of 4]

6 a) $800 = xy^0$ ***[1 mark]***

$12\ 800 = 800y^2$ ***[1 mark]***

$x = 800$ and $y = 4$ ***[1 mark]***

[3 marks available in total — as above]

b) $C = 800 \times 4^{-2}$ ***[1 mark]***

$C = £50$ ***[1 mark]***

[2 marks available in total — as above]

Pages 54-55: Graph Transformations

1 a)

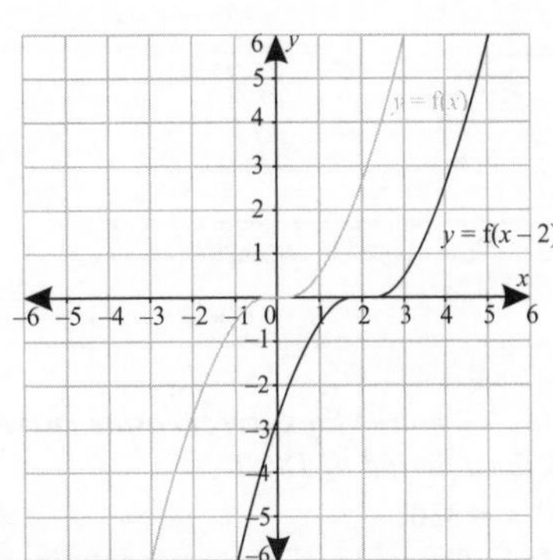

[2 marks available — 2 marks for the correct curve shifted 2 units to the right, otherwise 1 mark for an incorrect curve shifted 2 units to the right]

b) (2, 0) ***[1 mark]***

2 a) $y = f(x) - 4$ ***[1 mark]***

b) (–2, 1) ***[2 marks available — 1 mark for each correct coordinate, up to a maximum of 2]***

c) (4, 2) ***[2 marks available — 1 mark for each correct coordinate, up to a maximum of 2]***

d)

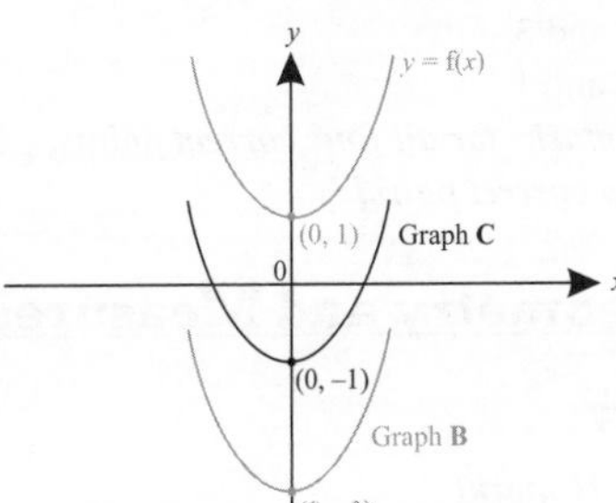

[1 mark]

e)

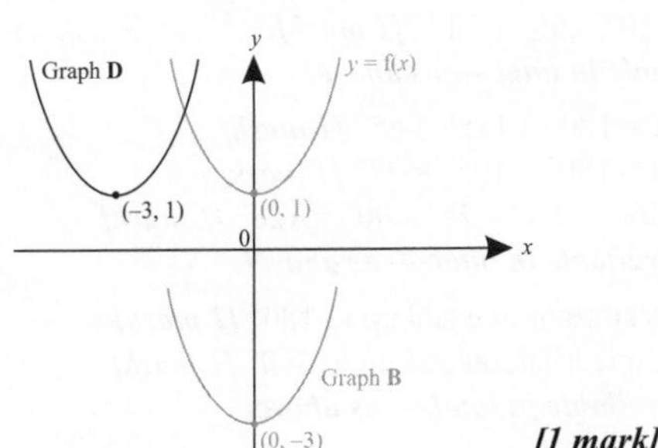

[1 mark]

3 a)

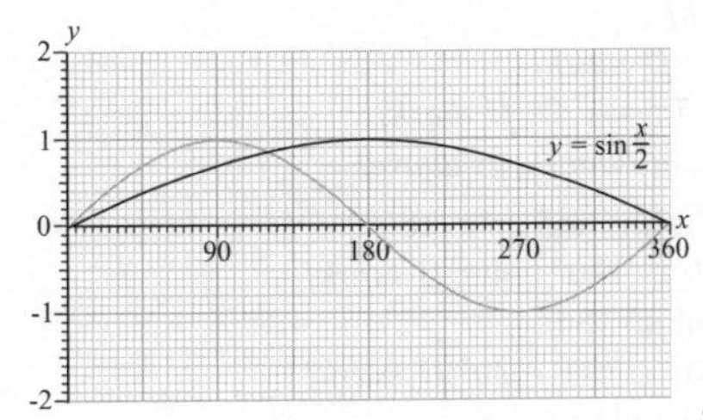

[1 mark]

b)

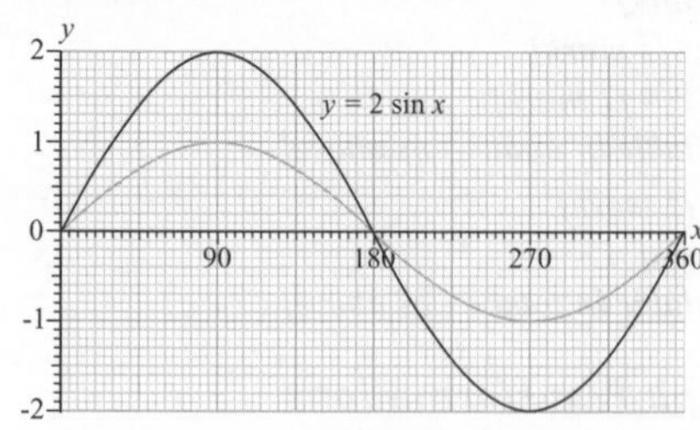

[1 mark]

4 a)

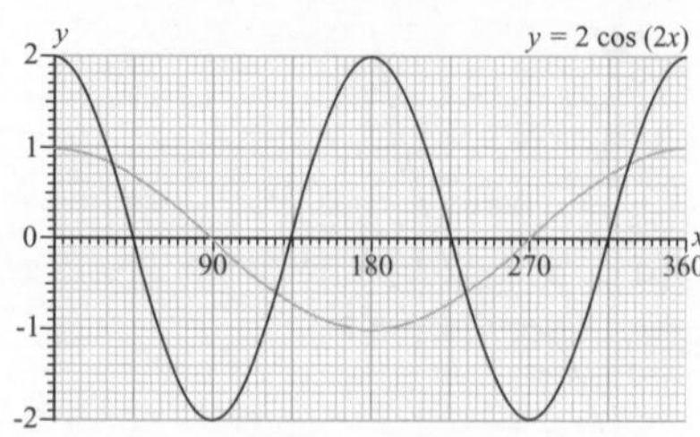

[2 marks available — 2 marks for correct cosine curve, otherwise 1 mark for a period of 180°]

b) $x = 150°$, $x = 210°$, $x = 330°$
[2 marks available — 2 marks for all correct solutions, otherwise 1 mark for 1 correct solution]

Page 56: Real-Life Graphs

1 a) Plan A: £25 ***[1 mark]***
Plan B: £28 ***[1 mark]***
[2 marks available in total — as above]

b) Mr Barker should use Plan A because it is cheaper. Using 85 units with Plan A would cost £26.50. 85 units with Plan B would cost £34. ***[2 marks available — 1 mark for correctly stating which plan, 1 mark for giving a reason]***

2 Graph A and 2, Graph B and 3
Graph C and 4, Graph D and 1
[2 marks available — 2 marks for all four correct points, otherwise 1 mark for two correct pairs]

Section Four — Geometry and Measures

Pages 57-58: Geometry

1 Angle BCA = angle BAC ***[1 mark]***
Angle $BCA = (180° - 48°) \div 2 = 66°$ ***[1 mark]***
Angle $BCD = 180° - 66° = 114°$ ***[1 mark]***
[3 marks available in total — as above]

2 a) Angle $CBE = 180° - 115° = 65°$ ***[1 mark]***
Angle $DEB = 180° - 103° = 77°$ ***[1 mark]***
Angle $x = 360° - 65° - 77° - 90° = 128°$ ***[1 mark]***
[3 marks available in total — as above]

b) Angles on a straight line add up to 180° ***[1 mark]***
Angles in a quadrilateral add up to 360° ***[1 mark]***
[2 marks available in total — as above]

3 $5x + 16x + 3x = 180°$
$24x = 180°$ ***[1 mark]***
$x = 180 \div 24 = 7.5°$ ***[1 mark]***
$ABC = 16x = 16 \times 7.5 = 120°$ ***[1 mark]***
[3 marks available in total — as above]

4 Angles on a straight line add up to 180°,
so angle $ABJ = 180° - 140° = 40°$ ***[1 mark]***
Allied angles add up to 180°,
so angle $JAB = 180° - 150° = 30°$ ***[1 mark]***
Angles in a triangle add up to 180°,
so angle $AJB = 180° - 40° - 30° = 110°$ ***[1 mark]***
Angles on a straight line add up to 180°,
so angle $x = 180° - 110° = 70°$ ***[1 mark]***
[4 marks available in total — as above]

5 a) Angles on a straight line add up to 180°,
so angle $FEC = 180° - 14° = 166°$ ***[1 mark]***
Angles in a quadrilateral add up to 360°,
so $x = 360° - 90 - 62° - 166° = 42°$ ***[1 mark]***
[2 marks available in total — as above]

b) Angles in a triangle add up to 180° ***[1 mark]***
so $y = 180° - 90° - 42° = 48°$ ***[1 mark]***
[2 marks available in total — as above]

6 $5x + (4x - 9°) = 180°$ ***[1 mark]***
Rearranging this: $9x = 189°$
Therefore $x = 21°$ ***[1 mark]***
$(4y - 12°) + 2y = 180°$ ***[1 mark]***
Rearranging this: $6y = 192°$
Therefore $y = 32°$ ***[1 mark]***
[4 marks available in total — as above]

Page 59: Polygons

1 Exterior angle = $180° - 150° = 30°$ ***[1 mark]***
Number of sides = $360° \div 30°$ ***[1 mark]***
$= 12$ ***[1 mark]***
[3 marks available in total — as above]

2 a) x is the same as an exterior angle, so $x = 360° \div 8$ ***[1 mark]***
$x = 45°$ ***[1 mark]***
[2 marks available in total — as above]

b) $y = (180° - 45°) \div 2$ ***[1 mark]***
$y = 67.5°$ ***[1 mark]***
[2 marks available in total — as above]

3 Number of sides = $360° \div 24°$ ***[1 mark]***
$= 15$ ***[1 mark]***
[2 marks available in total — as above]

4 Exterior angle = $360° \div 18 = 20°$ ***[1 mark]***
Interior angle = $180° - 20° = 160°$ ***[1 mark]***
The interior angles cannot be made to add up to 360°, so 18-sided regular polygons do not tessellate. ***[1 mark]***
[3 marks available in total — as above]

Page 60: Symmetry

1 a)

[2 marks available — 2 marks if all four lines of symmetry correctly drawn, otherwise 1 mark if two out of four lines of symmetry correctly drawn]

b) 4 ***[1 mark]***

2 E.g.

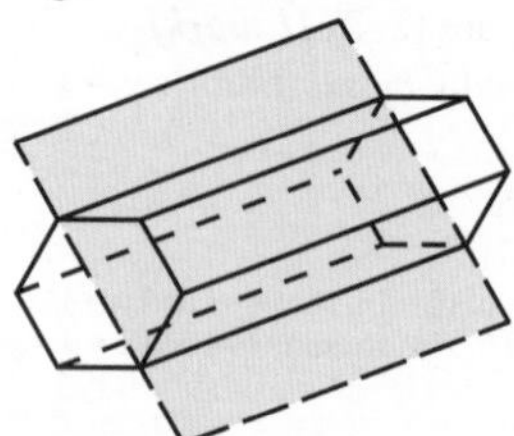

[2 marks available — 2 marks for this or any other correct plane of symmetry, otherwise 1 mark if just a line of symmetry on one face is drawn]

3 a) 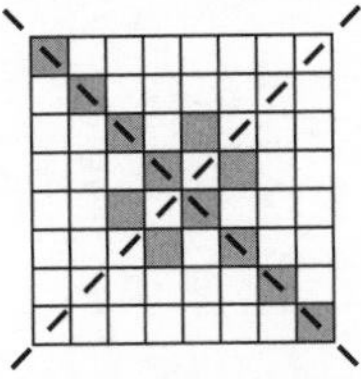

[2 marks available — 1 mark for each correct line of symmetry]

b) 2 *[1 mark]*

Pages 61-62: Circle Geometry

1 a) Angle $BCD = 150° \div 2 = 75°$ *[1 mark]*
(Angle at the centre is 2 × angle at circumference.) *[1 mark]*
[2 marks available in total — as above]

b) Opposite angles in a cyclic quadrilateral sum to 180°. *[1 mark]*

2 Angle $DBC = 62°$ *[1 mark]*
Angle $ABC = 90°$ *[1 mark]*
Angle $x = 90° - 62° = 28°$ *[1 mark]*
[3 marks available in total — as above]

3 a) $x = 28°$ *[1 mark]* $y = 24°$ *[1 mark]*
[2 marks available in total — as above]

b) Angles in the same segment are equal. *[1 mark]*

4 Angle $DCO = 90°$ *[1 mark]*
Angle $DOC = 180° - 90° - 24° = 66°$ *[1 mark]*
Angle $AOC = 66° \times 2 = 132°$ *[1 mark]*
Angle $ABC = 66°$ *[1 mark]*
Angle $CBE = 180° - 66° = 114°$ *[1 mark]*
[5 marks available in total — as above]

5 Angles *ODE* and *OBE* are both 90° because a tangent always meets a radius at 90°. *[1 mark]*
Angle $DOB = 100°$ because angles in a quadrilateral add up to 360°. *[1 mark]*
Angle $DCB = 50°$ because an angle at the centre is twice the angle at the circumference. *[1 mark]*
Angle $DAB = 130°$ because opposite angles of a cyclic quadrilateral sum to 180°. *[1 mark]*
[4 marks available in total — as above]

Pages 63-64: The Four Transformations

1 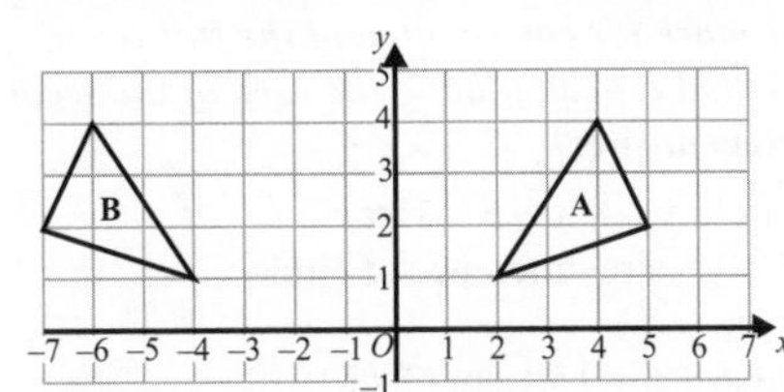

[2 marks available — 2 marks for shape correctly reflected and in the right place on the grid, otherwise 1 mark for shape correctly reflected but in wrong location]

2 a) and b)

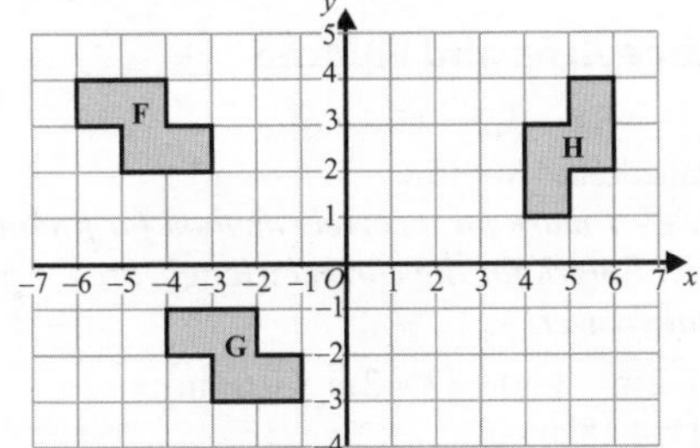

[1 mark available for part a) for correct translation]
[2 marks available for part b) — 1 mark for a rotation of 90° clockwise around any point, 1 mark for correct centre of rotation]

3 a) Rotation 90° anti-clockwise around the point (0, 0)
[3 marks available — 1 mark for rotation, 1 mark for correct angle and direction of rotation, 1 mark for correct centre of rotation]

b) 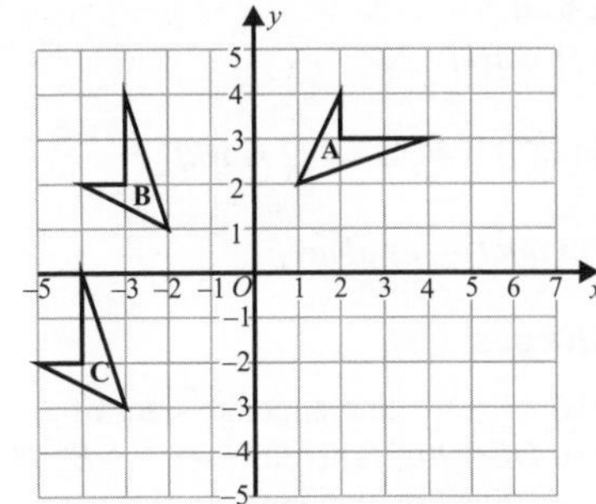

[1 mark for correct translation]

4 a) and b)

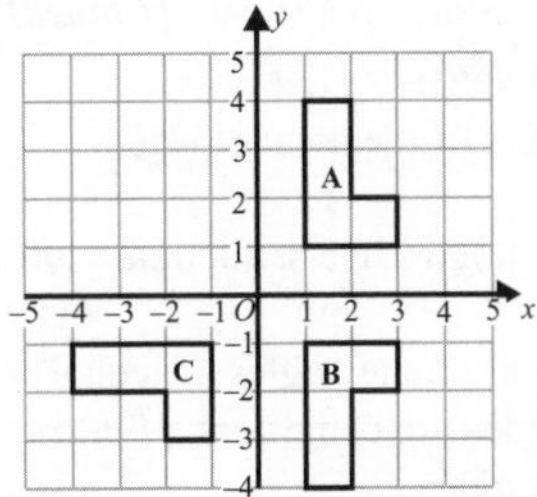

[2 marks available for part a) — 2 marks if shape correctly reflected and in the right place on the grid, otherwise 1 mark if shape correctly reflected but in wrong location]
[2 marks available for part b) — 1 mark for a rotation of 90° clockwise around any point, 1 mark for the correct centre of rotation]

c) Reflection in the line $y = -x$ *[2 marks available — 1 mark for reflection, 1 mark for correct line of reflection]*

5 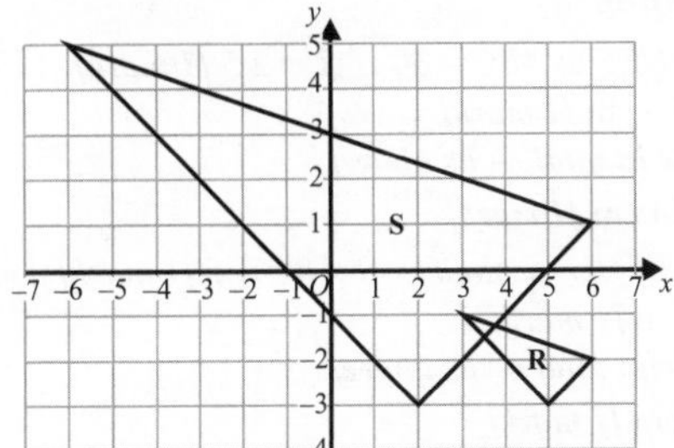

[3 marks available — 1 mark for any enlargement, 1 mark for enlarging by scale factor 4, 1 mark for correct position]

6 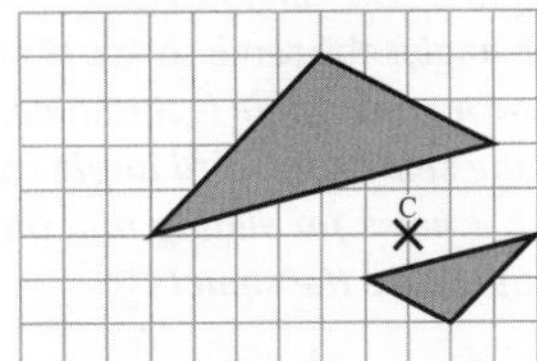

[3 marks available — 1 mark for any enlargement, 1 mark for enlarging by scale factor –2, 1 mark for correct position]

Page 65: More Transformation Stuff

1 Scale factor $= 16 \div 4 = 4$ *[1 mark]*

2 Area of enlarged shape $= 7 \times 3^2$ *[1 mark]*
$= 63$ cm^2 *[1 mark]*
[2 marks available in total — as above]

3 Scale factor $= 5 \div 2 = 2.5$ *[1 mark]*
Enlarged area $= 6 \times 2.5^2 = 37.5$ cm^2 *[1 mark]*
[2 marks available in total — as above]
Remember that you have to square the scale factor when you're scaling up areas.

4 $1^3 : 7^3 = 1 : 343$ *[1 mark]*

5 a) Scale factor from **A** to **C**:
$n^2 = 108\pi \div 12\pi = 9$ *[1 mark]*
$n = 3$ *[1 mark]*
Volume of **A** $= 135\pi$ cm$^3 \div 3^3$ *[1 mark]*
$= 5\pi$ cm^3 *[1 mark]*
[4 marks available in total — as above]

b) Scale factor from **A** to **B**:
$m^2 = 48\pi \div 12\pi = 4$ ***[1 mark]***
$m = 2$ ***[1 mark]***
Perpendicular height of B = 4 cm × 2 ***[1 mark]***
= 8 cm ***[1 mark]***
[4 marks available in total — as above]

Page 66: Congruent Shapes

1 F is the midpoint of AC so $AF = FC$ and opposite sides of a parallelogram are equal so $DE = FC$. Therefore $AF = DE$. ***[1 mark]***
E is the midpoint of CB so $CE = EB$, and opposite sides of a parallelogram are equal so $CE = FD$ Therefore $FD = EB$. ***[1 mark]***
D is the midpoint of AB, so $AD = DB$. ***[1 mark]***
Satisfies condition SSS so triangles are congruent. ***[1 mark]***
[4 marks available in total — as above]

2 $KP = OL$ (since they are diameters of identical circles)
[1 mark]
Angle KMP = angle ONL (since angles in a semicircle = 90°)
[1 mark]
Angle MKO = angle NLP (since alternate angles are equal) ***[1 mark]***
Satisfies condition AAS so triangles are congruent. ***[1 mark]***
[4 marks available in total — as above]

3 Angle CAE = angle EBD (angles in the same segment are equal)
[1 mark]
Angle ACE = angle EDB (angles in the same segment are equal)
[1 mark]
$AC = DB$ ***[1 mark]***
Satisfies condition AAS so triangles are congruent. ***[1 mark]***
[4 marks available in total — as above]

Page 67: Similar Shapes

1 a) Scale factor from DEF to $ABC = 30 \div 12 = 2.5$ ***[1 mark]***
$AB = 7 \times 2.5 = 17.5$ cm ***[1 mark]***
[2 marks available in total — as above]

b) $DF = 35 \div 2.5 = 14$ cm ***[1 mark]***

2 a) Scale factor from $EFGH$ to $ABCD = 9 \div 6 = 1.5$ ***[1 mark]***
$EF = 6 \div 1.5 = 4$ cm ***[1 mark]***
[2 marks available in total — as above]

b) $BC = 4 \times 1.5 = 6$ cm ***[1 mark]***

3 Angles in a rectangle are 90° so angle ABC = angle CEF
Corresponding angles are equal so angle BAC = angle ECF
Corresponding angles are equal so angle ACB = angle CFE
Triangles ABC and CEF have all three angles the same so are similar.
[3 marks available — 1 mark for showing one angle is the same, 1 mark for showing that the rest are the same (the third angle can be implied from two angles the same), 1 mark for stating that the triangles are similar because their angles are the same]

Page 68: Projections

1 a)

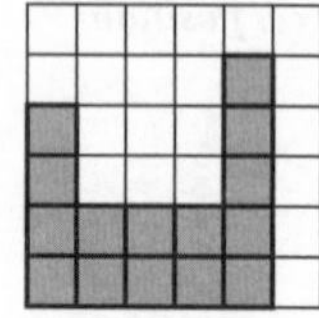

[1 mark]

b)

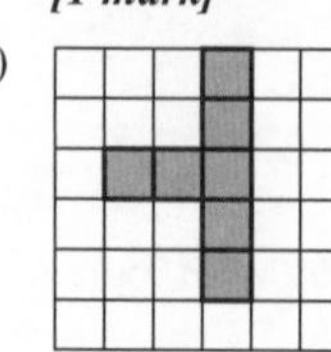

[1 mark]

It doesn't matter which way round you've drawn your plan view — just as long as it's the correct shape.

2

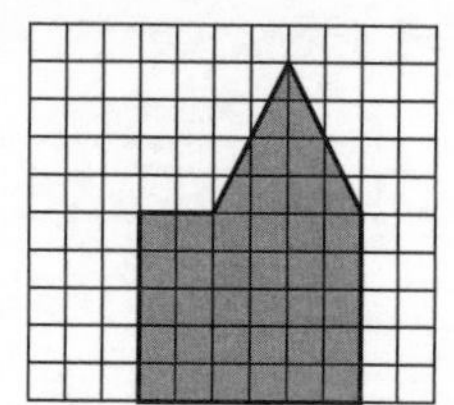

[2 marks available — 1 mark for rectangular part correct, 1 mark for triangular part correct]

Pages 69-70: Areas and Perimeters

1 Area of field = ½ × (105 + 80) × 60 = 5550 m² ***[1 mark]***
Price of weed killer per m² = 0.27 ÷ 10 = £0.027 ***[1 mark]***
Cost = area × price per square metre = 5550 × 0.027 ***[1 mark]***
= £149.85 ***[1 mark]***
[4 marks available in total — as above]

2 a) Lawn area = (30 m × 10 m) – (π × (5 m)²) = 221.460... m²
Boxes of seed needed = 221.460... m² ÷ 10 m² = 22.15
So Lynn must buy 23 boxes.
Total cost = 23 × £7 = £161
[6 marks available — 1 mark for a correct method for finding the lawn area, 1 mark for correctly calculating the lawn area, 1 mark for dividing the area by 10 m² to find the number of boxes, 1 mark for the correct number of boxes, 1 mark for a correct method for working out overall cost, and 1 mark for the correct answer]

b) Lawn perimeter = 30 m + 30 m + (π × 10 m) = 91.4 m (to 1 d.p.)
So Lynn should buy 92 m of edging.
[3 marks available — 1 mark for a correct method for finding the perimeter, 1 mark for correctly calculating the perimeter, 1 mark for correct final answer]

3 Area of a parallelogram = base × vertical height
So, vertical height = area ÷ base = 105 ÷ 15 = 7 cm
[2 marks available — 1 mark for dividing the area by the base, 1 mark for the correct answer]

4 Area of full circle = π × 12² = 144π cm²
Area of sector = (50 ÷ 360) × area of circle
= (50 ÷ 360) × 144π cm²
= 62.831... cm² = 62.8 cm² (3 s.f.)
[4 marks available — 1 mark for a correct method for finding the area of the full circle, 1 mark for correct area of the full circle, 1 mark for a correct method for calculating the area of the sector, and 1 mark for the correct answer]

5 Circumference of full circle = 2 × π × 6 = 12π cm
Length of arc = (30 ÷ 360) × circumference of circle
= (30 ÷ 360) × 12π = π cm
Perimeter of sector = π + 6 + 6 = 15.1 cm (3 s.f.)
[4 marks available — 1 mark for a correct method for finding the circumference of the full circle, 1 mark for a correct method for calculating the length of the arc, 1 mark for correct arc length, and 1 mark for the correct answer]

Pages 71-73: Surface Area and Volume

1 Area of triangle = ½ × 6.0 × 5.2 = 15.6 cm²
Area of whole octahedron = 8 × 15.6 = 124.8 cm²
[3 marks available — 1 mark for a correct method for finding the area of the triangle, 1 mark for the correct triangle area, 1 mark for the correct final answer]

2 Surface area = (2 × 2 m × 1 m) + (2 × 2 m × 0.03 m) + (2 × 1 m × 0.03 m) = 4.18 m²
Dan needs enough varnish to cover 4.18 m² × 2 = 8.36 m².
8.36 m² ÷ 2.45 m² = 3.412... tins. So Dan should buy 4 tins.
[4 marks available — 1 mark for a correct method for finding the surface area, 1 mark for the correct surface area, 1 mark for a correct method for calculating the number of tins, and 1 mark for the correct final answer]
Don't forget you need to round up here — not down. 3 tins wouldn't be enough, since you've worked out that Dan needs 3.412... tins.

3 Surface area of curved part of hemisphere =
½ × surface area of a sphere = ½ × 4 × π × 7² *[1 mark]*
= 307.876... cm² *[1 mark]*
Surface area of curved part of cone = π × 2 × 12 *[1 mark]*
= 75.398... cm² *[1 mark]*
Surface area of flat top of hemisphere = (π × 7²) – (π × 2²)
= 141.371... cm² *[1 mark]*
Total surface area = 307.876... + 75.398... + 141.371...
= 525 cm² (to 3 s.f.) *[1 mark]*
[6 marks available in total — as above]

4 Slanting length of cone = 16 cm *[1 mark]*
Length of arc = (90 ÷ 360) × (2 × π × 16) = 8π *[1 mark]*
The circumference of the base = 8π, so the diameter of the base is 8π ÷ π = 8. The radius is therefore 8 ÷ 2 = 4 cm *[1 mark]*
Curved surface area of cone = (π × 4 × 16) *[1 mark]*
Area of base of cone = (π × 4²) *[1 mark]*
Total surface area of cone = (π × 4 × 16) + (π × 4²)
= 251 cm² (to 3.s.f.) *[1 mark]*
[6 marks available in total — as above]

5 40 ÷ 8 = 5, so exactly 5 boxes fit into the width of each case.
16 ÷ 8 = 2, so exactly 2 boxes fit into the height of each case.
50 ÷ 8 = 6.25, so you can only fit 6 boxes along the length of the case, with a small gap at the end.
So each case can take a maximum of 5 × 2 × 6 = 60 boxes of fudge.
[3 marks available — 1 mark for a correct method, 1 mark for at least one division correct, and 1 mark for the correct final answer]
You need to think practically here — if you divided the volume of the case by the volume of one box, you'd get 62.5. But you can't put bits of boxes in to fill gaps. So you need to stop and think about what the best way of packing whole boxes into the case is.

6 A regular hexagon is made up of 6 identical triangles.
Area of triangle = 0.5 × 8 × 7 = 28 cm² *[1 mark]*
Area of whole hexagon cross-section = 28 × 6 = 168 cm² *[1 mark]*
Volume of prism = cross-sectional area × length =
168 × 6 = 1008 cm³ *[1 mark]*
[3 marks available in total — as above]

7 Area of pool base = π × (2 ÷ 2)² = π m² *[1 mark]*
Volume of pool = π × 0.4 = 0.4π m³ *[1 mark]*
Volume of water Amy should use = $0.4\pi \times \frac{3}{4}$ *[1 mark]*
= 0.94 m³ (to 2 d.p.) *[1 mark]*
[4 marks available in total — as above]

8 Volume = $\frac{1}{2} \times (\frac{4}{3} \times \pi \times 9^3) - \frac{1}{2} \times (\frac{4}{3} \times \pi \times 8^3)$ *[1 mark]*
= 1526.814... – 1072.330... *[1 mark]*
= 454 cm³ (3 s.f.) *[1 mark]*
[3 marks available in total — as above]
You still get full marks if you simplified the volume before multiplying everything through — e.g. you got $\frac{2}{3}\pi(729 - 512)$.

9 $113 = \frac{1}{3} \times \pi r^2 \times 12$ *[1 mark]*
$r^2 = 8.992...$
$r = 3.00$ (to 3 s.f.) *[1 mark]*
[2 marks available in total — as above]

Page 74: Density

1 a) Area of cross section = ½ × (3 + 4) × 4.5 = 15.75 *[1 mark]*
Volume = 15.75 × 6 = 94.5 cm³ *[1 mark]*
[2 marks available in total — as above]
b) Mass = 7.9 × 94.5 *[1 mark]* = 746.55 g *[1 mark]*
[2 marks available in total — as above]

2 a) Volume = 360 ÷ 1800 *[1 mark]*
= 0.2 m³ *[1 mark]*
[2 marks available in total — as above]
b) Mass = 2700 × 0.2 *[1 mark]*
= 540 kg *[1 mark]*
[2 marks available in total — as above]

3 a) Mass of syrup = 1.4 × 300 × π *[1 mark]*
= 1319.468... g
Mass of tin = 1500 – 1319.468... *[1 mark]*
= 180.531... = 181 g (3 s.f.) *[1 mark]*
[3 marks available in total — as above]
If you are using π in a calculation, make sure you don't round your answer until right at the very end.
b) Volume = 100 ÷ 1.4 *[1 mark]*
= 71.428... = 71.4 cm³ (to 3 s.f.) *[1 mark]*
[2 marks available in total — as above]

Page 75: Speed

1 a) Time = 22 miles ÷ 60 mph = 0.3666... hours *[1 mark]*
0.3666... hours × 60 = 22 minutes *[1 mark]*
It is 19:05, so he would arrive at the ground at
19:05 + 22 minutes = 19:27 *[1 mark]*
[3 marks available in total — as above]
b) Time he will take to cover the last 4 miles at 30 mph
= 4 miles ÷ 30 mph = 0.133... hours
0.133... hours × 60 = 8 minutes. *[1 mark]*
Time he must arrive at the ground = 19.45 – 15 minutes = 19:30
He has to drive the first (22 miles – 4 miles) = 18 miles, by 19:30 – 8 minutes = 19:22 *[1 mark]*
It is 19:05 now, so he must drive 18 miles in 17 minutes. *[1 mark]*
Speed = 18 miles ÷ (17 minutes ÷ 60) = 63.5294...
= 64 mph to nearest mph *[1 mark]*
[4 marks available in total — as above]

2 a) E.g. 2500 m = 2.5 km. 2.5 km = 2.5 ÷ 1.6 = 1.5625 miles.
102 s ÷ 60 = 1.7 minutes ÷ 60 = 0.02833... hours.
Speed = 1.5625 miles ÷ 0.02833... hours
= 55 mph (to nearest mph)
[3 marks available — 1 mark for converting 2500 metres to miles, 1 mark for converting 102 seconds into hours, 1 mark for the correct final answer]
It doesn't matter whether you do the conversion to miles per hour at the start or the end of the calculation — you could find the speed in m/s, km/s or kmh, and then change it to mph. Whichever way, you should get the same answer.
b) E.g. time = 1.5625 miles ÷ 50 mph = 0.03125 hours
0.03125 hours × 60 × 60 = 113 s (to nearest second)
[2 marks available — 1 mark for dividing the distance by the speed limit, 1 mark for the correct answer]

Page 76: Distance-Time Graphs

1 a) 15 ÷ 1 *[1 mark]*
= 15 *[1 mark]*
[2 marks available in total — as above]
b) The speed at which Selby is travelling. *[1 mark]*
c) 3 hours *[1 mark]*
As he was at point A at 0 hours, all you have to do is read off the x-value at point C to see how long Selby's journey was.
d) 2.5 hours *[1 mark]*
e)

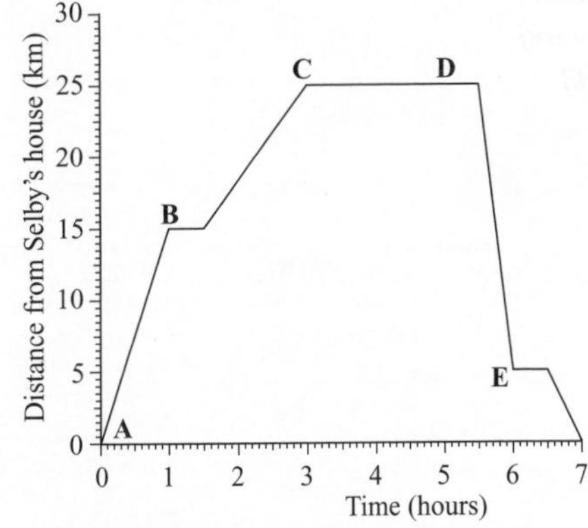

[2 marks available — 1 mark for a flat line from point E for 30 minutes, and 1 mark for a straight line from this point to (7,0)]

f) $7 - 0.5 - 2.5 - 0.5 = 3.5$ hours ***[1 mark]***
Selby isn't cycling whenever the graph shows a horizontal line. So, subtract these times from the total amount of time he is out.

Pages 77-78: Units

1 1 foot ≈ 30 cm
9.5×30 ***[1 mark]***
= 285 cm ***[1 mark]***
[2 marks available in total — as above]

2 E.g. 5 miles ≈ 8 km
Convert km into miles: $(5 \div 8) \times 5 = 3.125$ miles
Convert minutes into hours: $37.5 \div 60 = 0.625$ hours
$3.125 \div 0.625 = 5$ mph
[3 marks available — 1 mark for converting km to miles, 1 mark for converting minutes into hours, 1 mark for correct answer]

3 E.g. 1 kg ≈ 2.2 lb
$2500 \text{ g} \div 1000 = 2.5$ kg
Convert kg into lbs: $2.5 \times 2.2 = 5.5$ lbs
$5.5 \div 1.5 = 3.6666...$
Maximum number of books = 3
[4 marks available — 1 mark for converting g to kg, 1 mark for converting kg into lb, 1 mark for dividing 5.5 by 1.5, 1 mark for correct answer]

4 $39\,200 \div 10\,000$ ***[1 mark]***
$= 3.92 \text{ m}^2$ ***[1 mark]***
[2 marks available in total — as above]

5 150 litres × 1000 ***[1 mark]*** = 150 000 cm^3
= 150 000 $\text{cm}^3 \div 1\,000\,000$ ***[1 mark]***
= 0.15 m^3 ***[1 mark]***
[3 marks available in total — as above]

6 a) 10 °C ***[1 mark]***
b) Temperature at noon = 10 °C + 15 °C = 25 °C
From graph, 25 °C = 77 °F
Increase in temperature = 77 °F – 50 °F = 27 °F
5 hours between 7 o'clock and 12 o'clock,
so average hourly increase = $27 \div 5 = 5.4$ °F
[3 marks available — 1 mark for finding 25 °C in °F from graph, 1 mark for dividing change in temperature by change in time, 1 mark for correct answer]

7 4.5 litres ≈ 1 gallon
6.2 litres = $6.2 \div 4.5 = 1.377...$ gallons
8 km ≈ 5 miles
100 km = $(100 \div 8) \times 5 = 62.5$ miles
Miles per gallon for car B: $62.5 \div 1.377... = 45.362...$ mpg
Therefore car A is more efficient to hire.
[3 marks available — 1 mark for converting volumes and distances to the same units, 1 mark for finding the fuel efficiency in changed units, 1 mark for the correct answer]
You could also convert car A's miles per gallon into kilometres per litre to compare to car B. As long as you show all of your steps, you'll get the marks if your answer is correct.

8 a) $3(r + t)$ ***[1 mark]***
b) $s^2 + 4t^2$ ***[1 mark]***
c) $2rt^2$ ***[1 mark]***

Pages 79-80: Loci and Constructions

1 a)
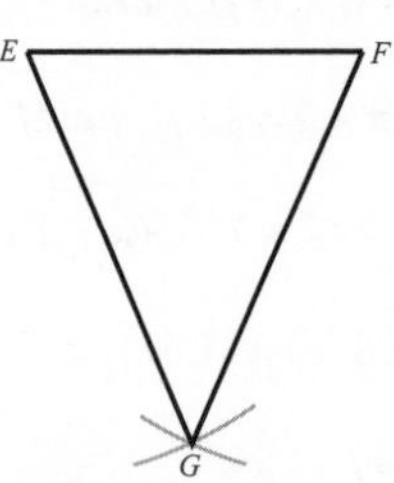

[2 marks available — 1 mark for arcs drawn with a radius of 4.5 cm, 1 mark for completed triangle]

b)
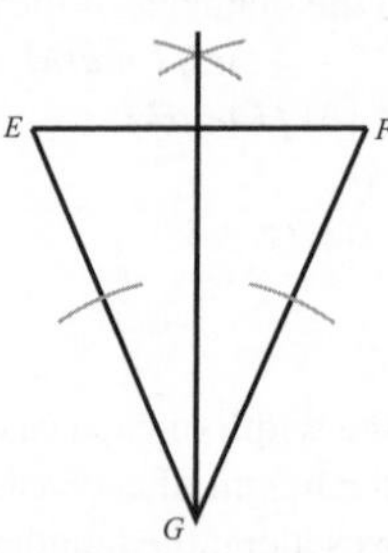

[2 marks available — 1 mark for correct construction arcs, 1 mark for correct bisector]

2
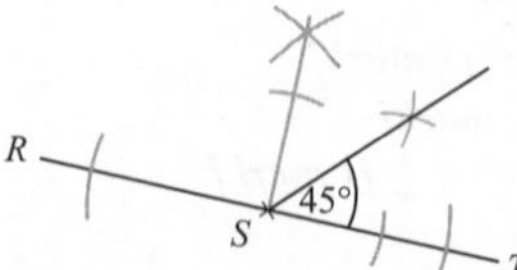

[2 marks available — 1 mark for intersecting arcs, 1 mark for perpendicular line]

3
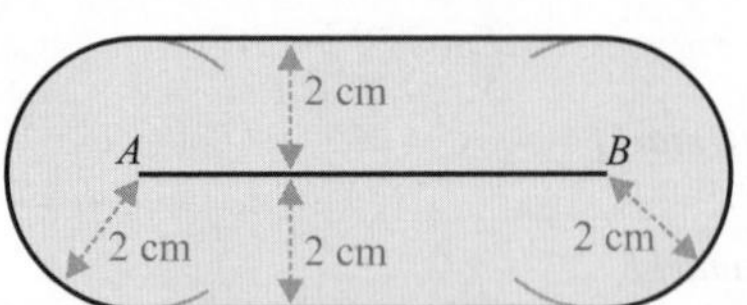

[4 marks available — 1 mark for correct construction arcs for right angle, 1 mark for correct right angle, 1 mark for correct construction lines for angle bisector, 1 mark for correct 45° angle]
Here you have to first construct a 90° angle to the line RST at S, then bisect this 90° angle to give the 45° angle. Your 45° angle could be the other side of the perpendicular line though.

4
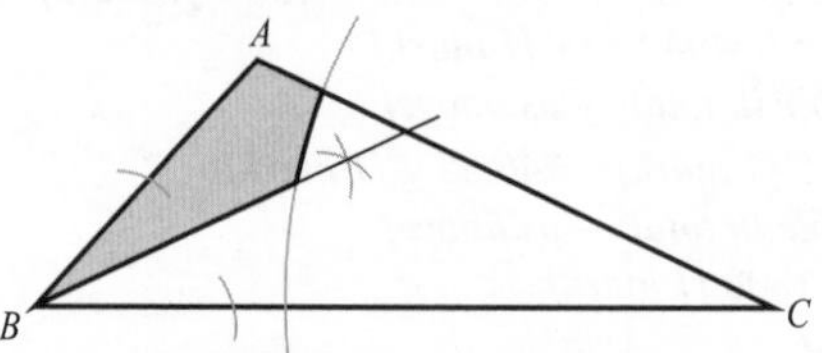

Scale: 1 cm represents 1 m

[2 marks available — 1 mark for correct semicircles, 1 mark for correct shaded area]

5

[4 marks available — 1 mark for radius of 6.5 cm with centre at C, 1 mark for construction arcs on AB and BC for angle bisector at ABC, 1 mark for correct angle bisector at ABC, and 1 mark for the correct shading]
You'll only get all four marks if you show the examiner you've constructed both the bisector of the angle and the arc from point C. So make sure you remember to leave in your construction lines.

6

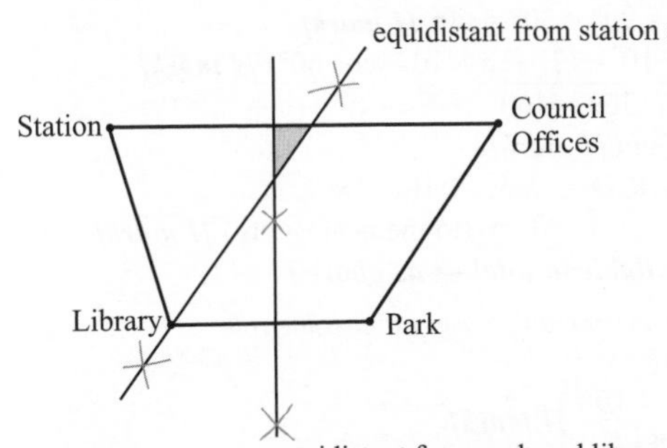

[3 marks available — 1 mark for perpendicular bisector between Library and Park, 1 mark for perpendicular bisector between Station and Park, 1 mark for the correct shaded area]

7 a)

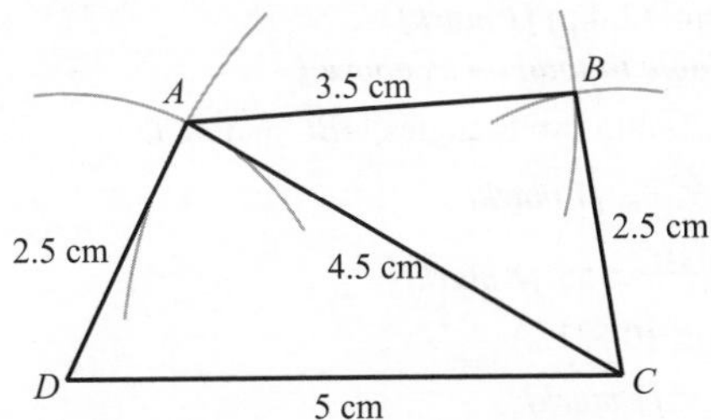

[3 marks available — 3 marks for all correct lengths, otherwise 2 marks for 2 correct lengths, or 1 mark for 1 correct length]

b) On the diagram, $BD = 5.2$ cm, ***[1 mark]***
so in the real field $BD = 5.2 \times 10 = 52$ m ***[1 mark]***
[2 marks available in total — as above]

Page 81: Bearings

1 a)

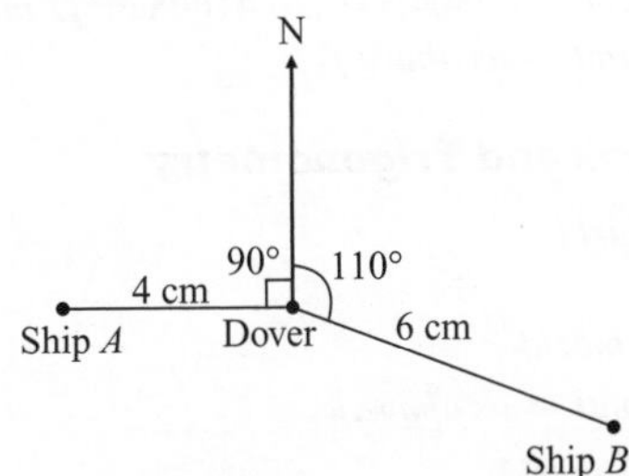

[4 marks available — 1 mark for Ship A 4 cm from Dover, 1 mark for correct bearing for ship A, 1 mark for ship B 6 cm from Dover, and 1 mark for correct bearing for Ship B]
This diagram has been drawn a bit smaller to make it fit — your measurements should match the labels given on the diagram here.

b) 102° (accept answers between 100° and 104°) ***[1 mark]***

c) 180° – 102° = 78°
360 – 78 = 282° (accept answers between 280° and 284°)
[2 marks available — 1 mark for correctly using 102°, 1 mark for correct answer]
You could also do this by adding 180° to 102°.

2 a)

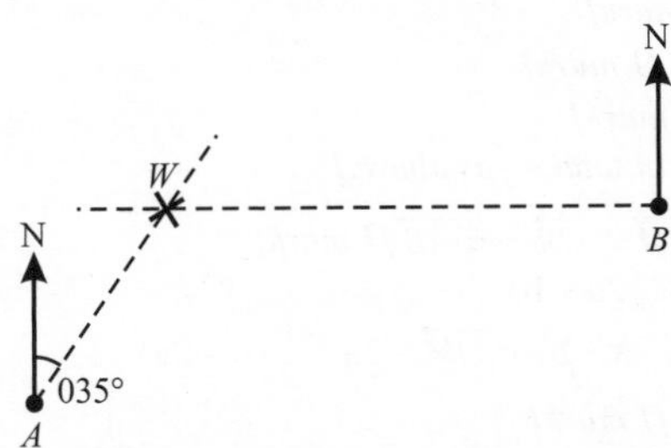

[2 marks available — 1 mark for correct bearing of 035° and 1 mark for marking W directly west of B]

b)

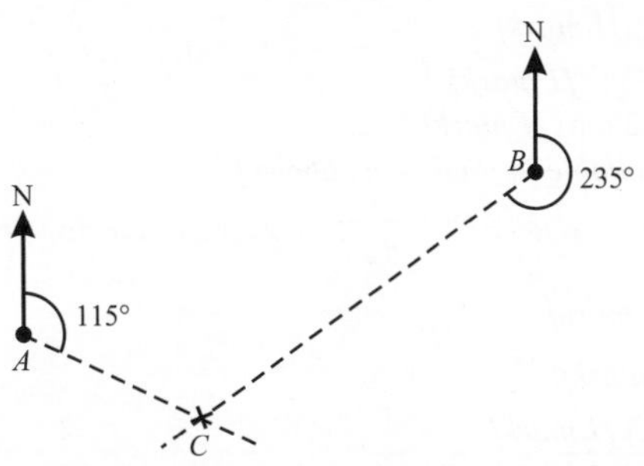

[3 marks available — 1 mark for correct bearing from A, 1 mark for correct bearing from B and 1 mark for correctly identifying intersection at point C]

c) 164° (accept answers between 162° and 166°) ***[1 mark]***

Section Five — Pythagoras and Trigonometry

Page 82: Pythagoras' Theorem

1 $AB^2 = 4^2 + 8^2$ ***[1 mark]***
$AB = \sqrt{16+64} = \sqrt{80}$ ***[1 mark]***
$AB = 8.94$ cm (2 d.p) ***[1 mark]***
[3 marks available in total — as above.]

2 $3.5^2 = x^2 + 2.1^2$ ***[1 mark]***
$x = \sqrt{12.25 - 4.41} = \sqrt{7.84}$ ***[1 mark]***
$x = 2.8$ m ***[1 mark]***
[3 marks available in total — as above.]

3 Let h be the height of the triangle:
$13^2 = 5^2 + h^2$ ***[1 mark]***
$h = \sqrt{169 - 25} = \sqrt{144}$ ***[1 mark]***
$h = 12$ cm ***[1 mark]***
Area, $A = \frac{1}{2} \times 10 \times 12$
$A = 60$ cm^2 ***[1 mark]***
[4 marks available in total — as above.]

4 Length of EA:
$28.3^2 = 20^2 + EA^2$ ***[1 mark]***
$EA = \sqrt{800.89 - 400}$
$EA = 20.02...$ ***[1 mark]***
Length of CE:
$54.3^2 = 20^2 + CE^2$ ***[1 mark]***
$CE = \sqrt{2948.49 - 400}$
$CE = 50.48...$ ***[1 mark]***
Perimeter $= 28.3 + 54.3 + EA + CE = 153.1$ cm (1 d.p) ***[1 mark]***
[5 marks available in total — as above.]

Pages 83-84: Trigonometry — Sin, Cos, Tan

1 $\sin x = \frac{14}{18}$ ***[1 mark]***
$x = \sin^{-1}\left(\frac{14}{18}\right)$ ***[1 mark]***
$x = 51.1°$ (1 d.p) ***[1 mark]***
[3 marks available in total — as above.]

2 $\tan 52° = \frac{4}{y}$ ***[1 mark]***
$y = \frac{4}{\tan 52°}$ ***[1 mark]***
$y = 3.13$ m (3 s.f) ***[1 mark]***
[3 marks available in total — as above.]

3 a) *Split ABC into two right-angled triangles, and find half of AC (call it x).*
$\cos 34° = \frac{x}{10}$ ***[1 mark]***
$x = 10 \times \cos 34°$ ***[1 mark]***
$x = 8.29...$
$AC = 8.29... \times 2 = 16.58$ m (2 d.p) ***[1 mark]***
[3 marks available in total — as above.]

b) $\sin 34° = \frac{h}{10}$ ***[1 mark]***
$h = 10 \times \sin 34°$ ***[1 mark]***
$h = 5.59$ m (2 d.p) ***[1 mark]***
[3 marks available in total — as above.]
You could also use $\tan 34° = \frac{h}{8.29}$ to work out the answer.

4 $\tan 3.6° = \frac{12}{x}$ ***[1 mark]***
$x = \frac{12}{\tan 3.6°}$ ***[1 mark]***
$x = 191$ cm (3 s.f) ***[1 mark]***
[3 marks available in total — as above.]

5 a) $\tan x = \frac{6}{9}$ ***[1 mark]***
$x = \tan^{-1}\left(\frac{6}{9}\right)$ ***[1 mark]***
$x = 33.7°$ (1.d.p) ***[1 mark]***
[3 marks available in total — as above.]

b) *EG bisects the angle FEH, so find angle FEM:*
$\tan x = \frac{6}{5}$ ***[1 mark]***
$x = \tan^{-1}\left(\frac{6}{5}\right)$ ***[1 mark]***
$x = 50.19...°$
$FEH = 50.19... \times 2 = 100.4°$ (1 d.p) ***[1 mark]***
[3 marks available in total — as above.]

6 *Call the distance from the centre of the circle to the centre of an edge, x. The radius bisects the internal angle forming angle a.*

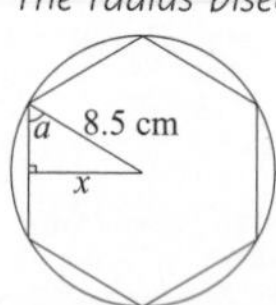

Sum of the internal angles of a hexagon = 4 × 180° = 720°
Each internal angle of a hexagon = 720° ÷ 6 = 120° ***[1 mark]***
$a = 120 \div 2 = 60°$ ***[1 mark]***
$\sin 60° = \frac{x}{8.5}$ ***[1 mark]***
$x = 8.5 \times \sin 60°$ ***[1 mark]***
$x = 7.36$ cm (2 d.p) ***[1 mark]***
[5 marks available in total — as above.]
You could also use the calculation cos 30° × 8.5 to find the value of x. As long as you make sure you show your working, you'll get full marks if your answer is correct.

Pages 85-86: The Sine and Cosine Rules

1 a) $AC^2 = 10^2 + 7^2 - (2 \times 10 \times 7 \times \cos 85°)$ ***[1 mark]***
$AC = \sqrt{149 - 140 \times \cos 85°}$ ***[1 mark]***
$AC = 11.7$ cm (3 s.f) ***[1 mark]***
[3 marks available in total — as above.]

b) Area = $\frac{1}{2} \times 10 \times 7 \times \sin 85°$ ***[1 mark]***
Area = 34.9 cm^2 (3 s.f) ***[1 mark]***
[2 marks available in total — as above.]

2 a) $\frac{BD}{\sin 30°} = \frac{8}{\sin 70°}$ ***[1 mark]***
$BD = \frac{8}{\sin 70°} \times \sin 30°$ ***[1 mark]***
$BD = 4.26$ m (3 s.f) ***[1 mark]***
[3 marks available in total — as above.]

b) $\frac{4}{\sin BDC} = \frac{4.26}{\sin 60°}$ ***[1 mark]***
$\sin BDC = \frac{\sin 60°}{4.26} \times 4$
Angle $BDC = \sin^{-1}(0.813...)$ ***[1 mark]***
Angle $BDC = 54.4°$ (3 s.f) ***[1 mark]***
[3 marks available in total — as above.]

3 a) $\sin 30° = \frac{5}{AC}$ ***[1 mark]***
$AC = \frac{5}{\sin 30°}$ ***[1 mark]***
$AC = 10$ cm ***[1 mark]***
[3 marks available in total — as above]

b) Angle $CAD = 90° - 30° = 60°$ ***[1 mark]***
$CD^2 = 18^2 + 10^2 - (2 \times 18 \times 10 \times \cos 60°)$ ***[1 mark]***
$CD = \sqrt{424 - 360 \cos 60°}$
$CD = 15.6...$ cm ***[1 mark]***
Perimeter of $ACD = 15.6... + 10 + 18$
= 44 cm (to the nearest cm) ***[1 mark]***
[4 marks available in total — as above.]

4 *First you need to find one angle using the cosine rule. E.g. use angle CAB.*
$\cos A = \frac{14^2 + 12^2 - 19^2}{2 \times 14 \times 12}$ ***[1 mark]***
$A = \cos^{-1}\left(\frac{-21}{336}\right)$ ***[1 mark]***
$A = 93.58...°$ ***[1 mark]***
Area = $\frac{1}{2} \times 14 \times 12 \times \sin 93.58...°$ ***[1 mark]***
Area = 83.84 cm^2 (2.d.p) ***[1 mark]***
[5 marks available in total — as above.]

5 First, split $ABCD$ into two triangles, ABC and ACD.
$\frac{55}{\sin ACB} = \frac{93}{\sin 116°}$ ***[1 mark]***
$\sin ACB = \frac{\sin 116°}{93} \times 55$ ***[1 mark]***
Angle $ACB = \sin^{-1}(0.531...)$
$ACB = 32.109...°$ ***[1 mark]***
Angle $BAC = 180° - 116° - 32.109...°$ so,
Area of $ABC = \frac{1}{2} \times 93 \times 55 \times \sin(180 - 116 - 32.10...)°$ ***[1 mark]***
Area of $ABC = 1351.106...$cm^2 ***[1 mark]***
Angle $ACD = 78° - 32.109...°$ so
Area of $ACD = \frac{1}{2} \times 93 \times 84 \times \sin(78 - 32.10...)°$ ***[1 mark]***
Area of $ACD = 2804.531...$cm^2 ***[1 mark]***
Area of $ABCD = 1351.106... + 2804.531... = 4160$ cm^2 ***[1 mark]***
[8 marks available in total — as above.]

Page 87: 3D Pythagoras and Trigonometry

1 $BH^2 = 6^2 + 3^2 + 4^2$ ***[1 mark]***
$BH = \sqrt{61}$ ***[1 mark]***
$BH = 7.81$ cm (3 *s.f*) ***[1 mark]***
[3 marks available in total — as above.]

2 a) $FD^2 = 8^2 + 2^2 + 5^2$ ***[1 mark]***
$FD = \sqrt{93}$ ***[1 mark]***
So maximum length of stick = 9.6 cm (2 s.f) ***[1 mark]***
[3 marks available in total — as above.]

b) $\sin FDG = \frac{5}{\sqrt{93}}$ ***[1 mark]***
$FDG = \sin^{-1}\left(\frac{5}{\sqrt{93}}\right)$ ***[1 mark]***
$FDG = 31°$ (2 s.f.) ***[1 mark]***
[3 marks available in total — as above.]

Page 88: Vectors

1 a) $\overrightarrow{CD} = -2\mathbf{a}$ ***[1 mark]***
b) $\overrightarrow{AC} = 2\mathbf{d} + 2\mathbf{a}$ ***[1 mark]***
c) $\overrightarrow{BL} = \mathbf{d} - \mathbf{a}$ ***[1 mark]***
[3 marks available in total — as above.]

2 a) $\overrightarrow{OM} = \overrightarrow{OA} + \overrightarrow{AM} = \overrightarrow{OA} + \frac{1}{2}\overrightarrow{AB}$ ***[1 mark]***
$\overrightarrow{AB} = \mathbf{b} - 2\mathbf{a}$ or $-2\mathbf{a} + \mathbf{b}$
$\overrightarrow{OM} = 2\mathbf{a} + \frac{1}{2}(-2\mathbf{a} + \mathbf{b})$ or $\overrightarrow{OM} = 2\mathbf{a} + \frac{1}{2}(\mathbf{b} - 2\mathbf{a})$
$= \mathbf{a} + \frac{1}{2}\mathbf{b}$ ***[1 mark]***
[2 marks available in total — as above.]

b) $\overrightarrow{OX} = \overrightarrow{OA} + \overrightarrow{AX}$ ***[1 mark]***
As AX:XB = 1:3, AX must be one-quarter of AB, so:
$\overrightarrow{OX} = \overrightarrow{OA} + \frac{1}{4}\overrightarrow{AB}$
$\overrightarrow{OX} = 2\mathbf{a} + \frac{1}{4}(\mathbf{b} - 2\mathbf{a})$ ***[1 mark]***
$\overrightarrow{OX} = \frac{3}{2}\mathbf{a} + \frac{1}{4}\mathbf{b}$ ***[1 mark]***
[3 marks available in total — as above.]

3 a) $\overrightarrow{BX} = \overrightarrow{BC} + \overrightarrow{CX} = \overrightarrow{BC} - \overrightarrow{XC}$
$\overrightarrow{BC} = 6\overrightarrow{BW} = 6\mathbf{b}$ ***[1 mark]***
As AX = 2XC, CX must be one third of AC, so:
$\overrightarrow{CX} = -\overrightarrow{XC} = -\frac{1}{3}\overrightarrow{AC}$ (or $\overrightarrow{CX} = \frac{1}{3}\overrightarrow{CA}$) ***[1 mark]***
$\overrightarrow{AC} = \overrightarrow{AB} + \overrightarrow{BC} = 3\mathbf{a} + 6\mathbf{b}$ (or $\overrightarrow{CA} = -3\mathbf{a} - 6\mathbf{b}$) ***[1 mark]***
$\overrightarrow{CX} = -\frac{1}{3}(3\mathbf{a} + 6\mathbf{b}) = -\mathbf{a} - 2\mathbf{b}$
$\overrightarrow{BX} = 6\mathbf{b} - \mathbf{a} - 2\mathbf{b} = 4\mathbf{b} - \mathbf{a}$ ***[1 mark]***
[4 marks available in total — as above.]
You could have solved this a little differently, for instance starting by writing $\overrightarrow{BX} = \overrightarrow{BA} + \overrightarrow{AX}$...

b) *From part a)* $\overrightarrow{BX} = 4\mathbf{b} - \mathbf{a}$:
ABCD is a parallelogram, so:
$\overrightarrow{CD} = \overrightarrow{BA} = -\overrightarrow{AB} = -3\mathbf{a}$ ***[1 mark]***
$\overrightarrow{CM} = \frac{1}{2}\overrightarrow{CD} = -\frac{3}{2}\mathbf{a}$ ***[1 mark]***
$\overrightarrow{BM} = \overrightarrow{BC} + \overrightarrow{CM}$
$= 6\mathbf{b} - \frac{3}{2}\mathbf{a} = \frac{3}{2}(4\mathbf{b} - \mathbf{a})$ ***[1 mark]***
B, X and M must be three points on a straight line because the lines BM and BX are both scalar multiples of the vector $4\mathbf{b} - \mathbf{a}$. ***[1 mark]***
[4 marks available in total — as above.]

Section Six — Statistics and Probability

Pages 89-90: Sampling and Data Collection

1 a) E.g. How many different after-school activities do you attend each week?

0	1 – 2	3 – 4	5 or more
☐	☐	☐	☐

[2 marks available — 1 mark for an appropriate question, 1 mark for at least 3 boxes which don't overlap and which cover all possible answers]

b) E.g. the results of her survey are likely to be biased as she is only asking people who attend an after school activity. ***[1 mark]***
The key idea here is "bias" — the results of her survey are likely to be an unfair representation of what all pupils at the school think.

2 a) E.g. no time frame is specified, so the response boxes are vague and could be interpreted differently by different people. ***[1 mark]***

b) E.g. Mike could assign a number to each person in his year group, generate a list of random numbers using a calculator/computer/random number table. ***[1 mark]***
He should then match these two sets of numbers up to create the sample. ***[1 mark]***
[2 marks available in total — as above]

3 No time frame is given. / The response boxes do not cover all possible outcomes. / The response boxes overlap.
[2 marks available — 1 mark for each of the above, up to a maximum of 2]

4 a) E.g. she needs to find the fraction of the total number of teenagers in each age group, then multiply each of these by the sample size (100) to get the number of teenagers from each group to be included in the sample. She should then choose these teenagers at random.
[2 marks available — 1 mark for a description of the calculation, 1 mark for saying to select the sample at random]

b) Teenagers aged 14
= (total aged 14 ÷ total teenagers) × size of sample
= (192 ÷ 800) × 100 ***[1 mark]***
= 24 ***[1 mark]***
[2 marks available in total — as above]

5 (116 ÷ 720) × 75 ***[1 mark]***
= 12.083... = 12 ***[1 mark]***
[2 marks available in total — as above]

6 (487 ÷ 2033) × 150 ***[1 mark]***
= 35.932... = 36 ***[1 mark]***
[2 marks available in total — as above]

Page 91: Mean, Median, Mode and Range

1 Total mark for boys = $15b$
Total mark for girls = $13g$
so, mean mark for all pupils = $\frac{15b + 13g}{28}$
[2 marks available — 1 mark for correct total marks for boys and girls, 1 mark for correct answer]

2 Total running time for first 20 days = 20 × 56.2 = 1124
Total running time for all 30 days = 30 × 54.4 = 1632
Total running time for last 10 days = 1632 – 1124 = 508
Mean running time for last 10 days = 508 ÷ 10 = 50.8 minutes
[3 marks available — 1 mark for calculating the total running time for the first 20 days OR for all 30 days, 1 mark for calculating the total running time for the last 10 days, 1 mark for the correct answer]

3 a) 23, 26, 36 (in any order)
range = 13, median = 26
[3 marks available — 3 marks for all correct answers, otherwise 2 marks for correct median AND correct range, otherwise 1 mark for correct median OR correct range]

b) 32 + 23 + 31 + 28 + 36 + 26 = 176 ***[1 mark]***
4 × 27.25 = 109 ***[1 mark]***
176 – 109 = 67 ***[1 mark]***
so, goats weighing 31 kg and 36 kg ***[1 mark]***
[4 marks available in total — as above]

Page 92: Averages and Spread

1 a)

0	3 4 4 5 5 7 8 8 9
1	0 1 2

Key: 0 | 3 = 3

[3 marks available — 1 mark for correct entries, 1 mark for correct order, 1 mark for key]

b) E.g. the interquartile range will remain the same, as all the values have decreased by 50p. This 50p will cancel out when you subtract the lower quartile from the upper quartile. ***[1 mark]***

2 Median (June) = 29
Median (Nov) = 15
Interquartile range (June) = 37 – 15 = 22
Interquartile range (Nov) = 22 – 7 = 15
E.g. the median rainfall was higher in June than in November, but the interquartile range was greater in November than in June.
[6 marks available — 1 mark for the June median, 1 mark for the November median, 1 mark for the June interquartile range, 1 mark for the November interquartile range, 1 mark for a suitable comment on the median, 1 mark for a suitable comment on the interquartile range]

3 E.g. the median time taken by the boys is the same as the median time taken by the girls. The interquartile range for the boys is smaller than the interquartile range for the girls.
[2 marks available — 1 mark for correct comparison of median OR longest time OR shortest time OR lower quartile OR upper quartile, 1 mark for correct comparison of interquartile range OR range]

Page 93: Frequency Tables — Finding Averages

1 a) 8 + 3 + 5 + 8 + 4 + 1 = 29
[2 marks available — 1 mark for the correct calculation, 1 mark for the correct answer]

b) (0 × 8) + (1 × 3) + (2 × 5) + (3 × 8) + (4 × 4) + (5 × 1) = 58
[2 marks available — 1 mark for the correct calculation, 1 mark for the correct answer]

c) 58 ÷ 29 = 2
[2 marks available — 1 mark for the correct calculation, 1 mark for the correct answer]

2 a) $(0 \times 2) + (2 \times 4) + (3 \times 7) + (5 \times 11) + (7 \times 6) + (8 \times 3) + (10 \times 3)$
[1 mark]
$= 180$ ***[1 mark]***
[2 marks available in total — as above]

b) i) $180 \div (2 + 4 + 7 + 11 + 6 + 3 + 3) = 5$
[2 marks available — 1 mark for the correct calculation, 1 mark for the correct answer]
ii) 5 ***[1 mark]***
iii) Value in position $(36 + 1) \div 2 = 18.5$
18th value = 5 and 19th value = 5, so median = 5
[2 marks available — 1 mark for the correct position, 1 mark for correct value]

Page 94: Grouped Frequency Tables

1 a) $40 < x \leq 50$ ***[1 mark]***

b) $(32 + 1) \div 2 = 16.5$, so the median is halfway between the 16th and 17th values, so it lies in the group containing the 16th and 17th values, which is $40 < x \leq 50$ ***[1 mark]***

c)

Exam mark	Frequency	Mid-interval value	Frequency × mid-interval value
$10 < x \leq 20$	2	$(10 + 20) \div 2 = 15$	$2 \times 15 = 30$
$20 < x \leq 30$	5	$(20 + 30) \div 2 = 25$	$5 \times 25 = 125$
$30 < x \leq 40$	7	$(30 + 40) \div 2 = 35$	$7 \times 35 = 245$
$40 < x \leq 50$	8	$(40 + 50) \div 2 = 45$	$8 \times 45 = 360$
$50 < x \leq 60$	4	$(50 + 60) \div 2 = 55$	$4 \times 55 = 220$
$60 < x \leq 70$	6	$(60 + 70) \div 2 = 65$	$6 \times 65 = 390$

$(30 + 125 + 245 + 360 + 220 + 390) \div 32$
$= 1370 \div 32 = 42.8125 = 42.8$ (to 3 s.f.)
[4 marks available — 1 mark for all mid-interval values, 1 mark for calculation of frequency × mid-interval value, 1 mark for dividing 1370 by 32, 1 mark for the correct answer]

2 a) i) $(10 + 1) \div 2 = 5.5$, so the median is halfway between the 5th and 6th values, so it lies in the group containing the 5th and 6th values, which is $3 \leq x \leq 5$ ***[1 mark]***
ii) $(1 \times 2) + (4 \times 4) + (7 \times 3) + (10 \times 1) \div 10$
$= 49 \div 10 = 4.9$ cm
[4 marks available — 1 mark for all mid-interval values, 1 mark for calculation of frequency × mid-interval value, 1 mark for dividing 49 by 10, 1 mark for the correct answer]

b) E.g. as we do not have original data we do not know the exact data values and have to approximate using the mid-interval values. ***[1 mark]***

Pages 95-96: Cumulative Frequency

1 a)

Exam mark (%)	≤ 20	≤ 30	≤ 40	≤ 50	≤ 60	≤ 70	≤ 80	≤ 100
Cumulative Frequency	3	13	25	49	91	107	116	120

[1 mark]

b)

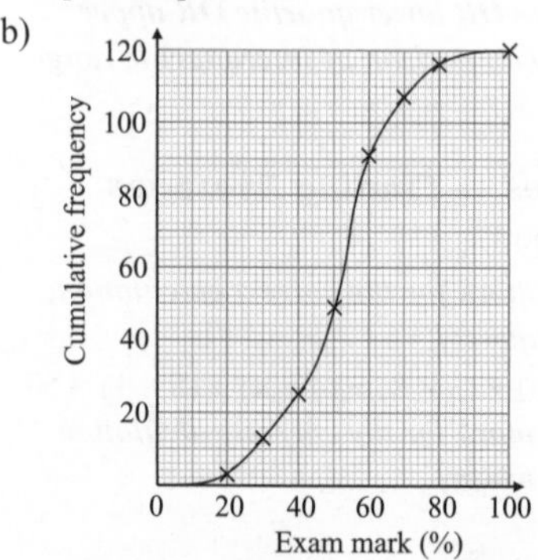

[2 marks available — 1 mark for plotting points correctly, 1 mark for joining them with a smooth curve or straight lines]

A common mistake in exams is not plotting the points at the top end of the interval. But you wouldn't make that mistake, would you?

c) Median plotted at 60 gives a value of 53%
[1 mark, accept answers ± 2%]

d) Lower quartile at 30 gives a value of 43%
Upper quartile at 90 gives a value of 60%
Inter-quartile range = 60 – 43 = 17%
[2 marks available — 1 mark for correct method, 1 mark for correct answer, accept answers ± 4%]

2 a)

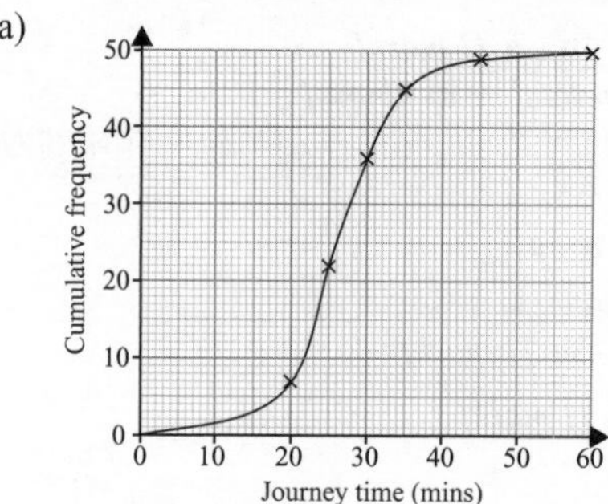

[2 marks available — 1 mark for plotting points correctly, 1 mark for joining them with a smooth curve or straight lines]

b) Number of journeys between 27 and 47 minutes = 49 – 28 = 21
[2 marks available — 1 mark for reading the cumulative frequencies off at 27 and 47 minutes, 1 mark for correct answer, accept answers ± 3]

c) 48 journeys took less than 40 mins so 2 journeys took longer.
Percentage of total number = $(2 \div 50) \times 100 = 4\%$
[2 marks available — 1 mark for correct method, 1 mark for correct answer, accept answers ± 2%]

d)

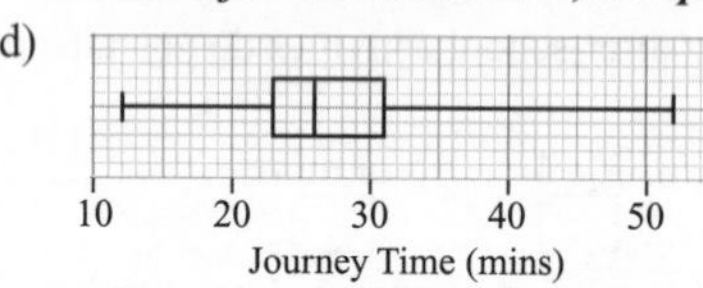

[3 marks available — 1 mark for plotting end points correctly, 1 mark for plotting median correctly (± 1) and 1 mark for plotting lower and upper quartiles correctly (± 1)]

Page 97: Histograms and Frequency Density

1

Number of minutes of TV watched (m)	Frequency
$40 \leq m < 60$	20
$60 \leq m < 70$	70
$70 \leq m < 80$	40
$80 \leq m < 120$	80
$120 \leq m < 140$	60

[2 marks available — 1 mark for using frequency = frequency density × class width, 1 mark for correct answers]

2

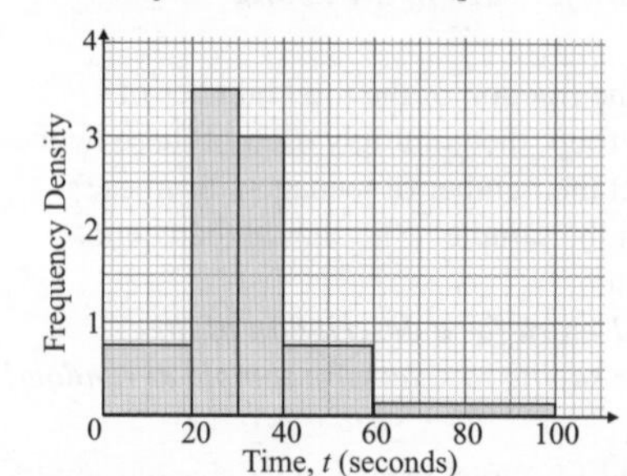

[3 marks available — 1 mark for finding frequency densities, 2 marks for all bars drawn correctly, otherwise 1 mark for one bar drawn correctly]

Page 98: Other Graphs and Charts

1 14 girls took part in swimming.

	Girls	Boys	Total
Swimming	14	10	24
Athletics	32	18	50
Football	6	35	41
Total	52	63	115

[4 marks available — 1 mark for a two-way table (or for a list of at least 2 combinations), 1 mark for attempting to find an unknown value, 1 mark for all correct values, 1 mark for correct final answer]

2 a)

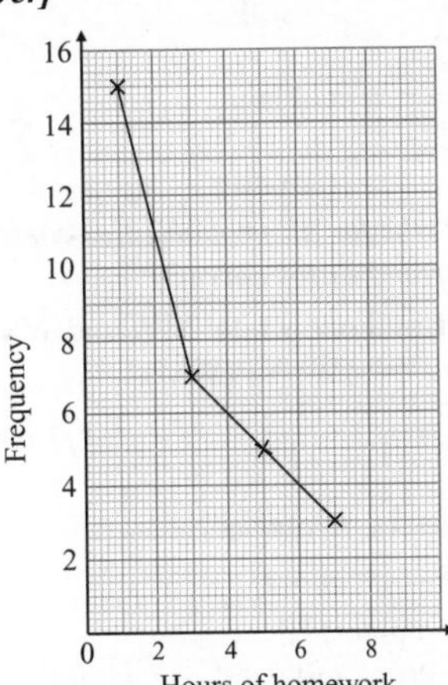

[2 marks available — 1 mark for plotting points correctly, 1 mark for joining them with straight lines]

b) $0 \le x < 2$ ***[1 mark]***

Page 99: Scatter Graphs

1 a) Strong positive correlation
[2 marks available — 1 mark for strong correlation, 1 mark for positive correlation]

b)

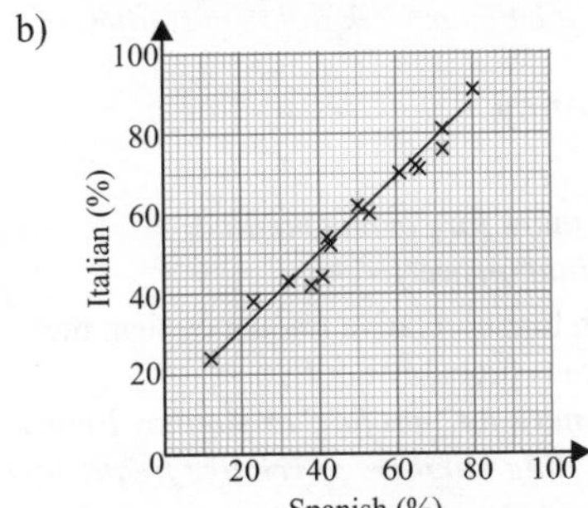

[1 mark for line of best fit starting between (10, 16) and (10, 28) and ending between (80, 82) and (80, 96)]

c) 56%
[2 marks available — 1 mark for indicating 66 on the y-axis, 1 mark for an answer between 48% and 62%]

2 a)

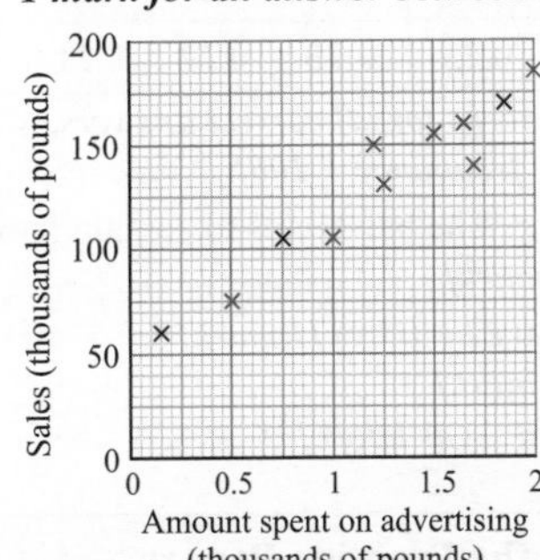

[1 mark if all three points are plotted correctly]

b) Positive correlation ***[1 mark]***

c) £1150
[3 marks available — 1 mark for a line of best fit, 1 mark for indicating 125 on the y-axis, 1 mark for correctly reading off from your line of best fit, allow answers ± £100]

Page 100: Probability Basics

1 Probability of not blinking $= 1 - \frac{2}{5}$ ***[1 mark]***
$= \frac{3}{5}$ ***[1 mark]***
[2 marks available in total — as above]

2 a) Number of red counters = 10 – 4 = 6 ***[1 mark]***
Probability of getting a red counter $= \frac{6}{10} = \frac{3}{5}$ ***[1 mark]***
[2 marks available in total — as above]

b) No green counters so probability of getting a green = 0 ***[1 mark]***

3 Let P(spotty sock) = y
Then P(stripy sock) = $2y$ ***[1 mark]***
$0.4 + y + 2y = 1$ ***[1 mark]***
$3y = 0.6$ ***[1 mark]***
$y = 0.2$
The probability he gets a spotty sock is 0.2 ***[1 mark]***
[4 marks available in total — as above]

Page 101: Listing Outcomes and Expected Frequency

1 a)

Cards (columns) / Dice (rows)

	2	4	6	8	10
1	3	5	7	9	11
2	4	6	8	10	12
3	5	7	9	11	13
4	6	8	10	12	14
5	7	9	11	13	15
6	8	10	12	14	16

[2 marks available — 2 marks for all numbers correct, otherwise 1 mark for at least 5 numbers correct]

b) 3 ways of scoring exactly 9 ***[1 mark]***
They are (1,8), (3,6) and (5,4)
Total number of possible outcomes 6 × 5 = 30
Probability of scoring exactly 9 $= \frac{3}{30} = \frac{1}{10}$ ***[1 mark]***
[2 marks available in total — as above]

c) Zynah wins if the score is between 8 and 11 (including 8 and 11).
There are 12 ways of scoring between 8 and 11 ***[1 mark]***
They are (1,8), (1,10), (2,6), (2,8), (3,6), (3,8), (4,4), (4,6), (5,4), (5,6), (6,2) and (6,4)
Probability that Zynah wins $= \frac{12}{30} = \frac{2}{5}$ ***[1 mark]***
[2 marks available in total — as above]

2 a) 0.02 + 0.21 ***[1 mark]***
= 0.23 ***[1 mark]***
[2 marks available in total — as above]

b) P(win) = 0.02 + 0.36 + 0.23 + 0.21 + 0.08 = 0.9 ***[1 mark]***
So P(lose) = 1 – 0.9 = 0.1
36 × 0.1 ***[1 mark]***
= 3.6 ***[1 mark]***
= 4 (accept 3) ***[1 mark]***
[4 marks available in total — as above]
He can only lose whole games so 3.6 isn't a sensible answer. Since the question asks you to estimate, it's okay to round, so you'd get the mark for writing either 3 or 4.

Page 102: The AND / OR Rules

1 a) P(not 2) = 1 – P(2) = 1 – 0.15 = 0.85
[2 marks available — 1 mark for 1 – 0.15, 1 mark for the correct answer]

b) P(even) = P(2) + P(4) = 0.15 + 0.25
= 0.4 ***[1 mark]***
So P(odd) = 1 – 0.4 ***[1 mark]***
= 0.6 ***[1 mark]***
[3 marks available in total — as above]
You could answer this by working out P(5) and then adding that to P(1) + P(3) but part c) asks for P(5) which is a bit of a hint that you don't need P(5) to answer b).

c) *either:* From part b) P(odd) = 0.6
P(odd) = P(1) + P(3) + P(5)
0.6 = 0.3 + 0.2 + P(5) ***[1 mark]***
0.1 = P(5) ***[1 mark]***
or: P(5) = 1 – P(1, 2, 3 or 4) ***[1 mark]***
P(5) = 1 – (0.3 + 0.15 + 0.2 + 0.25) = 0.1 ***[1 mark]***
[2 marks available in total — as above]

d) P(lands on 3 twice) = P(3) × P(3) = 0.2 × 0.2 = 0.04
[2 marks available — 1 mark for a correct method, 1 mark for the correct final answer]

2 P(2 orange and a brown) = P(orange then orange then brown)
+ P(orange then brown then orange)
+ P(brown then orange then orange)

$$=\left(\frac{12}{20}\times\frac{11}{19}\times\frac{8}{18}\right)+\left(\frac{12}{20}\times\frac{8}{19}\times\frac{11}{18}\right)+\left(\frac{8}{20}\times\frac{12}{19}\times\frac{11}{18}\right)$$

$$=3\times\frac{12\times11\times8}{20\times19\times18}=\frac{44}{95}$$

[4 marks available — 1 mark for the correct probability for picking each bead, 1 mark for multiplying the probabilities of the three beads together, 1 mark for adding the probabilities for each possible case together, 1 mark for the correct final answer]

Pages 103-104: Tree Diagrams

1 a)

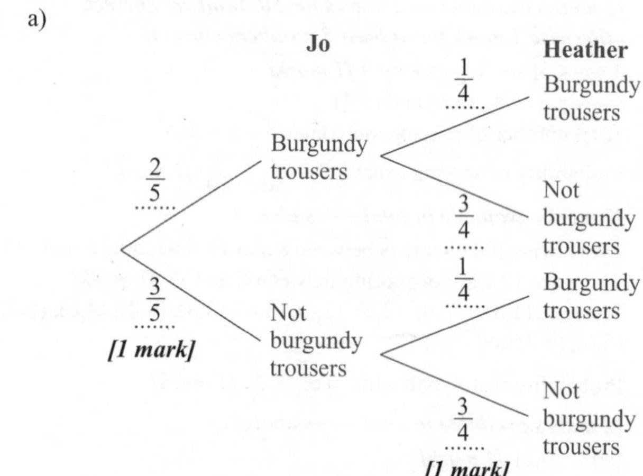

[2 marks available in total — as above]

b) P(neither wear burgundy trousers) = $\frac{3}{5}\times\frac{3}{4}$ ***[1 mark]***
= $\frac{9}{20}$ ***[1 mark]***
[2 marks available in total — as above]

2 E.g. use a probability tree diagram:

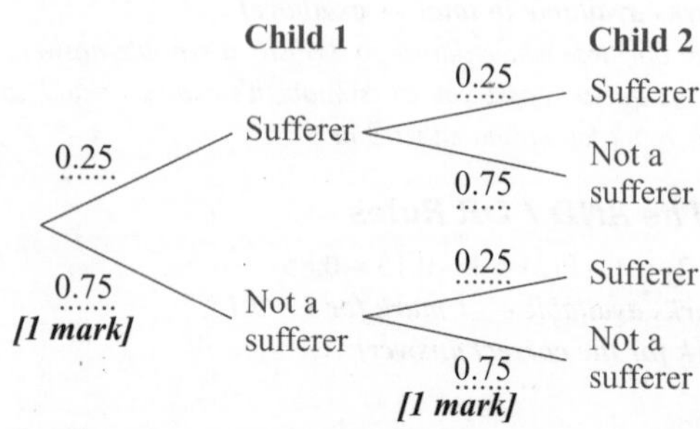

P(at least one of them has the disease)
= 1 – P(neither have the disease)
= 1 – (0.75 × 0.75) ***[1 mark]***
= 1 – 0.5625 = 0.4375 ***[1 mark]***
[4 marks available in total — as above]

3 a)

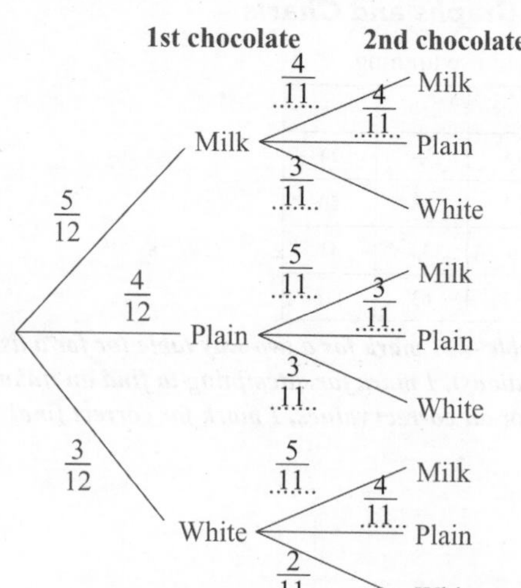

[2 marks available — 2 marks for all probabilities correct, 1 mark for four or more probabilities correct]

b) Outcomes that are one milk and one white: MW and WM
P(one milk and one white) = P(MW) + P(WM)
$=\left(\frac{5}{12}\times\frac{3}{11}\right)+\left(\frac{3}{12}\times\frac{5}{11}\right)$ ***[1 mark]***
$=\frac{5}{22}$ ***[1 mark]***
[2 marks available in total — as above]

c) P(at least 1 plain) = 1 – P(no plain)
= 1 – (P(MM) + P(WW) + P(one milk and one white))
$=1-\left(\left(\frac{5}{12}\times\frac{4}{11}\right)+\left(\frac{3}{12}\times\frac{2}{11}\right)+\frac{5}{22}\right)$
$=1-\left(\frac{10}{66}+\frac{3}{66}+\frac{15}{66}\right)=1-\frac{28}{66}=\frac{38}{66}=\frac{19}{33}$
[3 marks available — 1 mark for working out at least one of P(MM) and P(WW) correctly, 1 mark for a correct calculation to find the final answer, 1 mark for the correct final answer]
You could also answer this by working out P(first one plain) + P(MP) + P(WP), but it's a bit more work to get to the answer.

Page 105: Relative Frequency

1 a) 50 × 0.12 = 6
[2 marks available — 1 mark for correct method, 1 mark for the correct final answer]

b) E.g. 1 and 3 have a much higher relative frequency than the other numbers so the dice is probably not fair.
[2 marks available —1 mark for 'not fair' or similar, 1 mark for an explanation including numbers or relative frequency]

c) E.g. she should not expect the same result as 50 is a small number of trials and there are a large number of possible outcomes.
[1 mark]

2 a)

Number on counter	1	2	3	4	5
Frequency	23	25	22	21	9
Relative Frequency	0.23	0.25	0.22	0.21	0.09

[2 marks available — 2 marks for all correct answers, otherwise 1 mark for any frequency ÷ 100]

b) Elvin is likely to be wrong. The bag seems to contain fewer counters numbered 5. ***[1 mark]***

c) P(odd number) = (0.23 + 0.22 + 0.09) ***[1 mark]***
= 0.54 ***[1 mark]***
[2 marks available in total — as above]

How to get answers for the Practice Papers

You can print out worked solutions to Practice Papers 1 & 2 by accessing your free Online Edition of this book (which also includes step-by-step video solutions).

There's more info about how to get your Online Edition at the front of this book.